n	1000/n	n	1000/n	n	1000/n	n	1000/n	n	1000/n	[illegible]	[illegible]	[illegible]	[illegible]
475	2.105 263	550	1.818 182	625	1.600 000	700	1.428 571	775	1.290 323	[illegible]	[illegible]	[illegible]	[illegible]
476	2.100 840	551	1.814 882	626	1.597 444	701	1.426 534	776	1.288 660	[illegible]	[illegible]	[illegible]	[illegible]
477	2.096 436	552	1.811 594	627	1.594 896	702	1.424 501	777	1.287 001	852	[illegible]	[illegible]	[illegible]
478	2.092 050	553	1.808 318	628	1.592 357	703	1.422 475	778	1.285 347	853	1.172 333	[illegible]	[illegible]
479	2.087 683	554	1.805 054	629	1.589 825	704	1.420 455	779	1.283 697	854	1.170 960	929	[illegible]
480	2.083 333	555	1.801 802	630	1.587 302	705	1.418 440	780	1.282 051	855	1.169 591	930	1.075 269
481	2.079 002	556	1.798 561	631	1.584 786	706	1.416 431	781	1.280 410	856	1.168 224	931	1.074 114
482	2.074 689	557	1.795 332	632	1.582 278	707	1.414 427	782	1.278 772	857	1.166 861	932	1.072 961
483	2.070 393	558	1.792 115	633	1.579 779	708	1.412 429	783	1.277 139	858	1.165 501	933	1.071 811
484	2.066 116	559	1.788 909	634	1.577 287	709	1.410 437	784	1.275 510	859	1.164 144	934	1.070 664
485	2.061 856	560	1.785 714	635	1.574 803	710	1.408 451	785	1.273 885	860	1.162 791	935	1.069 519
486	2.057 613	561	1.782 531	636	1.572 327	711	1.406 470	786	1.272 265	861	1.161 440	936	1.068 376
487	2.053 388	562	1.779 359	637	1.569 859	712	1.404 494	787	1.270 648	862	1.160 093	937	1.067 236
488	2.049 180	563	1.776 199	638	1.567 398	713	1.402 525	788	1.269 036	863	1.158 749	938	1.066 098
489	2.044 990	564	1.773 050	639	1.564 945	714	1.400 560	789	1.267 427	864	1.157 407	939	1.064 963
490	2.040 816	565	1.769 912	640	1.562 500	715	1.398 601	790	1.265 823	865	1.156 069	940	1.063 830
491	2.036 660	566	1.766 784	641	1.560 062	716	1.396 648	791	1.264 223	866	1.154 734	941	1.062 699
492	2.032 520	567	1.763 668	642	1.557 632	717	1.394 700	792	1.262 626	867	1.153 403	942	1.061 571
493	2.028 398	568	1.760 563	643	1.555 210	718	1.392 758	793	1.261 034	868	1.152 074	943	1.060 445
494	2.024 291	569	1.757 469	644	1.552 795	719	1.390 821	794	1.259 446	869	1.150 748	944	1.059 322
495	2.020 202	570	1.754 386	645	1.550 388	720	1.388 889	795	1.257 862	870	1.149 425	945	1.058 201
496	2.016 129	571	1.751 313	646	1.547 988	721	1.386 963	796	1.256 281	871	1.148 106	946	1.057 082
497	2.012 072	572	1.748 252	647	1.545 595	722	1.385 042	797	1.254 705	872	1.146 789	947	1.055 966
498	2.008 032	573	1.745 201	648	1.543 210	723	1.383 126	798	1.253 133	873	1.145 475	948	1.054 852
499	2.004 008	574	1.742 160	649	1.540 832	724	1.381 215	799	1.251 564	874	1.144 165	949	1.053 741
500	2.000 000	575	1.739 130	650	1.538 462	725	1.379 310	800	1.250 000	875	1.142 857	950	1.052 632
501	1.996 008	576	1.736 111	651	1.536 098	726	1.377 410	801	1.248 439	876	1.141 553	951	1.051 525
502	1.992 032	577	1.733 102	652	1.533 742	727	1.375 516	802	1.246 883	877	1.140 251	952	1.050 420
503	1.988 072	578	1.730 104	653	1.531 394	728	1.373 626	803	1.245 330	878	1.138 952	953	1.049 318
504	1.984 127	579	1.727 116	654	1.529 052	729	1.371 742	804	1.243 781	879	1.137 656	954	1.048 218
505	1.980 198	580	1.724 138	655	1.526 718	730	1.369 863	805	1.242 236	880	1.136 364	955	1.047 120
506	1.976 285	581	1.721 170	656	1.524 390	731	1.367 989	806	1.240 695	881	1.135 074	956	1.046 025
507	1.972 387	582	1.718 213	657	1.522 070	732	1.366 120	807	1.239 157	882	1.133 787	957	1.044 932
508	1.968 504	583	1.715 266	658	1.519 757	733	1.364 256	808	1.237 624	883	1.132 503	958	1.043 841
509	1.964 637	584	1.712 329	659	1.517 451	734	1.362 398	809	1.236 094	884	1.131 222	959	1.042 753
510	1.960 784	585	1.709 402	660	1.515 152	735	1.360 544	810	1.234 568	885	1.129 944	960	1.041 667
511	1.956 947	586	1.706 485	661	1.512 859	736	1.358 696	811	1.233 046	886	1.128 668	961	1.040 583
512	1.953 125	587	1.703 578	662	1.510 574	737	1.356 852	812	1.231 527	887	1.127 396	962	1.039 501
513	1.949 318	588	1.700 680	663	1.508 296	738	1.355 014	813	1.230 012	888	1.126 126	963	1.038 422
514	1.945 525	589	1.697 793	664	1.506 024	739	1.353 180	814	1.228 501	889	1.124 859	964	1.037 344
515	1.941 748	590	1.694 915	665	1.503 759	740	1.351 351	815	1.226 994	890	1.123 596	965	1.036 269
516	1.937 984	591	1.692 047	666	1.501 502	741	1.349 528	816	1.225 490	891	1.122 334	966	1.035 197
517	1.934 236	592	1.689 189	667	1.499 250	742	1.347 709	817	1.223 990	892	1.121 076	967	1.034 126
518	1.930 502	593	1.686 341	668	1.497 006	743	1.345 895	818	1.222 494	893	1.119 821	968	1.033 058
519	1.926 782	594	1.683 502	669	1.494 768	744	1.344 086	819	1.221 001	894	1.118 568	969	1.031 992
520	1.923 077	595	1.680 672	670	1.492 537	745	1.342 282	820	1.219 512	895	1.117 318	970	1.030 928
521	1.919 386	596	1.677 852	671	1.490 313	746	1.340 483	821	1.218 027	896	1.116 071	971	1.029 866
522	1.915 709	597	1.675 042	672	1.488 095	747	1.338 688	822	1.216 545	897	1.114 827	972	1.028 807
523	1.912 046	598	1.672 241	673	1.485 884	748	1.336 898	823	1.215 067	898	1.113 586	973	1.027 749
524	1.908 397	599	1.669 449	674	1.483 680	749	1.335 113	824	1.213 592	899	1.112 347	974	1.026 694
525	1.904 762	600	1.666 667	675	1.481 481	750	1.333 333	825	1.212 121	900	1.111 111	975	1.025 641
526	1.901 141	601	1.663 894	676	1.479 290	751	1.331 558	826	1.210 654	901	1.109 878	976	1.024 590
527	1.897 533	602	1.661 130	677	1.477 105	752	1.329 787	827	1.209 190	902	1.108 647	977	1.023 541
528	1.893 939	603	1.658 375	678	1.474 926	753	1.328 021	828	1.207 729	903	1.107 420	978	1.022 495
529	1.890 359	604	1.655 629	679	1.472 754	754	1.326 260	829	1.206 273	904	1.106 195	979	1.021 450
530	1.886 792	605	1.652 893	680	1.470 588	755	1.324 503	830	1.204 819	905	1.104 972	980	1.020 408
531	1.883 239	606	1.650 165	681	1.468 429	756	1.322 751	831	1.203 369	906	1.103 753	981	1.019 368
532	1.879 699	607	1.647 446	682	1.466 276	757	1.321 004	832	1.201 923	907	1.102 536	982	1.018 330
533	1.876 173	608	1.644 737	683	1.464 129	758	1.319 261	833	1.200 480	908	1.101 322	983	1.017 294
534	1.872 659	609	1.642 036	684	1.461 988	759	1.317 523	834	1.199 041	909	1.100 110	984	1.016 260
535	1.869 159	610	1.639 344	685	1.459 854	760	1.315 789	835	1.197 605	910	1.098 901	985	1.015 228
536	1.865 672	611	1.636 661	686	1.457 726	761	1.314 060	836	1.196 172	911	1.097 695	986	1.014 199
537	1.862 197	612	1.633 987	687	1.455 604	762	1.312 336	837	1.194 743	912	1.096 491	987	1.013 171
538	1.858 736	613	1.631 321	688	1.453 488	763	1.310 616	838	1.193 317	913	1.095 290	988	1.012 146
539	1.855 288	614	1.628 664	689	1.451 379	764	1.308 901	839	1.191 895	914	1.094 092	989	1.011 122
540	1.851 852	615	1.626 016	690	1.449 275	765	1.307 190	840	1.190 476	915	1.092 896	990	1.010 101
541	1.848 429	616	1.623 377	691	1.447 178	766	1.305 483	841	1.189 061	916	1.091 703	991	1.009 082
542	1.845 018	617	1.620 746	692	1.445 087	767	1.303 781	842	1.187 648	917	1.090 513	992	1.008 065
543	1.841 621	618	1.618 123	693	1.443 001	768	1.302 083	843	1.186 240	918	1.089 325	993	1.007 049
544	1.838 235	619	1.615 509	694	1.440 922	769	1.300 390	844	1.184 834	919	1.088 139	994	1.006 036
545	1.834 862	620	1.612 903	695	1.438 849	770	1.298 701	845	1.183 432	920	1.086 957	995	1.005 025
546	1.831 502	621	1.610 306	696	1.436 782	771	1.297 017	846	1.182 033	921	1.085 776	996	1.004 016
547	1.828 154	622	1.607 717	697	1.434 720	772	1.295 337	847	1.180 638	922	1.084 599	997	1.003 009
548	1.824 818	623	1.605 136	698	1.432 665	773	1.293 661	848	1.179 245	923	1.083 424	998	1.002 004
549	1.821 494	624	1.602 564	699	1.430 615	774	1.291 990	849	1.177 856	924	1.082 251	999	1.001 001

D1241519

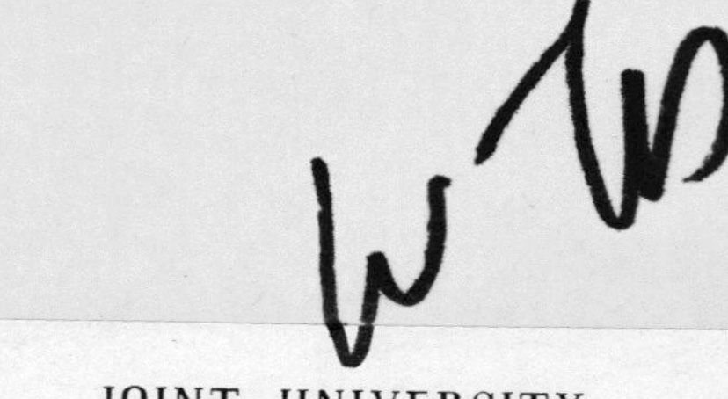

JOINT UNIVERSITY
LIBRARIES

NASHVILLE TENNESSEE

Science

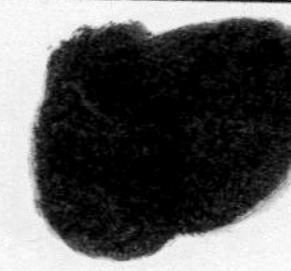

543888

INTERPRETED INFRARED SPECTRA
Volume 3

INTERPRETED INFRARED SPECTRA

Volume 3

Including a Cumulative Index

Herman A. Szymanski

Chairman, Chemistry Department
Canisius College
Buffalo, New York

PLENUM PRESS DATA DIVISION

NEW YORK • 1967

Library of Congress Catalog Number 64-7764

©1967 Plenum Press Data Division
A Division of Plenum Publishing Corporation
227 West 17 Street, New York, N. Y. 10011
All rights reserved

No part of this publication may be reproduced in any form without written permission from the publisher

Printed in the United States of America

QD
95
.S97
v.3
Science

543888

FOREWORD

The more I examine so-called "group frequencies" the more I become convinced that the only method of positively identifying an unknown from its infrared spectrum is by an exact matching of each band, using a computer sort. Group frequencies — at best — can give only the class of compound, and that only when the structure is not too complex. For example, phenols can be identified by the group frequencies in the 3000 and 1400-1100 cm^{-1} regions. However, if the molecule contains an ether group, its group frequency may be obscured and the molecule misidentified. This volume can therefore best serve the scientist who knows the class of compound he is working with and can refer to the examples of spectra of this class.

It must be noted, however, that the position of the absorption band in many cases represents uniquely the environment of the vibrating group. For example, in cyclohexanols the position of the carbon—oxygen stretch indicates whether the group is axial or equatorial.

In this volume I have again attempted to provide a well-rounded selection of carefully chosen examples of spectra for each class, and to reinforce it by the addition of vibrational analyses of typical molecules, correlation tables for families of common compounds, and other pertinent information culled from the literature. The reader should thus find between these covers most of the infrared data he may require for analyses of spectra of compounds of the classes covered.

CONTENTS

ACKNOWLEDGMENTS

The spectra on pages 135, 136 were contributed by Ronald E. Erickson, Dept. of Chemistry, Canisius College, Buffalo, New York.

The Journal of Physical Chemistry contributed the spectra on page 216.

Analytical Chemistry supplied the spectra on pages 180-183, 200, 201, 218-221, 224, 225, 234-237.

Proceedings of the Royal Society of London contributed the spectra on pages 217, 222, 223, 227, 228, 238-245.

The spectra on pages 206, 208 were supplied by the American Petroleum Institute, Catalog of Infrared Spectral Data, Research Project 44, Chemical Thermodynamic Properties Center, A. & M. College of Texas, College Station, Texas.

All other spectra were contributed by Sadtler Research Laboratories, 1517 Vine Street, Philadelphia, Pennsylvania.

For all of these contributions we are sincerely grateful.

INTRODUCTION

The interpretation of infrared spectra is based on the so-called "group frequencies" which related molecules have in common. A group frequency is a vibration associated with an isolated structural group in a molecule. For example, the −OH group in a series of compounds has an absorption band in the 3500-2500 cm^{-1} region which is assigned as the stretching vibration of that group.

Since group frequencies are related to vibrations of molecules, they are derived from analysis of the vibration of molecules. Generally only small and fairly symmetrical molecules are susceptible to complete vibrational analysis, but the group frequencies obtained from such analyses can be extended to larger and unsymmetrical molecules. It will be the general plan of this series to follow this analytical process in considering the interpretation of spectra. First we will present vibrational analyses of representative compounds within a given class, then the group frequencies found for that class, and finally we will discuss the individual spectra. No spectrum will be presented unless the group frequency of all groups in the molecule have already been discussed.

The author feels that the vibrational analysis of a compound can lead to further correlations in a class. Many vibrations that are not considered "good group frequencies" may nevertheless be useful in limited correlation work. For example, a rocking vibration may be a valuable correlation for a series of closely related compounds, although it loses its value for compounds of other classes. Thus, it is possible that new group frequencies can be found by extending the vibrational analysis of a molecule to related compounds of the same class.

The vibrational analysis of a molecule is accomplished by calculation with a series of force constants which are reasonable and lead to the observed frequencies. It is these force constants which can be used to obtain a definition of a group frequency. "A group frequency is related to a vibration for which the calculated value of the vibration is determined by only one or a few force constants."

Various symbols are used to indicate the motions that atoms undergo during a vibration. Although it is possible to use as few as six such symbols, the author has chosen to retain the symbols used in the original references, since in some cases motions pertinent to only the particular molecules under discussion may have been implied. The symbols used and their usual meanings are:

β = in-plane bend
γ = out-of-plane bend
δ = bend
δ' = deformation
ν = stretch
ω = wag
τ = torsion } usually equivalent
t = twist }
r = rock

in subscript
β = in plane
γ = out of plane
as = asymmetric
s = symmetric

Group Frequencies of Phenols, Ethers, and Peroxides

In this volume interpreted spectra of phenols, ethers, and peroxides are presented. It will be of value to the reader if we examine first a series of compounds where the central atom involved in the vibration is oxygen. We shall consider the groups attached to each bond of oxygen so that what can be termed a symmetric and asymmetric stretch of these groups with respect to oxygen can be described. The series to be discussed follow.

Compound	ν_{as}, cm^{-1}	ν_s, cm^{-1}	Remarks
H_2O	3756	3657	vapor state
HDO	3707	2723	vapor state
D_2O	2788	2672	vapor state
CH_3OH	≈3700	1025	vapor state
CH_3OCH_3	1122	940	vapor state
C_6H_5OH	1175*	≈3700	vapor state
$C_6H_5OC_6H_5$	1236	1198	liquid state
$C_6H_5OCH_3$	1172*	1020	liquid state

*This band is perturbed by another vibration. Some authors place this assignment at a higher frequency.

It is possible to consider that the ν_{as} and ν_s vibrations in the preceding list are isolated vibrations, that is, that one vibration is essentially the stretch of one group against the O atom and the second, the stretch of the second group. For $C_6H_5OCH_3$ one of the vibrations involves the unit C_6H_5O and the second the OCH_3. These could be designated as $\nu(C_6H_5O)$ and $\nu(OCH_3)$, but both are C–O stretching vibrations. The higher position of the $\nu(C_6H_5O)$ compared to $\nu(OCH_3)$ can be explained as being due to the partial double-bond character of the C–O unit of the aromatic ring. Thus structures such as the following are predicted for anisole, and the $\nu(C{=}O^{\oplus})$ stretch appears near 1200 cm^{-1}.

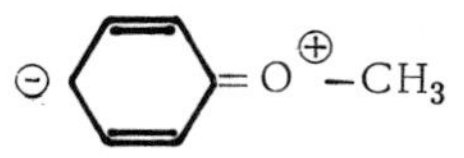

$$\ominus\ C_6H_5{=}O^{\oplus}{-}CH_3$$

As a first approximation to group frequencies for C–O we could then list the following:

Group	Band position
=C–O	1200 cm^{-1}
$\geq$C–O	1025 cm^{-1}

where we are indicating unsaturation on the carbon attached to the oxygen as =C–O. This unsaturation could be aromatic or olefinic.

In many of the spectra which are interpreted in this volume these group frequencies will be found to be fairly reasonable assignments. For structures where the partial double-bond character is large, the $\nu(=C-O)$ will appear higher than 1200 cm^{-1}. In those structures where electron-withdrawing groups can reduce the electron density of the C–O bond the frequency will be lower. In such cases as $(C_6H_5)_3COH$ the $\nu(C-O)$ appears lower than 1025 cm^{-1} and is found at 1000 cm^{-1}. We shall describe other examples of the influence of electron-withdrawing as well as electron-donating groups on the position of the $\nu(C-O)$, but first is necessary to examine further the data presented for ν_{as} and ν_s of CH_3OCH_3 and other related molecules.

The reader may have noted that from the previous discussion the $\nu(\geqq C-O)$ should appear near 1025 cm^{-1}, which it does in CH_3OH; but for CH_3OCH_3, bands at 1122 and 940 cm^{-1} are assigned as $\nu(\geqq C-O)$. The failure of our simple approximation of isolated group frequencies in the case of CH_3OCH_3 is due to a phenomenon termed "coupling".

Coupling occurs for vibrations where the central atom is attached to groups of similar mass by bonds of similar order. Thus, in CH_3OCH_3 both groups attached to the O atom have the same mass, and the bond attaching them to the O atom is similar. The ν_{as} and ν_s vibrations would be of nearly the same frequency if they occurred without coupling. Since coupling does occur these two frequencies appear above and below the 1025 cm^{-1} position predicted for the unperturbed vibration. The observed positions are 1122 and 940 cm^{-1}.

This coupling of frequencies occurs for many molecules. It is seen in the series H_2O, HDO, and D_2O, whose ν_{as} and ν_s are listed in the previous data. Thus, $\nu(OH)$ of HDO is between the ν_{as} and ν_s of H_2O, and the $\nu(OD)$ of HDO is between the ν_{as} and ν_s of D_2O just as the $\nu(C-O)$ of CH_3OH is between the ν_{as} and ν_s of CH_3OCH_3.

The phenomenon of coupling has been used to explain other vibrations as, for example, the $C=O$ stretch in such related molecules as $O=C=O$ and $(CH_3)_2C=O$. Again for $O=C=O$ the $\nu_{as}(C=O)$ and $\nu_s(C=O)$ couple and appear at positions higher and lower than for the $\nu(C=O)$ of $(CH_3)_2C=O$.

It has been shown that the separation of coupled frequencies is maximum if the bond angle between the central atom and the two attached groups is 180°, and the separation is zero if the angle is 90°. Thus for CO_2, where the angle is 180°, the ν_{as} appears 1000 cm^{-1} higher than the ν_s, while for H_2S, where the angle is 90°, the two frequencies coincide. In H_2O the angle is nearly 90° and the ν_{as} and ν_s are separated by only 100 cm^{-1}.

In summary of the suggestions presented above we can state that for unsymmetrical ethers, where we can assume coupling is not present, as well as for alcohols, phenols, and peroxides, we can expect the $\nu(C-O)$ vibration to appear near 1025 cm^{-1} if the O is attached to a saturated carbon atom, and to appear near 1200 cm^{-1} if the carbon atom is part of an unsaturated group.

All symmetrical saturated ethers such as diethyl and di-n-propyl will have coupled ν_{as} and ν_s vibrations. The ν_{as} will appear near 1110 cm^{-1} as a very strong band. The ν_s will be weak or absent and will not be a useful group frequency.

The group $(CH_3)_3C-O$ appears to give a ν_{as} (C−O) near 1175 cm^{-1} in both $(CH_3)_3C-O-H$ and $(CH_3)_3COC(CH_3)_3$.

While this volume is not concerned with acids and esters where the group $-\overset{O}{\overset{\|}{C}}-O-$ occurs, it will be of value to note the $C=O$ group, like unsaturated systems, gives partial double-bond character to the $C-O$ bond, and therefore the $C-O$ stretch appears near 1200 cm^{-1}, similar to its position for phenol and diphenyl ether.

It is in order now to describe further the effect of induction and resonance on the position of the $C-O$ stretch. As pointed out above, any grouping which increases the double-bond character of the $C-O$ group will give a spectrum with the $\nu(C-O)$ appearing at a higher frequency than for those groups where only a single bond occurs. We shall see many spectra of this type. Here we shall cite only a few examples.

As an example of the groups attached to the $C-O$ reducing the electron density of this bond and causing a $\nu(C-O)$ vibration at low frequency, the spectrum of $(C_6H_5)_3COC(C_6H_5)_3$ can be cited. In this case the aromatic ring is not attached to the O atom as it is in diphenyl ether, and it can only act as an electron-withdrawing group. The $\nu(C-O)$ for this compound is found at 1000 cm^{-1}.

We have cited the example previously of $C_6H_5OCH_3$ (anisole), where the $\nu(C-O)$ is near 1200 cm^{-1} for the C_6H_5O group. If now we introduce a $C=O$ group between the O atom and C_6H_5, it is not surprising that, since both the C_6H_5 and $C=O$ are resonant with the $C-O$ and increase its double-bond character, the compound $C_6H_5\overset{O}{\overset{\|}{C}}-OCH_3$ has the $\nu(C-O)$ at 1275 cm^{-1} – a position higher than for either $C_6H_5OCH_3$ or $CH_3\overset{O}{\overset{\|}{C}}-OCH_3$.

The final example of the influence of the groups attached to the O atom on the position of the C−O stretch is illustrated by a series of anisole derivatives where the following compound was synthesized.*

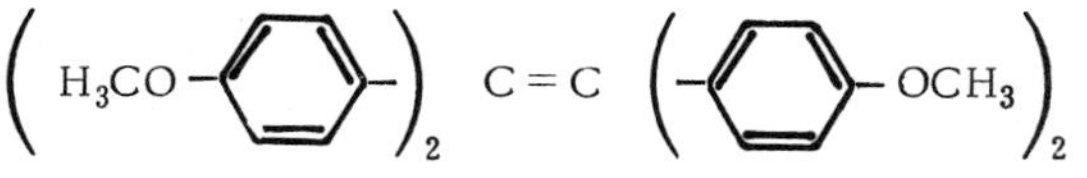

$$\left(H_3CO-C_6H_4-\right)_2 C=C \left(-C_6H_4-OCH_3\right)_2$$

From the above discussion we would predict this to give a spectrum having 1180 and 1050 cm^{-1} bands due to the CH_3O and C_6H_5O- group (a 1250 cm^{-1} band due to the C_6H_5-O- unit also appears). On examining its spectrogram (see p. 133) it is found that there are very strong bands in this complex corresponding to the above bands.

If now a charge-transfer complex is made of this molecule with ICl, it is found the 1050 cm^{-1} band shifts to 1000 cm^{-1}, and the 1180 cm^{-1} band to near 1140 cm^{-1}. This should not be unexpected, as the formation of the charge-transfer complex disturbs the electronic configuration to such an extent that the bond order of the C−O group must certainly change. This sort of change should be expected by the organic chemist. The spectrum of a compound in an unusual electronic environment should not show the expected position for group frequencies. However, they should be expected to appear shifted only to a small degree from the correct regions. We assign the frequency shift to a lowering of bond order of the C−O unit.

Notation of C−O Stretching Vibration

The notation for stretching vibration for all C−O examined in this text, according to the type of structure in which the group can be found, is shown in the following table.

Group	ν(C−O) notation	
	in complex structures	in simple structures (where grouping is obvious)
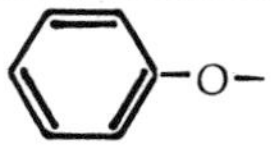 C_6H_5−O−	ν(=C−O)	
C=CH−O	ν(=C−O)	
$-CH_2OH$	$\nu(CH_2OH)$	$\nu(CH_2O)$
$-CH_2O-C$	$\nu(CH_2O)$	
−CHRO−C	ν(CHRO)	
−CRRO−C	ν(CRROC)	ν(CRRO)
CHROH	ν(CHROH)	ν(CHRO)
CR_2OH	$\nu(CR_2OH)$	$\nu(CR_2O)$
CH_3-O	$\nu(CH_3O)$	
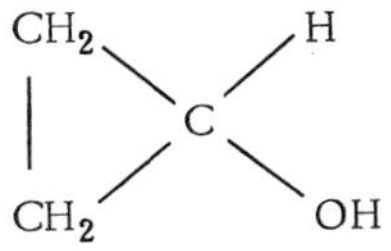 cyclopropanol (CH_2, CH_2 ring with C bearing H and OH)	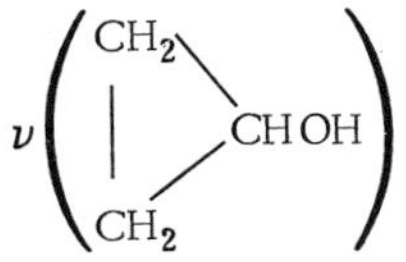 ν (cyclo-CH_2–CH_2–CHOH)	
CH_2OOH	$\nu(CH_2OO)$	$\nu(CH_2O)$
CHROOH	ν(CHROO)	ν(CHRO)

* Reported by R. Erickson, Ph. D. Thesis, University of Iowa, 1959.

PHENOLS

Vibrational Analysis

C_6H_5OH

Source: S. Pinchas, D. Sadek, D. Samuel, J. Chem. Phys. 69:2259 (1965).

Infrared band, cm^{-1} (CCl_4 solution)	Species	Assignment
3620		ν(OH)
3500		$\nu(OH)_{dimer}$
3076, 3046		ν(= CH)
3024		ν(= CH)
1598		ν(C = C)
1502		ν(C = C)
1472		ν(C = C)
1344		ν(C = C) + δ(OH)
1333		combination
1313		combination
1256	a_1	X-sensitive
1182		monomeric δ(OH) + ring
1152		β(= CH)
1072		β(= CH)
1044*		combination + β(= CH)
1027*		combination + β(= CH)
884	b_2	γ(= CH)
827*	a_2	γ(= CH)
812*	a_1	X-sensitive
751*	b_2	γ(= CH)
688*	b_2	δ'_γ(ring)
608	b_1	δ'(ring)
536	a_1	X-sensitive
510	b_2	X-sensitive
400*	b_1	$\beta(COH)_{monomeric}$
320*		$\gamma(COH)_{monomeric}$
272, 252*		$\gamma(COH)_{monomeric}$
235, 226*		$\gamma(COH)_{monomeric}$

*in cyclohexane

PHENOLS

C_6H_5OH

Source: J. H. S. Green, J. Chem. Soc. 2236 (1961)

Band, cm^{-1}			Fundamental and species	Assignments
infrared (CCl_4 solution)	infrared (vapor)	Raman (melt)		
3612 M	3623			
3091 S		3085	{ ν_{20b} (b_1) ν_{20a} (a_1)	ν(OH) ν(=CH)
3076			ν_2 (a_1)	ν(=CH)
		3063		
3046 M	3030	{ 3047 3023	ν_{13} (a_1) ν_{7b} (b_1)	ν(=CH) ν(=CH)
1810 S				combination
1842 S				combination
1777 S				combination
1596 S	1600	1604 VS 1595 VS }	ν_{8a} (a_1)	ν(C=C)
1498 S	1497		ν_{19a} (a_1)	ν(C=C)
1472 S			ν_{19b} (b_1)	ν(C=C)
1384 M				combination
1344 M	1344		ν_{14} (b_1)	ν(C=C)
	1333		ν_{14} (b_1)	ν(C=C)
1255 S	1259 1253 }	1250 M		X-sensitive
1220 S				combination
1182 S	1175			δ'(OH)
1167 S	1167	1167 S	ν_{9a} (a_1)	β(=CH)
1153 M	1142	1152 M	ν_{9a} (b_1)	β(=CH)
1071 M	1069 1057 }	1072 M	ν_{15} (b_1)	β(=CH)
1024 M	1033 1026 1015 }	1024 S	ν_{18a} (a_1)	β(=CH)
1000 M	999	1002 S	ν_1 (a_1)	ring
884 M	888 881 875 }		ν_{17b} (b_2)	γ(=CH)
825 M	823	828 M	ν_{10a} (a_2)	γ(=CH)

table continued.

C_6H_5OH, J.H.S. Green, continued.

Band, cm^{-1}			Fundamental and Species	Assigment
infrared (CCl_4 solution)	infrared (vapor)	Raman (melt)		
810 S	814 } 810 } 806 }	812 S	ν_{7a} (a_1)	X-sensitive
752 S	751 } 747 } 742 }	756 S	ν_{10b} (b_2)	γ(=CH)
688 S	691 } 686 } 681 }		ν_4 (b_2)	(CC)
617 W	591	617 S	ν_{6b} (b_1)	α(CCC)
526 W	533 } 526 } 514 }	532 S	ν_{6a} (a_1)	X-sensitive
502 W	496		ν_{16b} (b_2)	X-sensitive
		241 S	ν_{11} (b_2)	X-sensitive

C_6H_5OH

Source: J. C. Evans, Spectrochim. Acta 16:1382 (1960).

Infrared band, cm^{-1}				Raman, cm^{-1}	Assignment
vapor	solution	liquid	solid		
3661 } 3653 } 3648 }					ν(OH)
	3610				ν(OH)
	3500	3500 Sh		3500 B	ν(OH)
	3350	3350 VSB	3225	3350	
3078	3074	3070 W	3070 Sh		ν(=CH)
				3061	ν(=CH)
	3052	3050 Sh			ν(=CH)
	3046	3044 M	3043		ν(=CH)
	3021	3020 W	3019	3023	ν(=CH)
1608	1608	1604 S	1605	1603	ν(ring)*
1602	1600	1597 VS	1598	1595	ν(ring)*

table continued.

C_6H_5OH, J.C. Evans, continued.

Infrared band, cm^{-1}				Raman, cm^{-1}	Assignment
vapor	solution	liquid	solid		
1507					
1501	1502	1500 VS	1501	1500	ν(ring)*
1493					
1478					
1470	1473	1474 VS	1473	1471	ν(ring)*
1462					
1349					ν(ring)* + δ'(OH)
1343		1362 M	1370		ν(ring)* + δ'(OH)
1335		1343 W			ν(ring)* + δ'(OH)
	1290	1292 VVW	1292		β(=CH)
1268					
1260	1259		1252	1253	X-sensitive
1253					
		1228 VS	1230		δ'(OH) + ν(ring)*
		1198 Sh			
	1167	1168 W		1170	β(=CH)
1158					
1150	1151	1152 W	1152	1155	β(=CH)
1142					
1072	1070	1072 M		1072	β(=CH)
1032					
1026	1026	1025 W	1024	1024	β(=CH)
1018					
				1000	δ'(ring)
			981		
	972	978 VVW	974		γ(=CH)
	958	958 VVW	962		γ(=CH)
			888		
881	883	888 W	882	890	γ(=CH)
823	829	828 W	828	828	γ(=CH)
814	814	812 S	812	814	X-sensitive
686	691	690 VS	691		δ'(ring)
620	619	618 VW	618	617	δ'(ring)
533					
527	530	531 W	535	531	X-sensitive
518					
		410 B	415	415	δ'(ring)
			455		X-sensitive
		650 VB	720 B		γ(OH)

*In the notation on the interpreted spectra of this book this is indicated as ν(C = C).

NO_2
OH

Source: J. H. S. Green, W. Kynaston, S. A. Lindsey, Spectrochim. Acta 17:486 (1961).

Bands, cm^{-1}		Assignment
infrared (solid)	Raman	
3241 M		ν(OH)
3122 W		
3102 W		ν(=CH)
3030 Sh		combinations and overtones
2923 W		
2715 W		
2663 W		
1984 W		
1958 W		
1958 W		
1923 W		
1855 W		
1740 W		
1616 S	1612 W	ν(C=C)
1594 S	1588 M	ν(C=C)
1584 Sh		
1536 S	1534 M	$\nu_{as}(NO_2)$
1486 S		ν(C=C)
1456 S		
1421 W		
1376 S		
1337 S		ν(C=C)
1315 S	1321 S	$\nu_s(NO_2)$
1266 S		
1257 S		ν(=C−O)
1243 S	1246 S	
1182 S	1187 S	δ'(OH)
1165 M		
1137 M	1135 S	β(=CH)
1124 W		
1094 W		β(=CH)
1080 M		
1046 W		
1028 M	1029 W	β(=CH)
989 W		γ(=CH)
958 (W)		
870 M	868 M	γ(=CH)
820 M	821 M	ν(CX)
784 M		
747 S		δ'(CC)
696 W		
665 SB		ring

PHENOLS

Other Literature Pertaining to Ortho-Substituted Phenols

Infrared studies with substituted orthobromophenols, Part I. The hydroxyl frequencies in carbon tetrachloride solution. See: I. Brown, G. Eglinton, M. Martin-Smith, Spectrochim. Acta 18:1593 (1962).

Infrared studies with substituted orthobromophenols, Part II. The effect of the solvent on the hydroxyl stretching frequency. See: I. Brown, G. Eglinton, M. Martin-Smith, Spectrochim. Acta 19:463 (1963).

Infrared studies with substituted orthobromophenols, Part III. The effect of state on the hydroxyl stretching frequency. See: I. Brown, G. Eglinton, M. Martin-Smith, Spectrochim. Acta 19:1089 (1063).

Samples were examined as mulls or as liquid or solid film. Four general classifications of spectra are suggested, based on the position and intensity of the hydroxyl stretching band. These are termed "intra" where the hydrogen bond is OH . . .Br; "Inter" where the bond is OH . . . O; "mixture of intra and inter" and "inter" where the bond is OH. . . NO_2. Attention is directed to the types of interaction which can occur between the phenol and the mulling compound. These include dispersion as solid, dispersion as liquid droplets, and solution in the mulling material.

Intramolecular hydrogen bonding in orthotritylphenols.

See: A. W. Baker, A. T. Shulgin, Spectrochim. Acta 19:1611 (1963).

Contribution concerning the problem of the intramolecular hydrogen bonds in orthohalophenols.

See: H. Bourassa-Bataille, P. Sauvageau, C. Sandorfy, J. Can. Chem. 41:2241 (1963).

Conformers of ortho-cis-propenylphenols.

See: A. W. Baker, A. T. Shulgin, Spectrochim. Acta 20:153 (1964).

Para-Substituted Phenols

The vibrations of para-substituted phenols can be divided into three categories: those modes that are not sensitive to the mass or nature of the substitutent, those modes which are substituent-sensitive (ν_6, ν_{14}, ν_{15}, ν_{18}, and ν_{19} in the following tables), and those vibrations that are governed by the motion of one of the two substituents on the ring. The vibrations ν_{12}, ν_{17}, ν_{20}, and ν_{11}, are of this type in the table below, and can be classified as characteristic modes of the para-substituted phenols.

A band near 1350 cm^{-1}, while primarily a ring vibration, is coupled to the β(OH)* vibration. The band is therefore shifted and more intense than for non-phenolic derivatives. It shifts to lower frequencies if the phenol is run in dilute solutions.

The ν_{12} mode involves some ν(C—O) and interacts with β(OH) vibrations ν_{25} and ν_{26}. In solid and liquid phenols these vibrations appear as a strong broad band, but in dilute solutions two bands are seen. The bands are at lower frequencies in dilute solutions.

The ν_{17} mode is characteristic for these substituted phenols as it falls in a very narrow range. The band does shift to lower frequency if the phenol is run in dilute solution.

*In previous analyses this band was designated as δ'(OH). We shall use either designation according to what the original author has used in the data he presented.

Frequencies of Para-Substituted Phenols

Source: R.J. Jakobsen and E.J. Brewer, Appl. Spectr. 16(2): 32 (1962).

Infrared band, cm^{-1}	Fundamental and species	Assignment
1628-1585	$\nu_{16'}$ (a_1)	ν(C=C)
1620-1573	ν_{16} (b_2)	ν(C=C)
1525-1488	ν_{13} (a_1)	ν(C=C)
1480-1430	$\nu_{13'}$ (b_2)	ν(C=C)
1388-1344	ν_9 (b_2)	ν(C=C)
857-825	ν_2 (a_1)	ν(ring)
1307-1261	ν_3 (b_2)	β(=CH)
1186-1150	$\nu_{17'}$ (a_1)	β(=CH)
1116-1092	ν_{10} (b_2)	β(=CH)
1025-1005	ν_{14} (a_1)	β(=CH)
975-937	ν_{19} (a_2)	γ(=CH)
960-914	ν_7 (b_1)	γ(=CH)
854-818	ν_4 (b_1)	γ(=CH)
835-808	ν_{11} (a_2)	γ(=CH)
711-687	ν_8 (b_1)	$(CC)_{ring}$
652-630	ν_{18} (b_2)	α(CCC)
1239-1205	ν (b_2)	β (OH)
780-600	ν (b_1)	γ (OH)
1282-1235	ν_{12} (a_1)	ν(C−O)
1231-1069	$\nu_{15'}$ (a_1)	X-sensitive
791-603	ν_6 (a_1)	X-sensitive
510-290	$\nu_{18'}$ (a_1)	X-sensitive
456-360	ν_{17} (b_2)	X-sensitive
341-209	$\nu_{14'}$ (b_2)	X-sensitive
548-504	$\nu_{20'}$ (b_1)	X-sensitive
412-319	$\nu_{11'}$ (b_1)	X-sensitive
211-150	$\nu_{19'}$ (b_1)	X-sensitive

PHENOLS

H_3C– –OH

Source: R. J. Jakobsen, Spectrochim. Acta 21:433 (1965).

Band, cm^{-1}				Fundamental and species	Assignment
infrared			Raman (liquid)		
vapor	solution	liquid			
3717 MS	3720 M				$\nu(OH)_{monomer}$
		3344 VS			$\nu(OH)_{polymer}$
3067 MS	3070 W		3057 S	a_1	$\nu(=CH)$
	3032 W	3036 M	3037 M		$\nu(=CH)$
2915 M	2915 W		2919 S	b_2	$\nu(CH_3)$
1621 MS		1618 M	1612 S	a	$\nu(C=C)$
		1605 M	1600M	b_2	$\nu(C=C)$
1520 S		1515 VS		a_1	$\nu(C=C)$
1431 MW		1439 MS		b_2	$\nu(C=C)$
	1334		1380 MS		$\delta(CH_3)$
1332	1325 MW	1361 MS		b_2	$\nu(C=C)$
1255 SB	1253 VS	1235 VSB	1251 MS	a_1	X-sensitive (COH)
1178 SB	1170 VS	1235 VS			$\beta(OH)$
	1210 VS	1172 M	1212 S	a_1	$\beta(=CH)$
			1193 M		combination
			1170 M	b_2	$\beta(=CH)$
1117 W	1111 W	1114 Sh	1112 W		$r(CH_3)$
1105 W	1102 MS	1105 M			$\beta(=CH)$
	1038 W	1042 W	1032 W		$r(CH_3)$
1015 W		1016 W	1011 W		$\beta(=CH)$
	842 M	841 MS	842 VS	a_1	ring
811 S	818 VS	816 VS	823 S	a_2	$\gamma(=CH)$
739	738 M	738 M	740 M	a_1	X-sensitive $\nu(CC)$
698 W		702 W	700 M	b_1	$(CC)_{ring}$
503 S	504 S	508 S	512 S	b_1	X-sensitive $(CC)_{ring}$
459 W	460 MW	464 M	468 S	a_1	X-sensitive
420 M	424 MW	430 W		b_2	$\beta(CX)$
333 MW		338 MW	341 S	b_2	ring
294 SB	307 SB				$\gamma(OH)$

Other Phenols

The γ(OH) Vibration of Intramolecularly Hydrogen-Bonded Phenols

Source: R. A. Nyquist, Spectrochim. Acta 19:1655 (1963).

The spectra of various phenols in 10% CCl_4 solution in 0.1 mm cells were observed in the 3800-1335 cm^{-1} region; for 10% CS_2 solutions in 0.1 mm cells in the 1335-400 cm^{-1} region; and for 10% and 20% 2,2,4-trimethylpentane or CCl_4 solutions in 0.4 mm cells in the 450-280 cm^{-1} region. The γ(OH) vibration for non-bonded phenols is a simple torsion of the OH bond about the C—O axis. This vibration appears at low frequencies (for example, near 300 cm^{-1}). For hydrogen-bonded phenols this frequency is higher, and should increase directly with the strength of the hydrogen bond. Since it is known that the ν(OH) vibration is also a function of the hydrogen-bond strength, it is not surprising to find that a plot of γ(OH) versus ν(OH) frequencies gives a reasonably straight line. The reason for this is that the ν(OH) band lowers when the bond strength is increased, while the γ(OH) band rises. The γ(OH) vibration appears in the 800-300 cm^{-1} region, depending on the degree and strength of hydrogen bonding. It is usually a broad strong band, especially for the associated phenols.

Studies of hydrogen bonding, Part VII. Hydrogen-bond association of phenol and pentachlorophenol with carbonyl compounds and ethers.
See: T. Gramstad, Spectrochim. Acta 19:497 (1963).

Studies of hydrogen bonding, Part VIII. Hydrogen-bond association between phenol and sulfoxides and nitroso compounds.
See: T. Gramstad, Spectrochim. Acta 19:829 (1963).

The Hydroxyl-Group Stretching Frequency in Hydroxyazobenzenes
Source: A. G. Catchpole, W. B. Foster, R. S. Holden, Spectrochim. Acta 18:1353 (1964).

The OH stretching frequency of X—⟨C₆H₄⟩—N=N—⟨C₆H₄⟩—OH (where X is H, CH_3, NO_2, Br, I, Cl, and CH_3O) appears in the range 3597 to 3606 cm^{-1} in dilute solutions in carbon tetrachloride. For

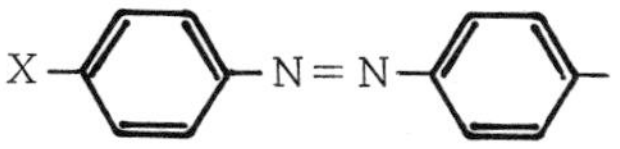

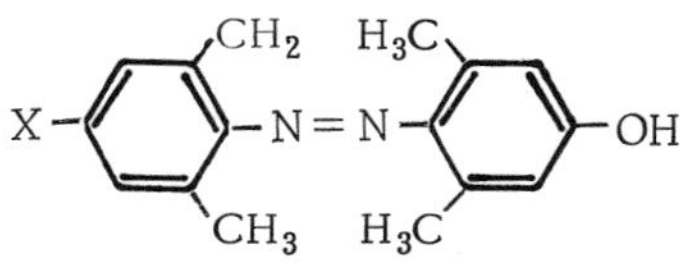

X—(ring with CH_2, CH_3)—N=N—(ring with H_3C, H_3C)—OH

the band appears in the 3606-3603 cm^{-1} region.

Temperature Dependency of Phenol OH Stretching Band Absorptivities

See: A.W. Baker, H.O. Kerlinger, A.T. Shulgin, Spectrochim. Acta 20:1467 (1964).

The Hydroxyl Stretching Bands of Phenols: Some Aspects of Half-Band Widths

See: A.W. Baker, H.O. Kerlinger, A.T. Shulgin, Spectrochim. Acta 20:1477 (1964).

PHENOLS

Infrared Examination of Carbon-Hydrogen Stretching Frequency in Pyrocatechols, Guaiacols, and Phenols

Source: W. Beckering, C. M. Frost, W.W. Fowkes, Anal. Chem. 36:2412 (1964).

The authors present a careful examination of the 2800-3000 cm^{-1} region showing that bands here can be used to distinguish unknown phenolic compounds. For the 78 compound examined, no two gave the same pattern of bands in this region. The data follows.

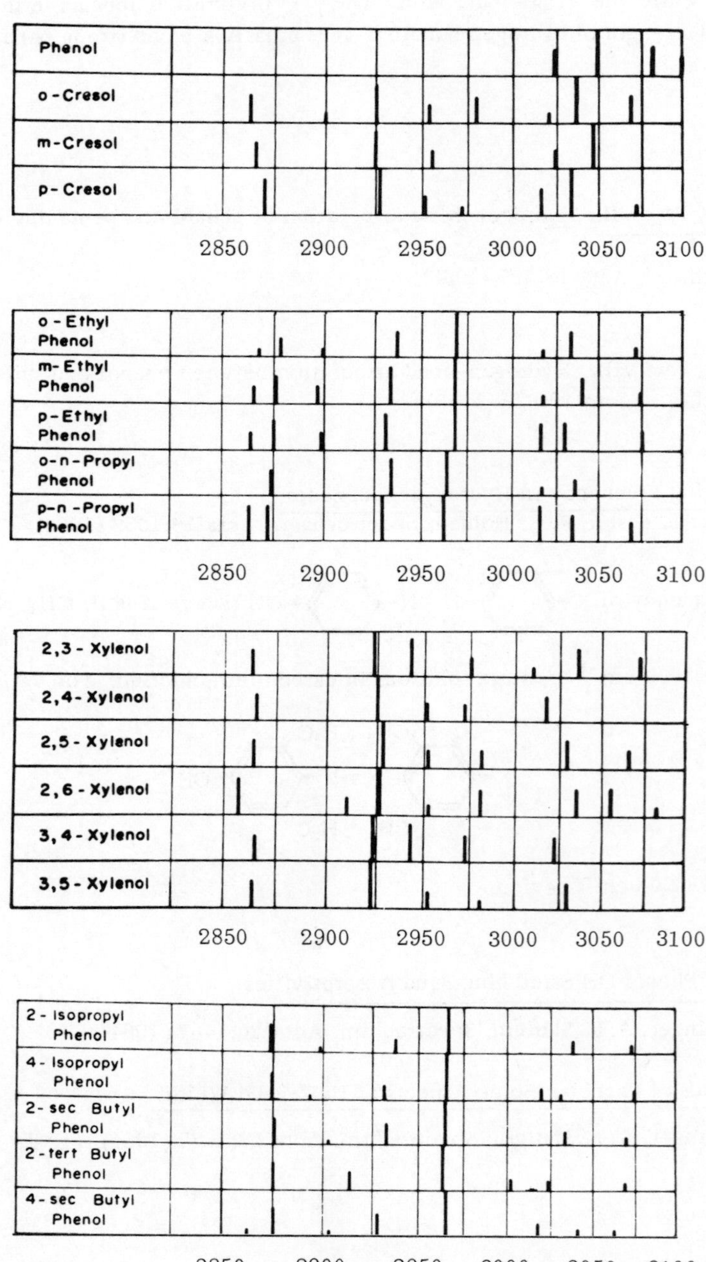

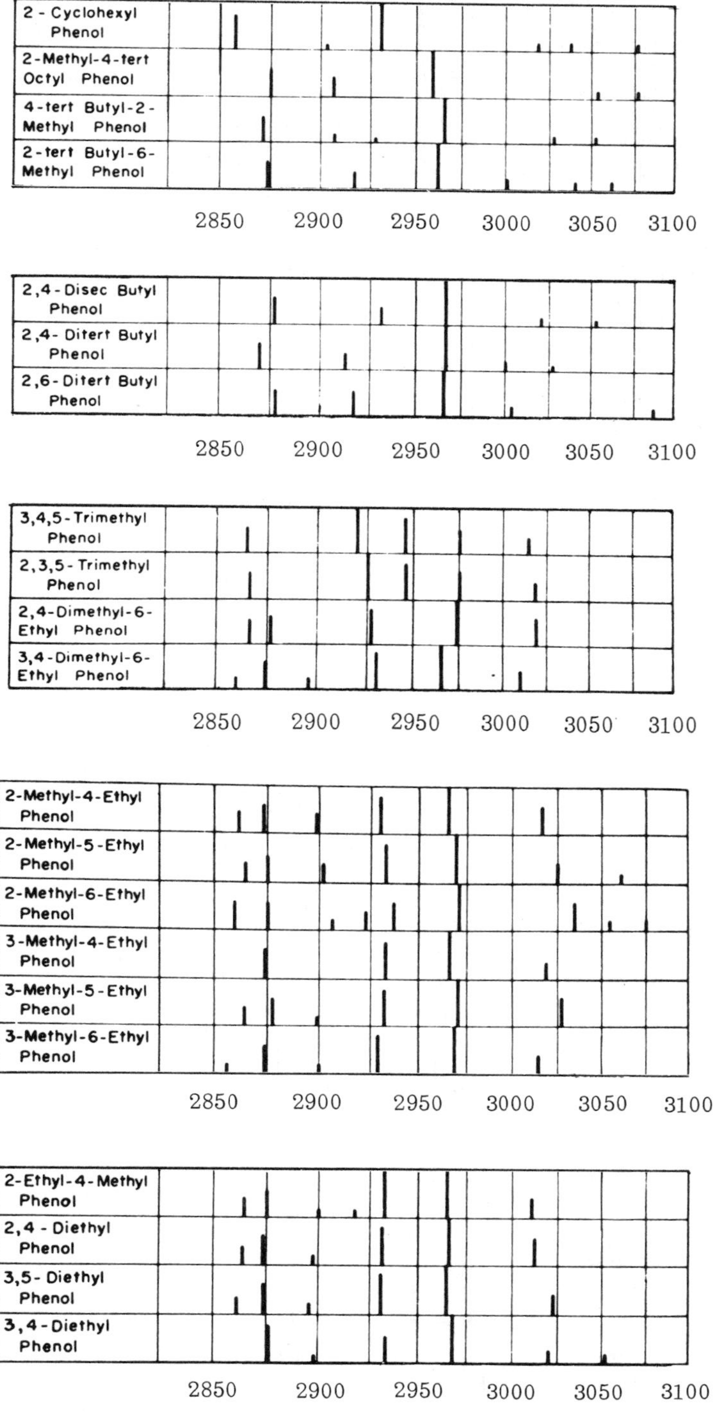
2 - Cyclohexyl Phenol
2-Methyl-4-tert Octyl Phenol
4-tert Butyl-2-Methyl Phenol
2-tert Butyl-6-Methyl Phenol
2850 2900 2950 3000 3050 3100
2,4-Disec Butyl Phenol
2,4- Ditert Butyl Phenol
2,6- Ditert Butyl Phenol
2850 2900 2950 3000 3050 3100
3,4,5-Trimethyl Phenol
2,3,5- Trimethyl Phenol
2,4-Dimethyl-6-Ethyl Phenol
3,4-Dimethyl-6-Ethyl Phenol
2850 2900 2950 3000 3050 3100
2-Methyl-4-Ethyl Phenol
2-Methyl-5-Ethyl Phenol
2-Methyl-6-Ethyl Phenol
3-Methyl-4-Ethyl Phenol
3-Methyl-5-Ethyl Phenol
3-Methyl-6-Ethyl Phenol
2850 2900 2950 3000 3050 3100
2-Ethyl-4-Methyl Phenol
2,4 - Diethyl Phenol
3,5- Diethyl Phenol
3,4-Diethyl Phenol
2850 2900 2950 3000 3050 3100

PHENOLS

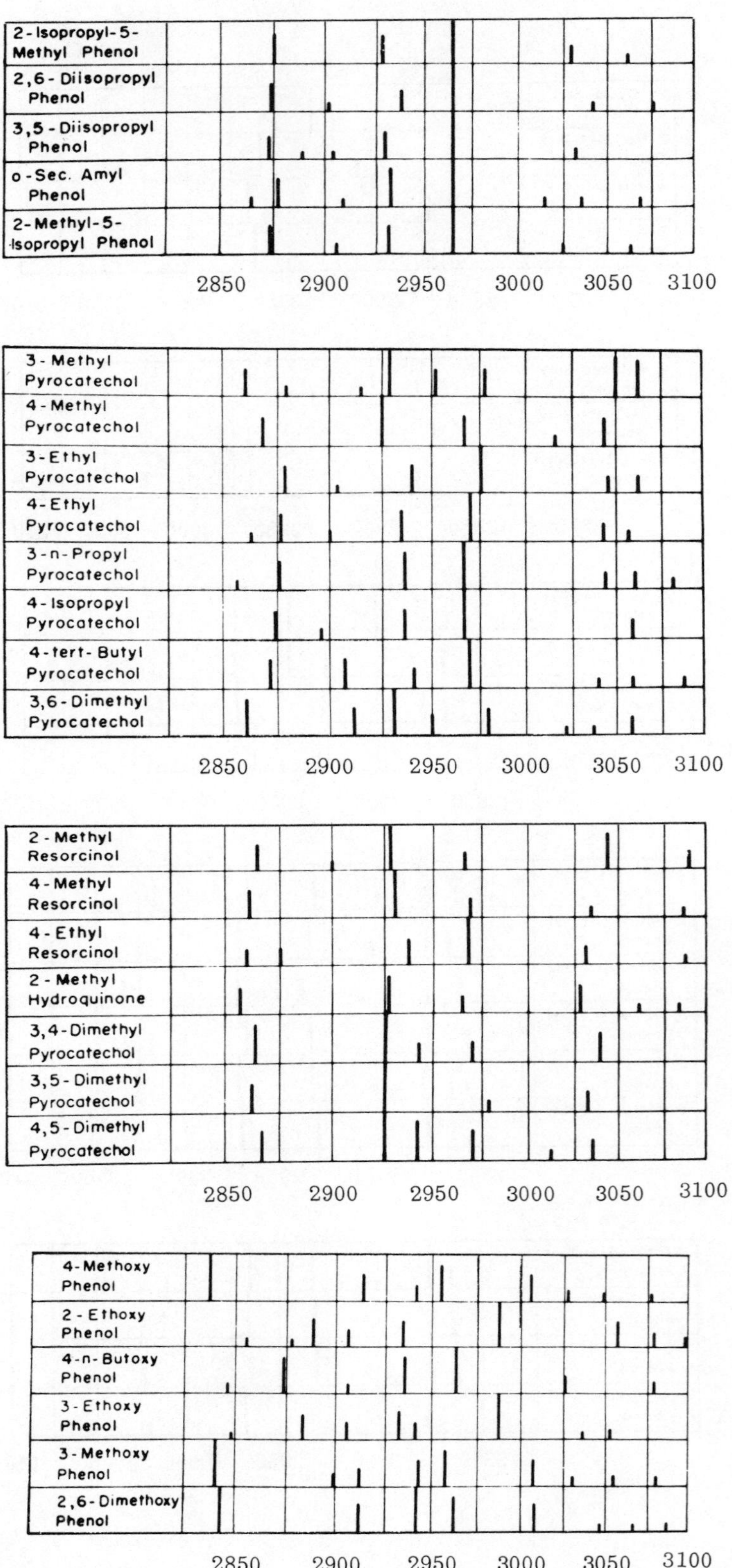

2-Isopropyl-5-Methyl Phenol
2,6-Diisopropyl Phenol
3,5-Diisopropyl Phenol
o-Sec. Amyl Phenol
2-Methyl-5-Isopropyl Phenol
2850 2900 2950 3000 3050 3100
3-Methyl Pyrocatechol
4-Methyl Pyrocatechol
3-Ethyl Pyrocatechol
4-Ethyl Pyrocatechol
3-n-Propyl Pyrocatechol
4-Isopropyl Pyrocatechol
4-tert-Butyl Pyrocatechol
3,6-Dimethyl Pyrocatechol
2850 2900 2950 3000 3050 3100
2-Methyl Resorcinol
4-Methyl Resorcinol
4-Ethyl Resorcinol
2-Methyl Hydroquinone
3,4-Dimethyl Pyrocatechol
3,5-Dimethyl Pyrocatechol
4,5-Dimethyl Pyrocatechol
2850 2900 2950 3000 3050 3100
4-Methoxy Phenol
2-Ethoxy Phenol
4-n-Butoxy Phenol
3-Ethoxy Phenol
3-Methoxy Phenol
2,6-Dimethoxy Phenol
2850 2900 2950 3000 3050 3100

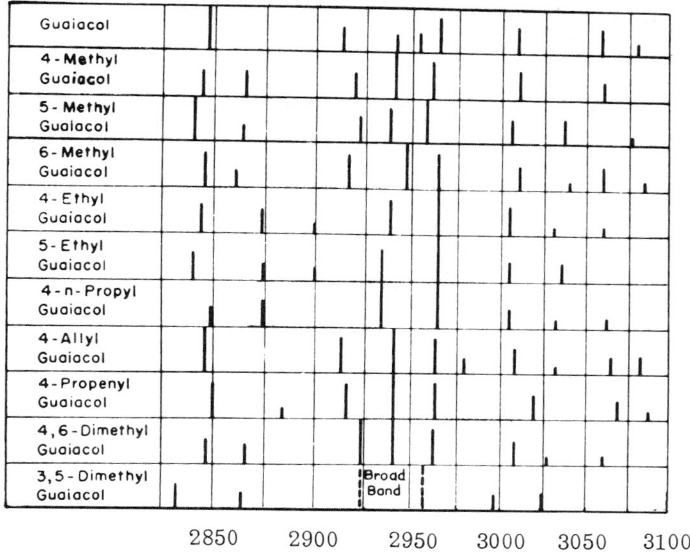

Correlation of Phenols

As with many groups frequencies, it is possible to locate characteristic bands for phenols in simple structures, but as the complexity of the molecule increases it becomes more difficult to find bands which can be used to positively identify the presence of a phenolic group. For example, even the very distinct OH stretching frequency can appear to be absent in the spectra of some phenols, even though this group is considered to give one of the most characteristic group frequencies.

The specific group frequencies which should be utilized for detecting the presence of a phenolic group are as follows:

ν(OH)	{ 3250-3000 cm^{-1} for the bonded state 3620-3400 cm^{-1} for the free state
δ'(OH) and ν(C—O)	1260-1220 and 1200-1160 cm^{-1}
ν(C=C) and δ'(OH)	1370-1320 cm^{-1}

The ν(OH) group frequency is usually present somewhere in the 3600-3000 cm^{-1} region, and for simple phenols, which are associated in the solid state, it will appear at a lower frequency than if the same compound is measured in dilute solution. There are examples of steric hindrance preventing H-bonding in the solid state, in which case no band shift will occur when the solid and dilute solution spectra are compared. We shall see several examples of this. A typical one is 2, 6 di-tertiary butyl phenol. There are also examples of internal H-bonding, where again no shift occurs in comparing solid to solution spectra. The ν(OH) in this case appears at a lower frequency than that found for the free state.

The OH deformation and C—O stretching vibrations interact, and therefore it is not possible to assign one vibration as the OH bend and a second as the ν(C —O). From the Vibrational Analysis section it appears these two bands should be near 1240 ± 20 cm^{-1} and 1180 ± 20 cm^{-1}. In solution these bands will usually shift to lower frequency. A third band near 1350 ± 20 cm^{-1} is primarily a ν(C=C) of the aromatic ring, but is coupled to the OH deformation and therefore stronger and shifted from the position found for aromatic rings. It can be therefore used as a characteristic band for phenols.

More bands will be found in the 1400-1100 cm^{-1} region of phenols than the above three group frequencies. Some of these are strong and often broad. While it has been suggested that some order for these bands can be correlated with the substitution on the phenolic ring, the rules work well only with alkyl substituents and will not be discussed here.

The discussion in the first section of this volume concerning the C_6H_5—O— vibration should be referred to here. In that section it is pointed out that anisole, like phenol, has a band near 1200 cm^{-1} which can be assigned as ν(=C—O). The partial double-bond character of the C—O bond is the explanation for the high position of this band compared to its position for aliphatic alcohols.

PHENOLS

Correlation Table

Group frequency designation	Symbol	Position (cm^{-1})	Intensity
OH stretch of phenols in dilute, inert solutions			
Associated state	ν(OH)	3250-3200	Variable
Dilute solution	ν(OH)	3610-3590	S
OH deformation and C—O stretch			
Associated state	δ'(OH) and ν(C—O)*	1390-1330 1260-1180	M S
Dilute solution	δ'(OH) and ν(C—O)*	1360-1300 1225-1150	M S
C=C stretch (this vibration usually double for phenols)	ν(C=C)	≈1660	S
=CH in-plane bend (this band seen often in simple phenols)	β(=CH)	1110	Variable

*ν(C=C) also occurs in the 1390-1300 cm^{-1} range.

Spectra of Phenols

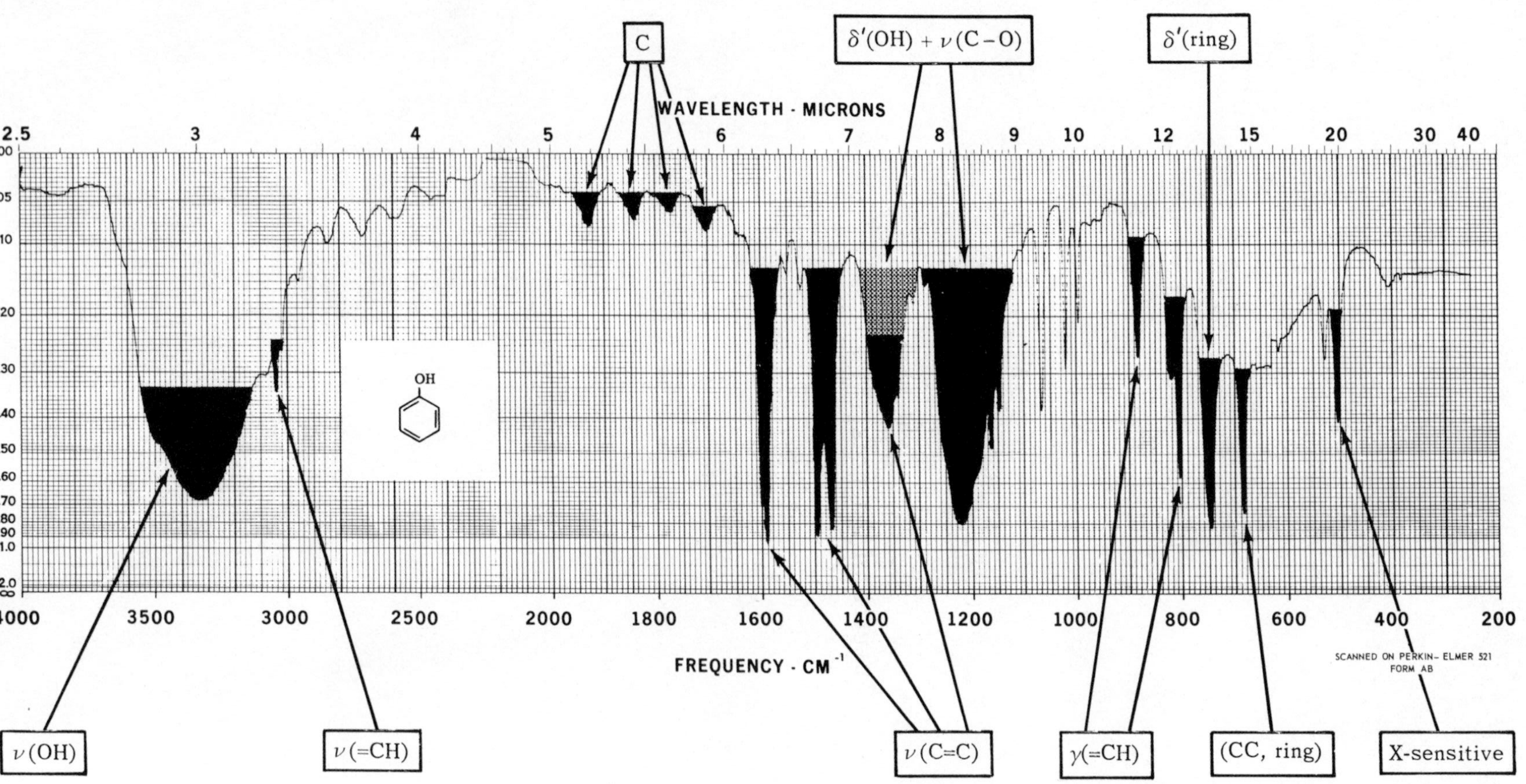

1. The first member of the phenols is of course phenol itself. This molecule has been subjected to many vibrational analyses, and in the first part of this section several of these were presented. The assignments on this spectrum are based on these papers. In general, two strong bands can be directly associated with the phenolic grouping. These are the ν(C–O) and a deformation of the COH. Most authors feel these modes interact, and suggest they result in strong bands near 1350 and 1200 cm^{-1}. We therefore assign both the two strong bands found in these regions as δ'(OH) + ν(C–O). There may be some value in assuming the 1350 cm^{-1} band is δ'(OH) and the 1200 cm^{-1} band the ν(C–O). This would make the ν(C–O) assignment agree with that found for anisoles, where the C – O group also occurs. However, it should be noted the ν(C = C) is also assigned as the 1350 cm^{-1} band in the analysis presented in the correlation section. The other assignments are for the C_6H_5 ring. The γ(= CH) assignments are those suggested in Volume 1, and appear in the expected positions. Note this is a high resolution (4000-200 cm^{-1}) spectrum. Several of these shall be presented in this volume.

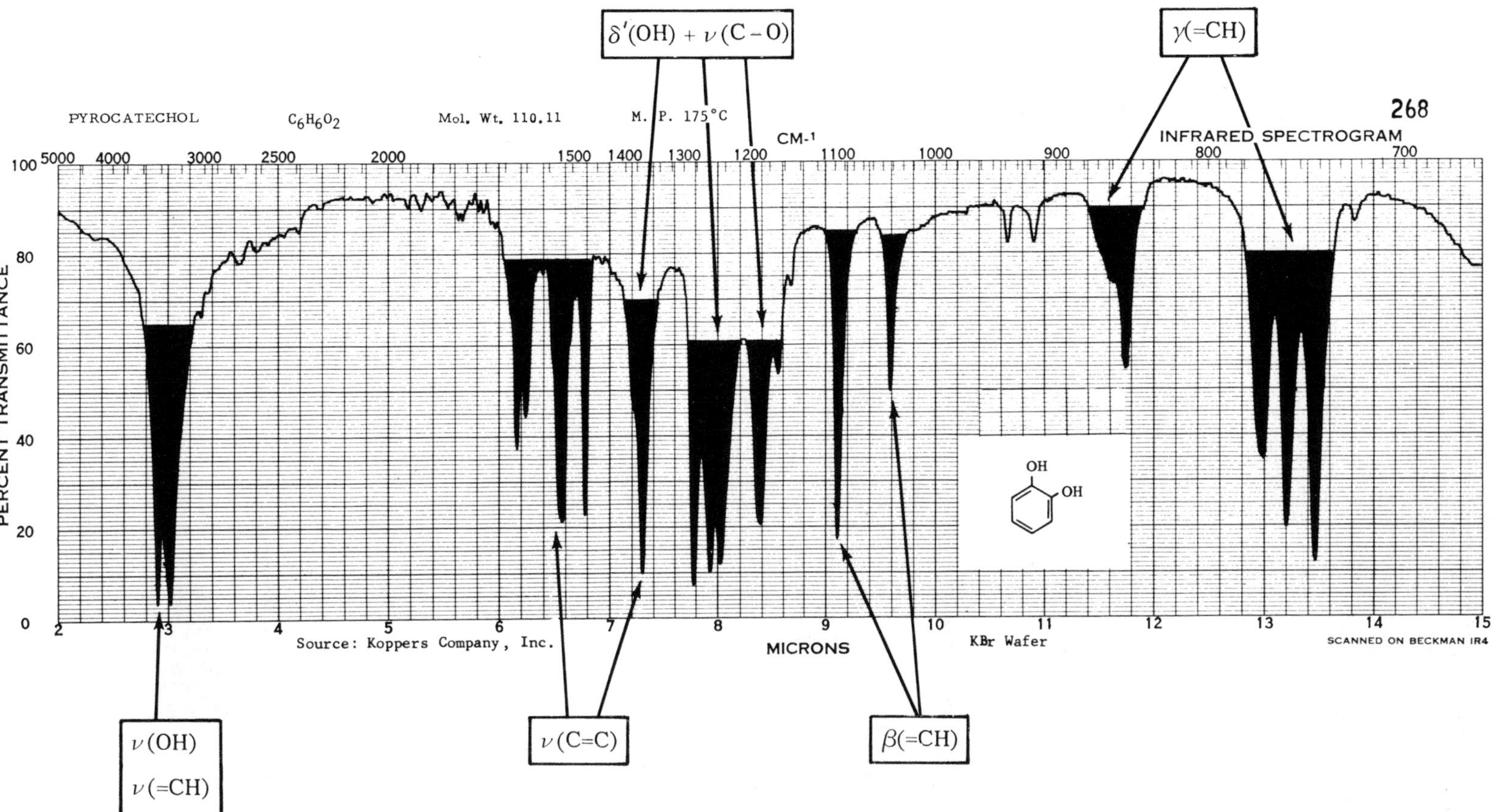

2. Catechol is an example of a 1,2-substituted ring phenol. The γ(= CH) should appear in the 770-735 cm^{-1} region, and strong bands are found here in this spectrum. They are multiple, however, instead of a single strong band. If this spectrum is similar to the vibrational analysis reported earlier for orthonitrophenol, then bands near 870, 785, 740, and 700 cm^{-1} would be found, and could be assigned as ring vibrations. We therefore assign all the strong bands below 900 cm^{-1} as ring vibrations. Note the double ν(OH) band, and contrast it with the next spectrum.

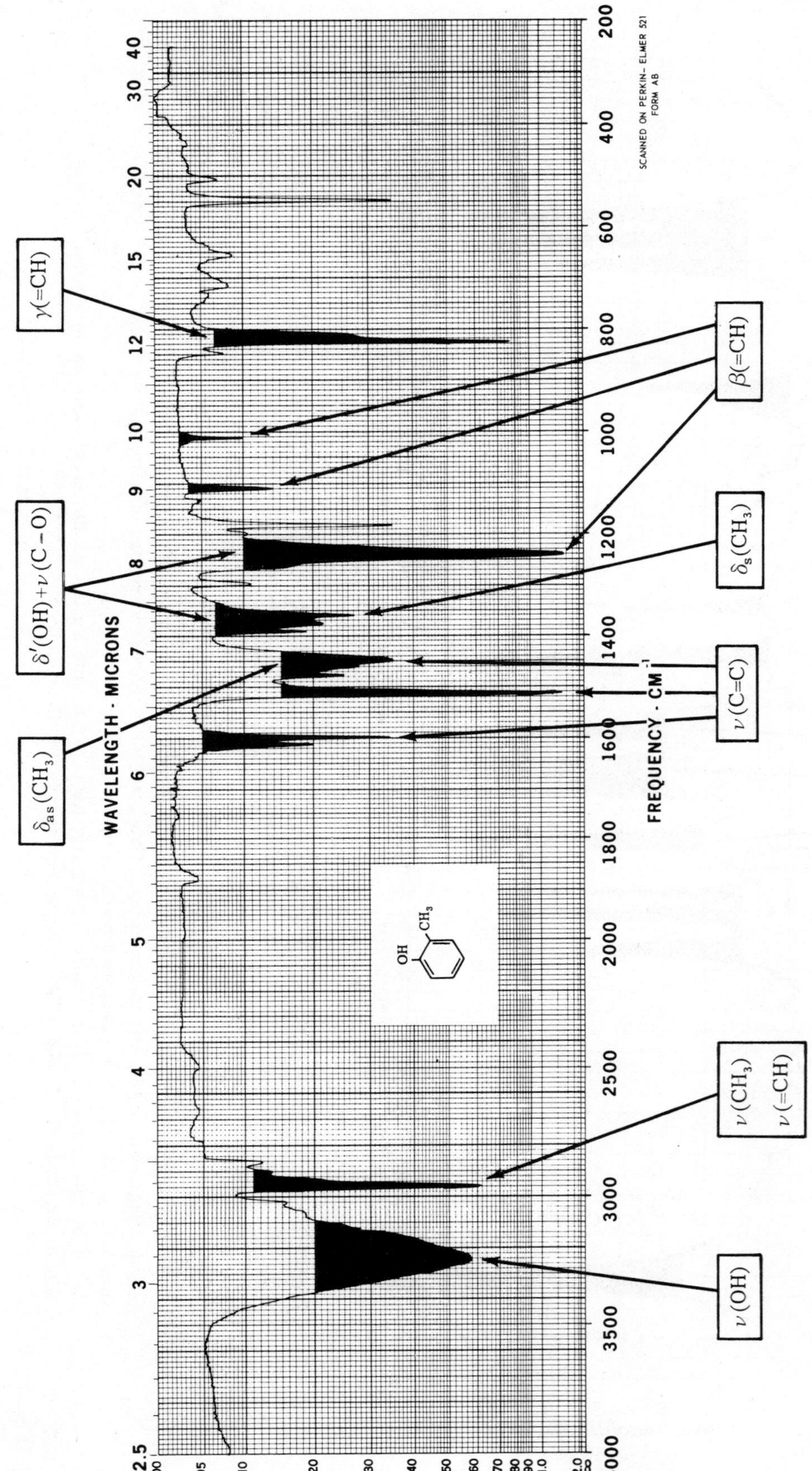

3. Since catechol and o-cresol are both 1,2-disubstituted ring compounds, the previous spectrum can be compared to this one for similar ring vibrations. The band near 840 cm^{-1} is present in both spectra and can certainly be assigned as a ring vibration. Note the band near 1250 cm^{-1} for catechol is a sharp band centered at 1220 cm^{-1} for this cresol. The two β(= CH) assignments near 1080 and 1030 cm^{-1} at nearby the same position in each spectrum indicate these are correctly assigned to the ring. This is again a high-resolution 4000-200 cm^{-1} spectrum.

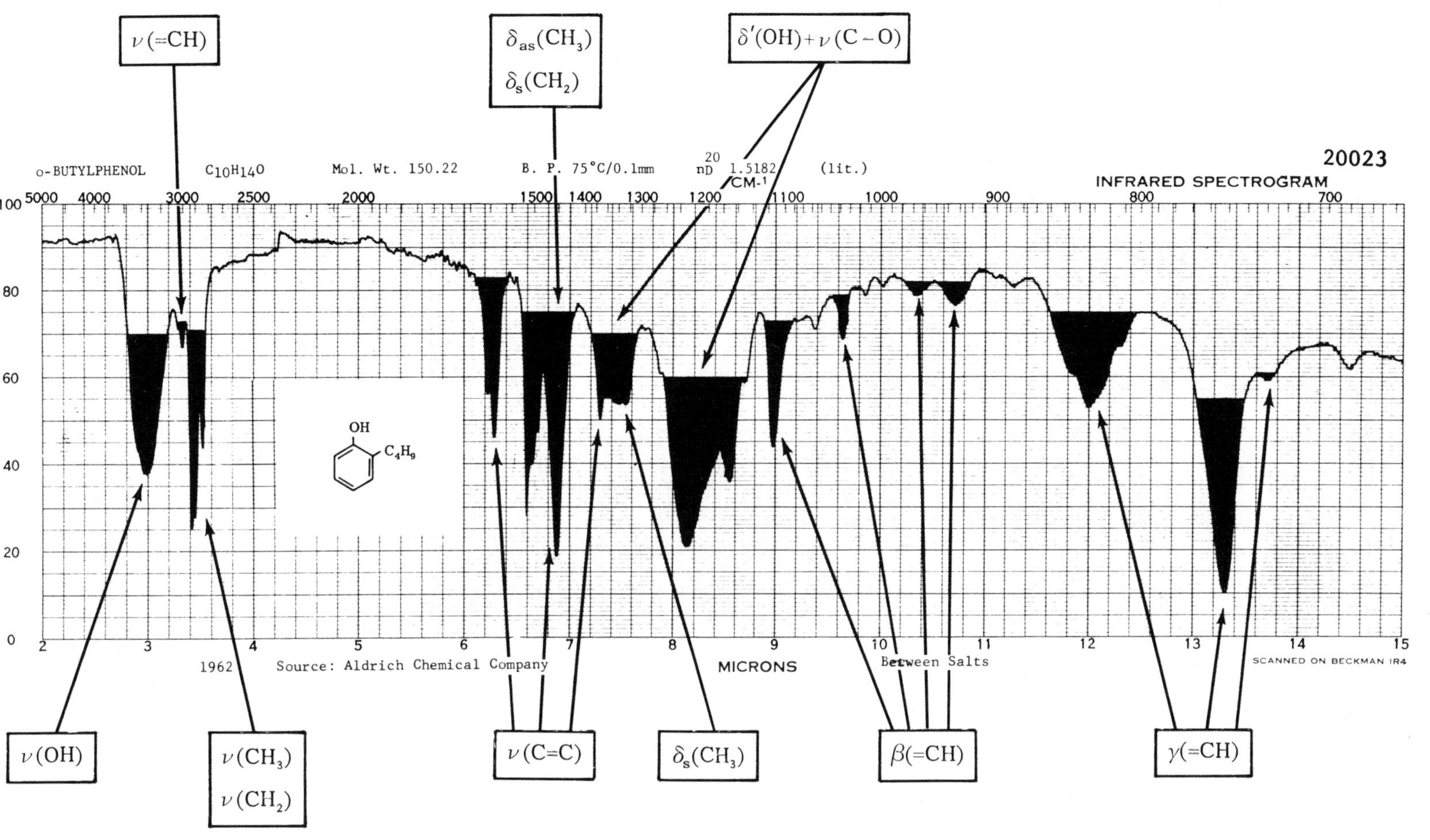

4. This compound differs from the previous o-cresol only in length of aliphatic chain attached to the ring. We would expect a similar spectrum, and this is the case. The assignments are the same.

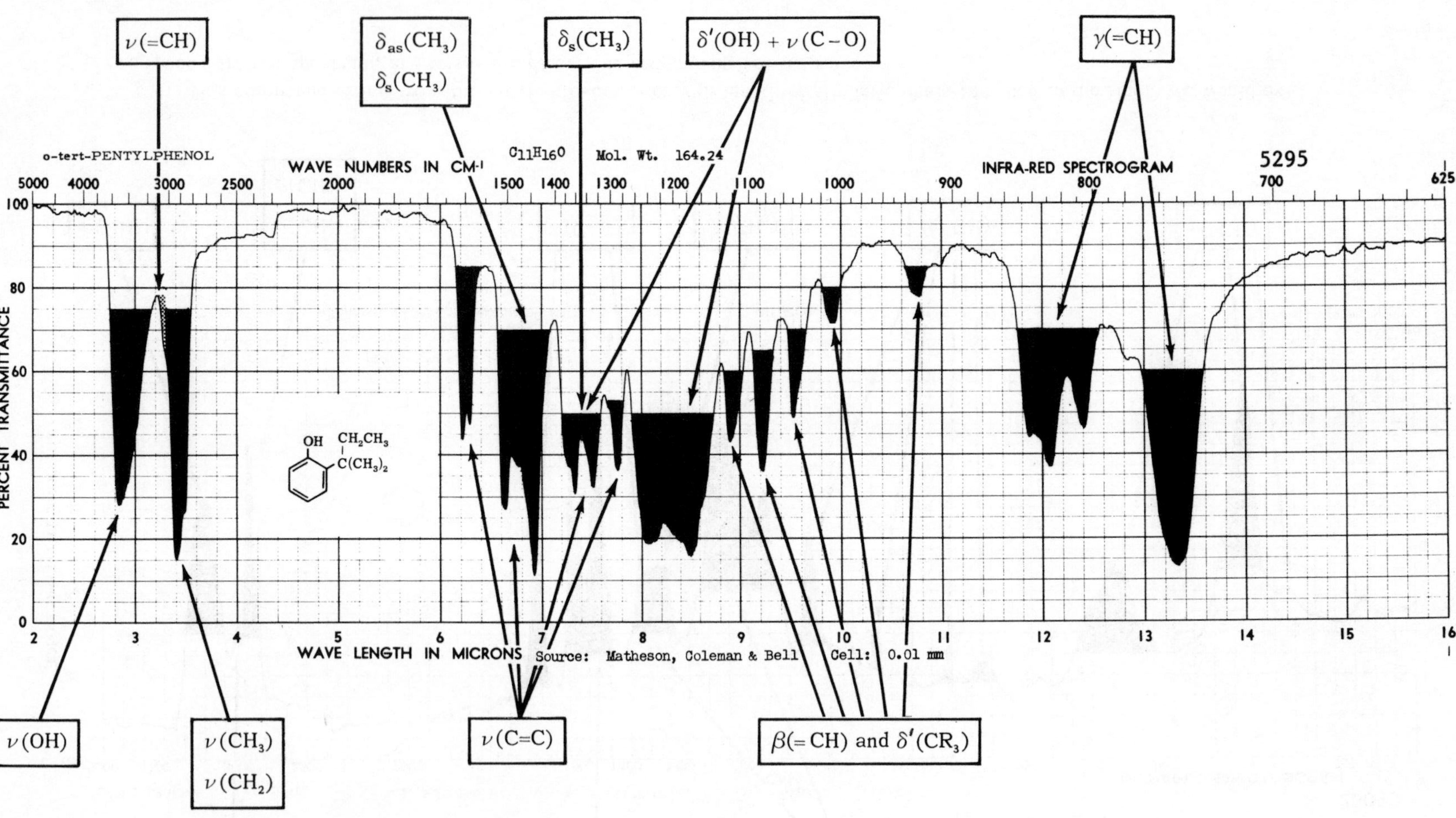

5. The spectrum here is similar to the two previous ones except for a few bands near 1100 cm^{-1}. These bands are presumably due to the tertiary alkyl group. Attention can be given to the broad band between 1220 and 1170 cm^{-1}. This band appeared in a similar region for the previous alkyl phenols, except catechol, where it was at a higher position. This shifting should be expected since the band is assigned to both the C−O and OH groups. The γ(=CH) bands retain fairly constant positions for all of the o-phenols examined here.

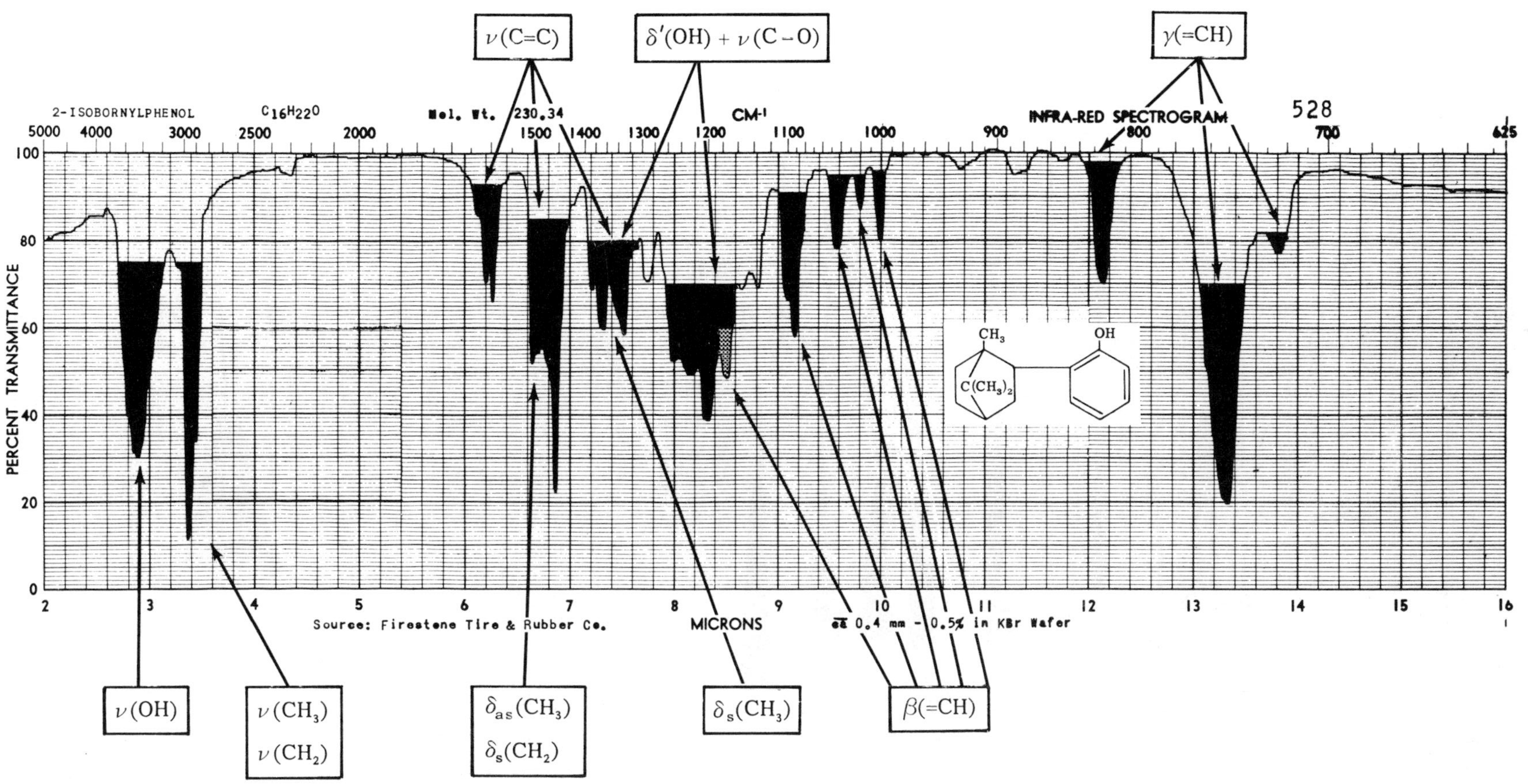

6. This spectra is similar to those of the previous alkyl o-phenols. It is therefore difficult to make assignments to the isobornyl radical. The fact illustrates how general classes of compounds can usually be identified by their infrared spectra, but slight differences in structure, especially of saturated alkyls, are not easily recognized.

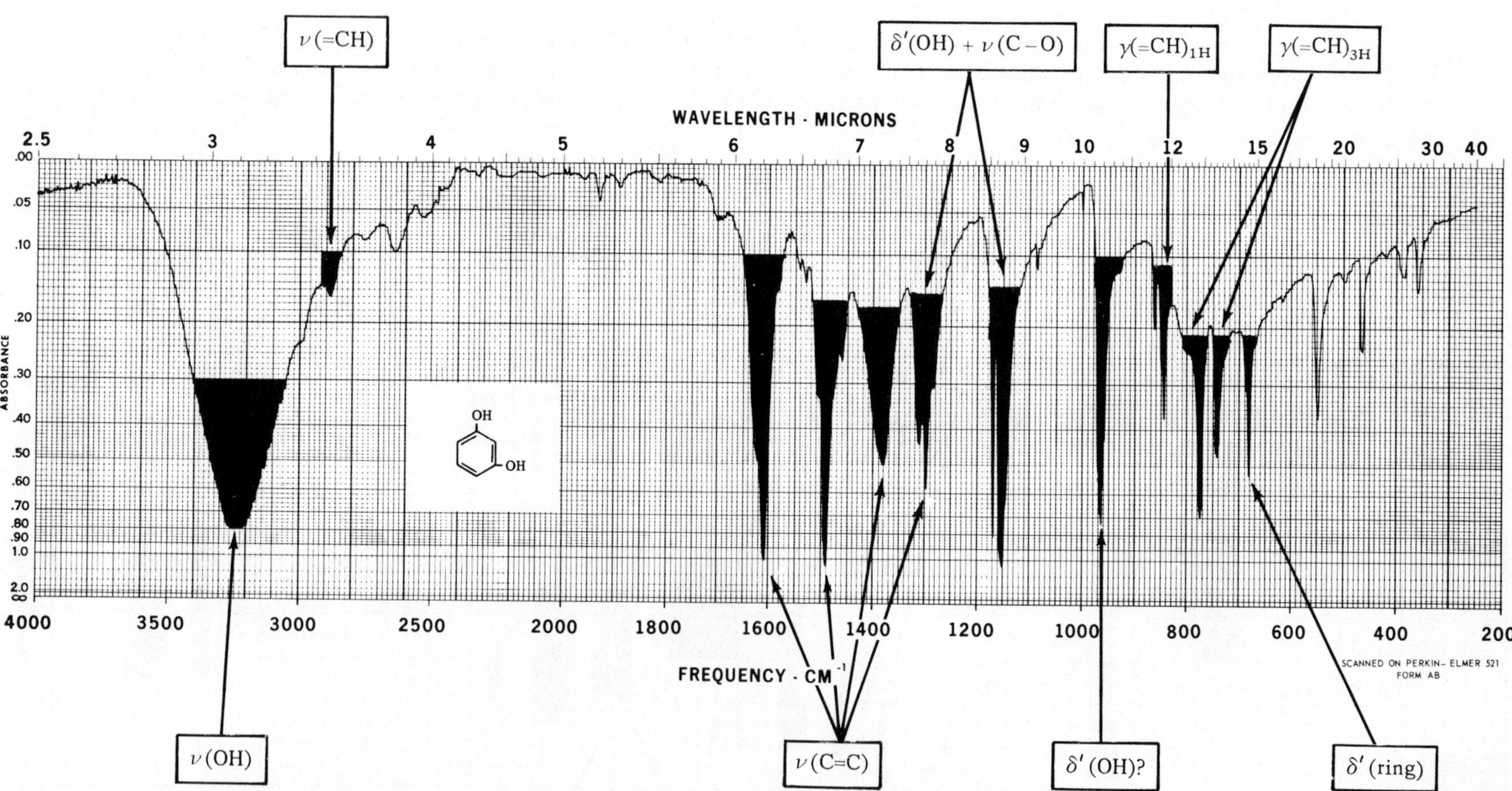

7. This is the first meta-substituted phenol we shall examine. Since o-phenols having two OH groups showed a higher 1250 cm^{-1} band, we shall examine this region first. For resorcinol the band is near 1300 cm^{-1}, a position even higher than for catechol, the o-dihydroxy compound. No explanation is offered for this except to note that in the following alkyl compounds this band is higher than for the previous ortho alkyl derivatives.

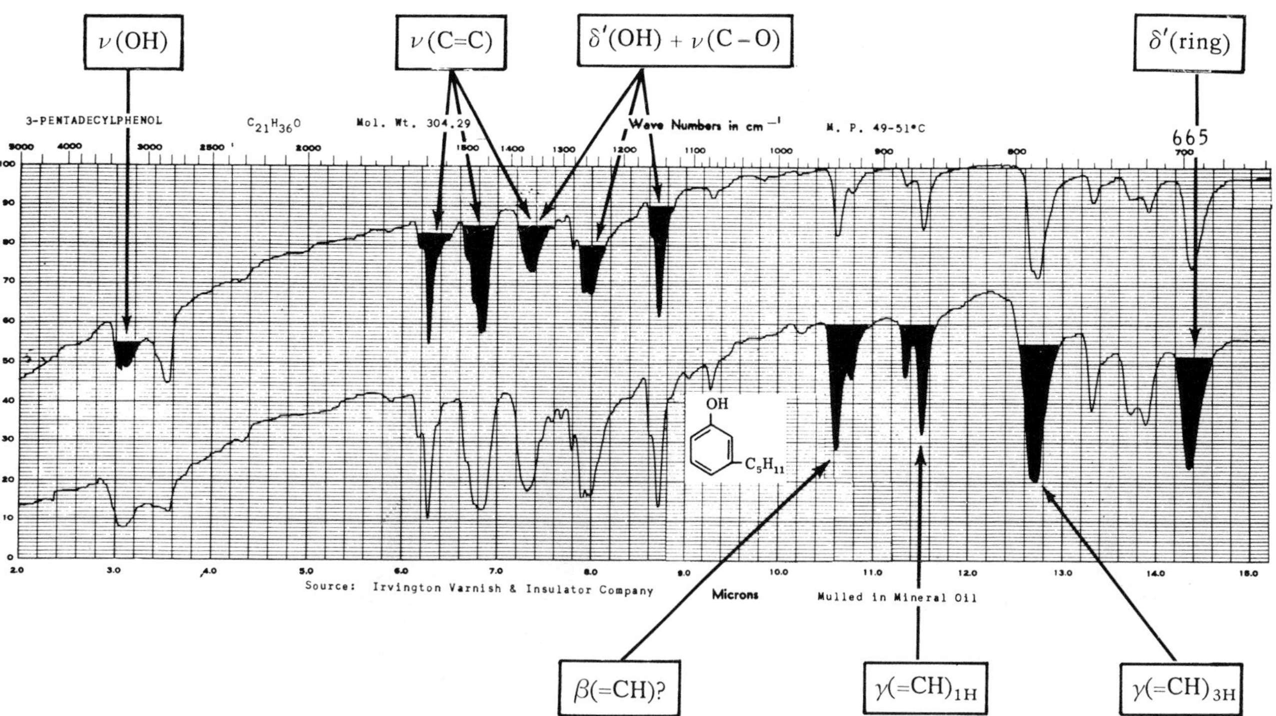

8. This spectrum is presented as an example of a 1,3-phenol derivative with the substituent a straight alkyl chain. The 1250 cm^{-1} band discussed in the previous spectrum is assigned to $\delta'(OH) + \nu(C-O)$; however, a lower frequency band near 1150 cm^{-1} is so intense that it is included in the assignment. The $\gamma(=CH)$ assignments for a 1,3-substituted ring should appear in the 810-750 and 725-680 cm^{-1} region, and bands in these positions are found. The position of $\nu(OH)$ suggests a very strongly hydrogen-bonded system.

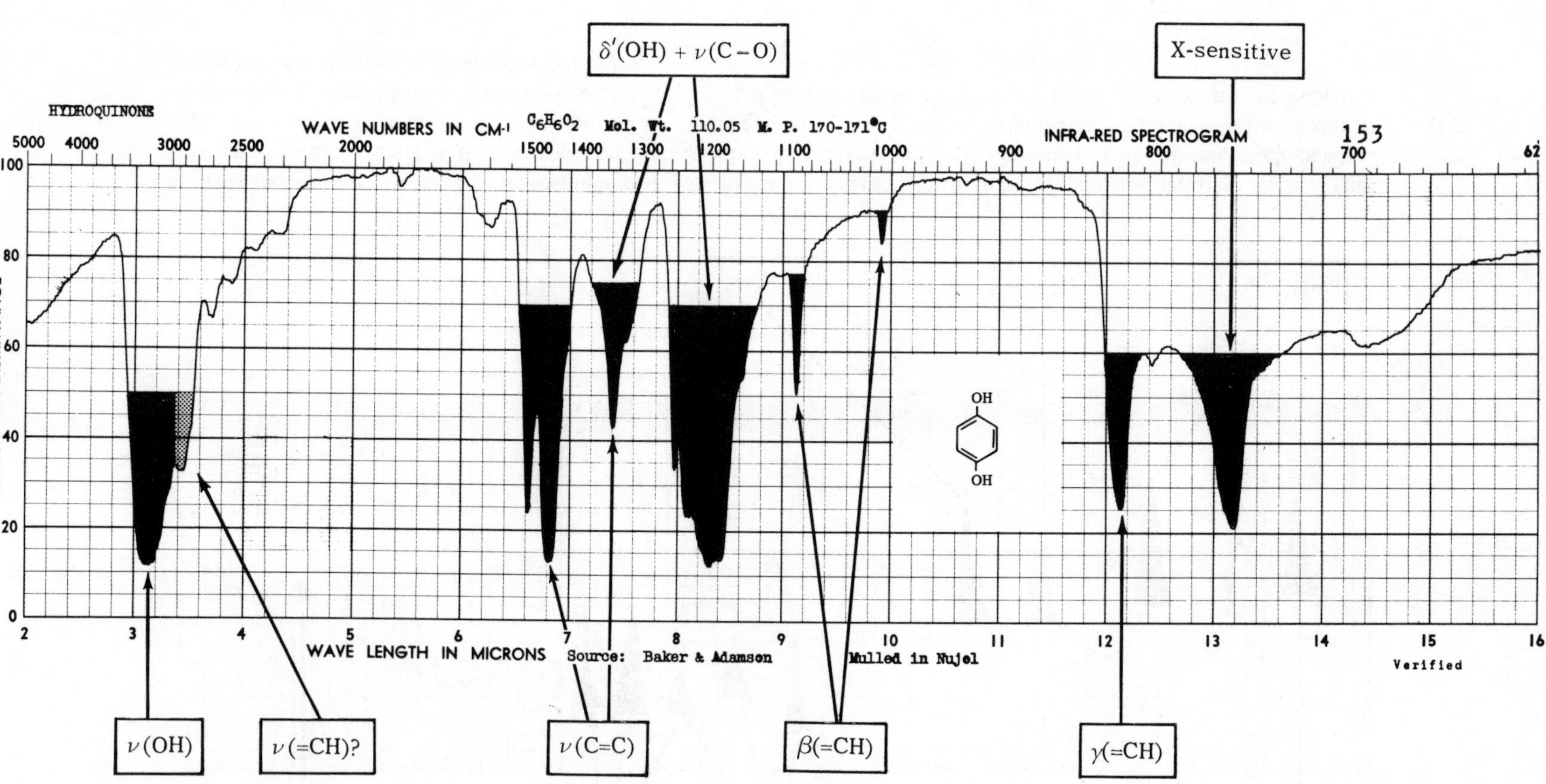

9. This is the first para-substituted phenol we shall discuss. Note for this compound, the band near 1290 cm^{-1} for the meta derivative is now shifted to 1250 cm^{-1}, and the 1250 cm^{-1} band for the ortho derivative is now at 1200 cm^{-1}. The position of this band appears to be a function of the ring substitution, and its position can, therefore, be used to distinguish between the ortho, meta, and para phenols.

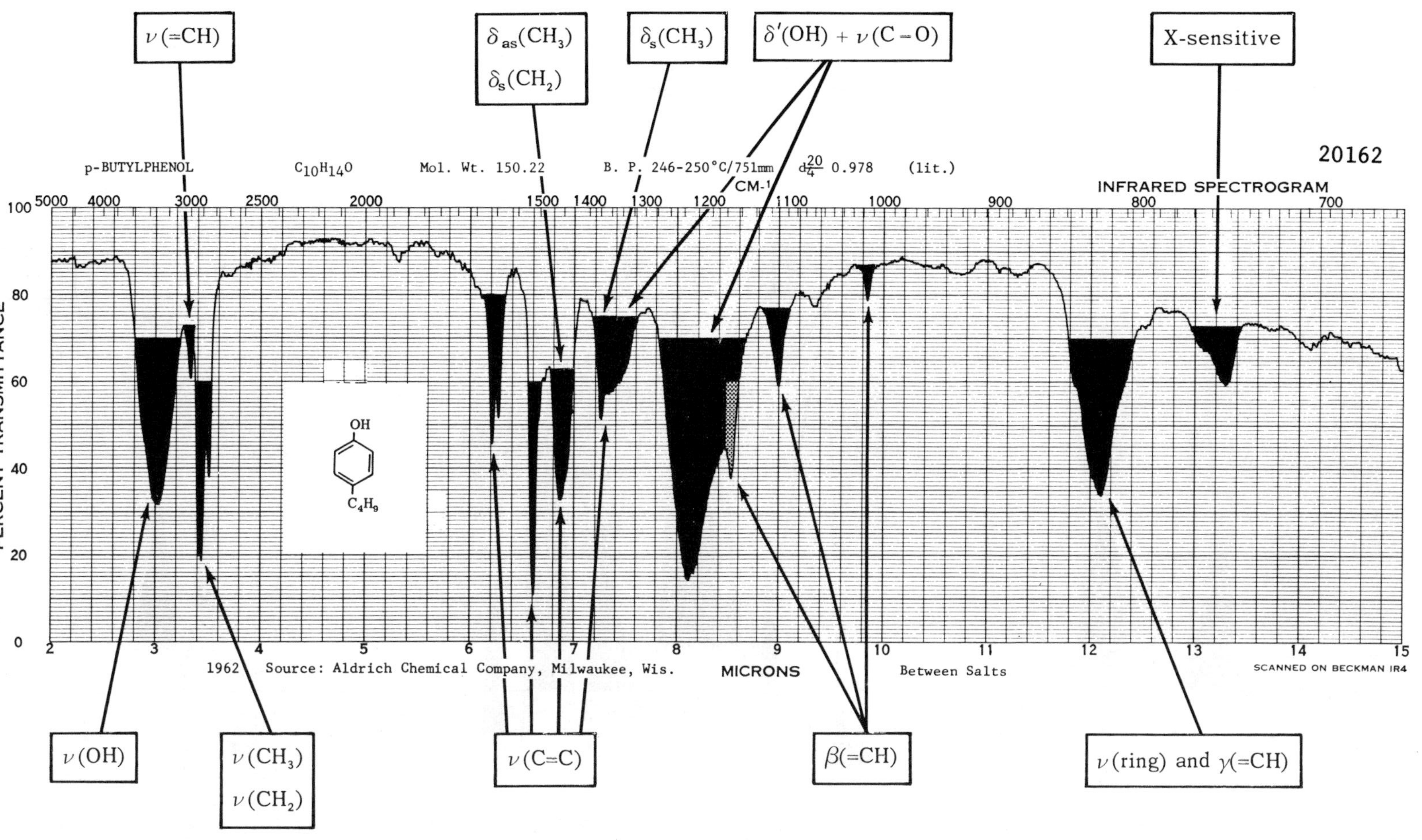

10. If we compare the spectrum of p-butylphenol to the previous one of hydroquinine, the following similarities can be noted. Nearly all major peaks are observed in the same position in both spectra. The band near 1220 cm^{-1} has a different contour in each spectrum, but its broadness in both is about the same. A band near 1110 cm^{-1} in this spectrum is shifted by about 20 cm^{-1} in the quinone spectrum. The γ(=CH) vibrations occur in about the same position for both compounds.

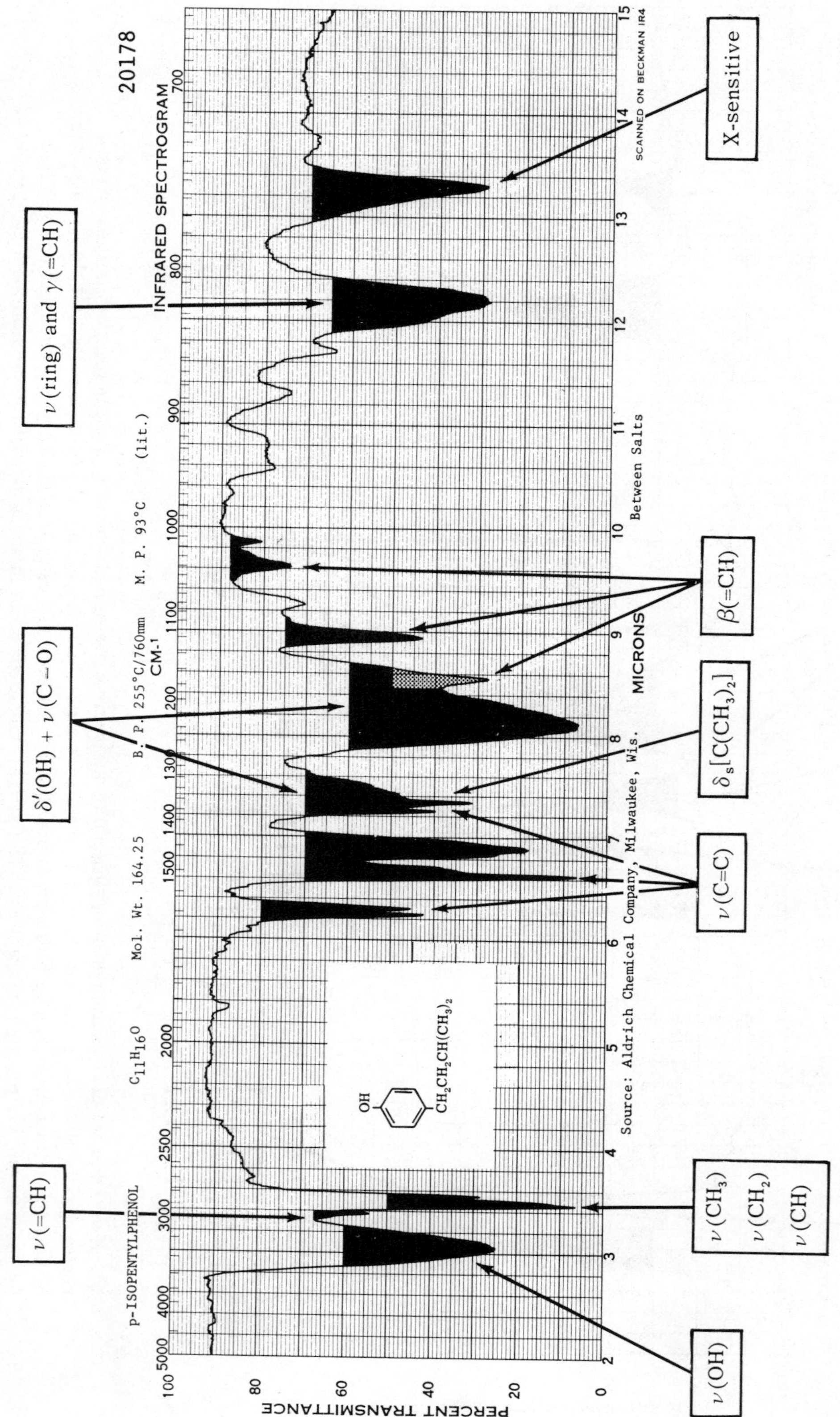

11. The spectrum of p-isopentylphenol is so similar to the previous spectrum that a casual inspection might identify them as of the same compound. Only a very exact measurement of band positions and the presence of a number of weak bands in the 1100-800 cm^{-1} region would allow a worker to distinguish between them.

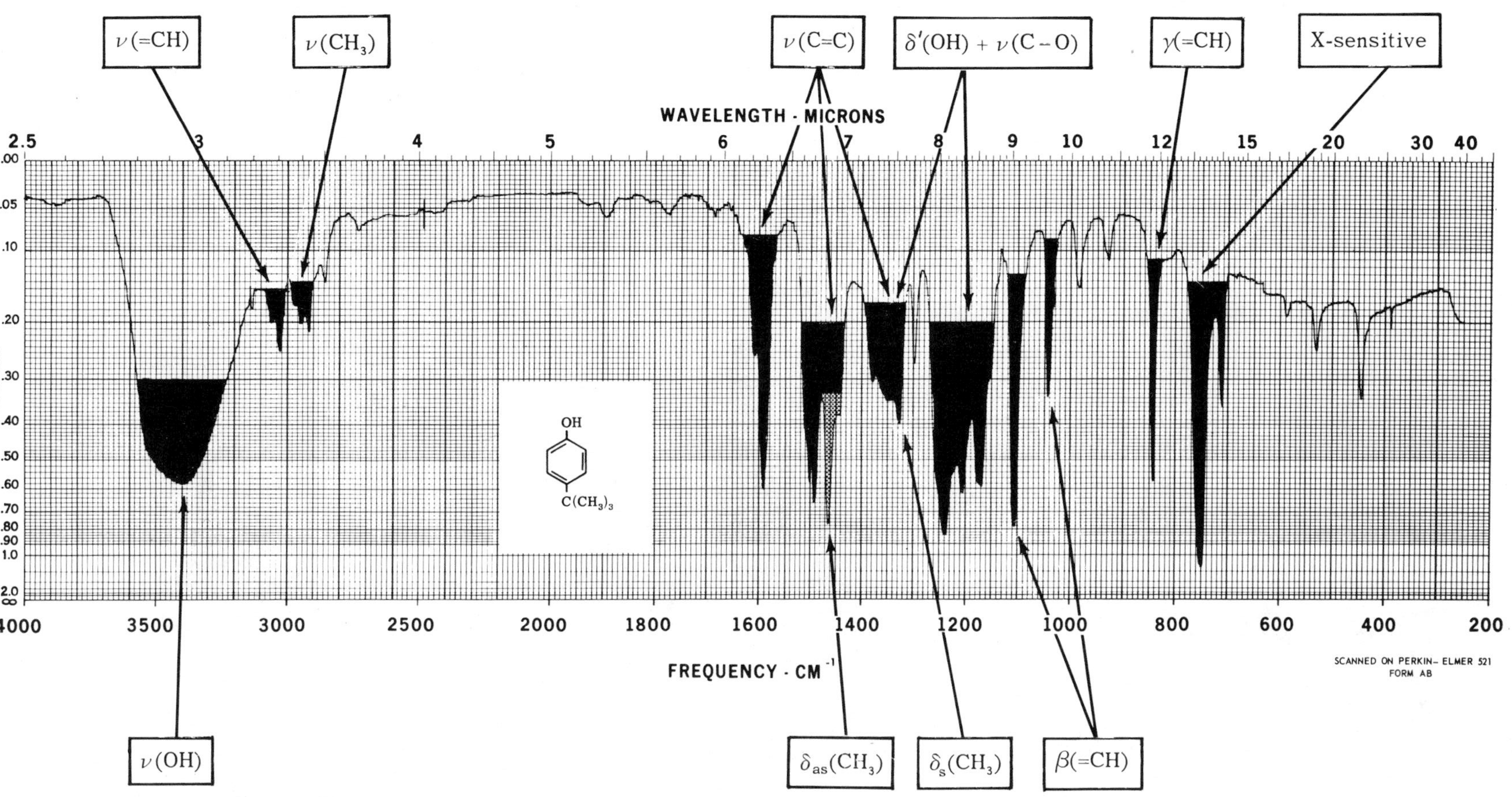

12. The presence of a tertiary butyl group in the para position results in a spectrum for this phenol that is similar to the previous two para compounds. It should be noted the position of the δ'(OH) + ν(C–O) bands are similar for this and previous para derivatives.

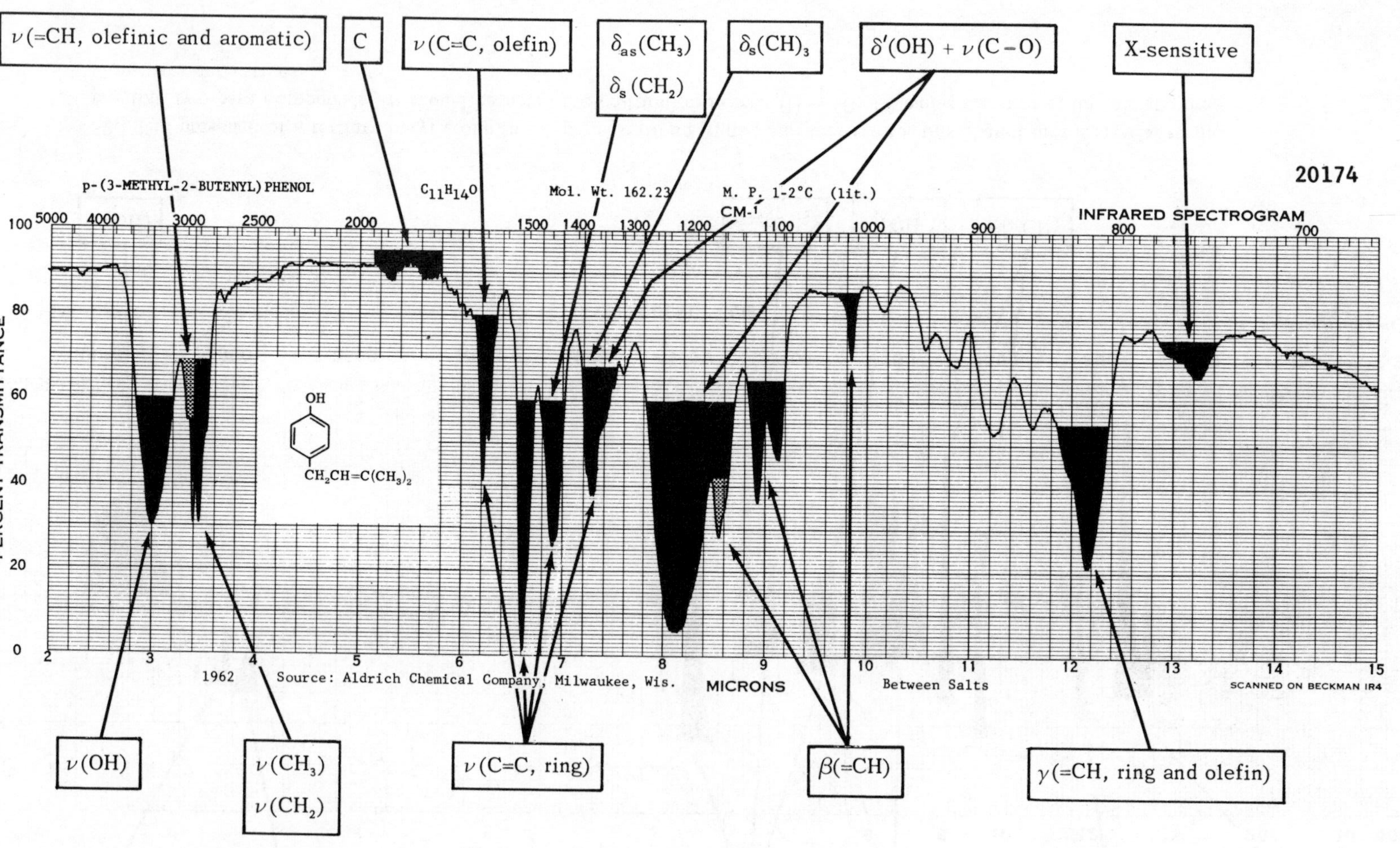

13. The combination of a phenol with an olefinic group results in the overlapping of some of the group frequencies from each group. It is therefore difficult to separate the olefinic from the aromatic group frequencies for this compound. Note the strong, broad band near 1200 cm^{-1}. This quite distinct phenolic band helps identify this as well as many other compounds as phenols.

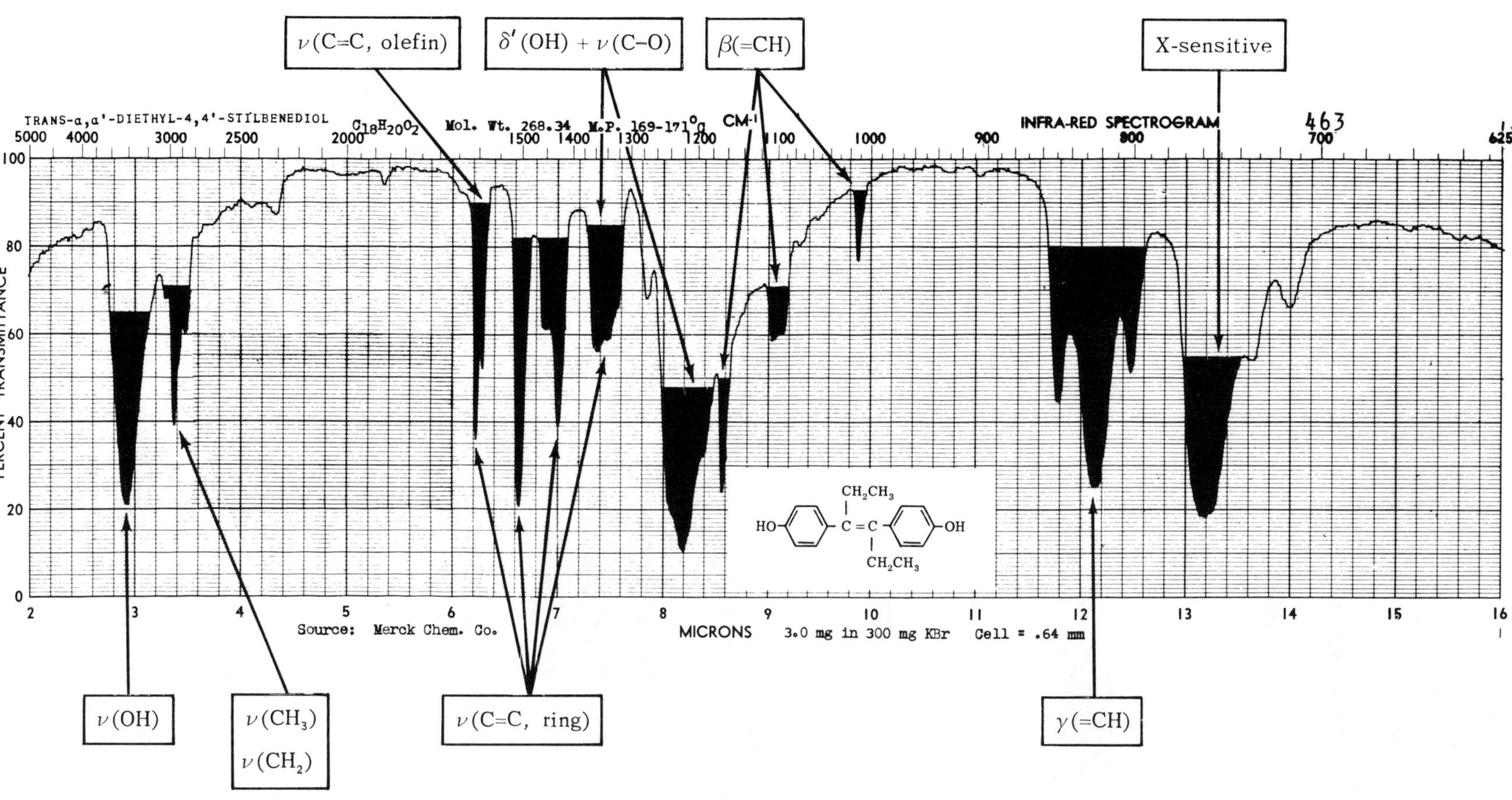

14. This spectrum is another example of a phenolic group combined with an olefin. Again the strong, broad phenolic band is seen near 1200 cm^{-1}. Note again this position is the same for all the para-substituted derivatives.

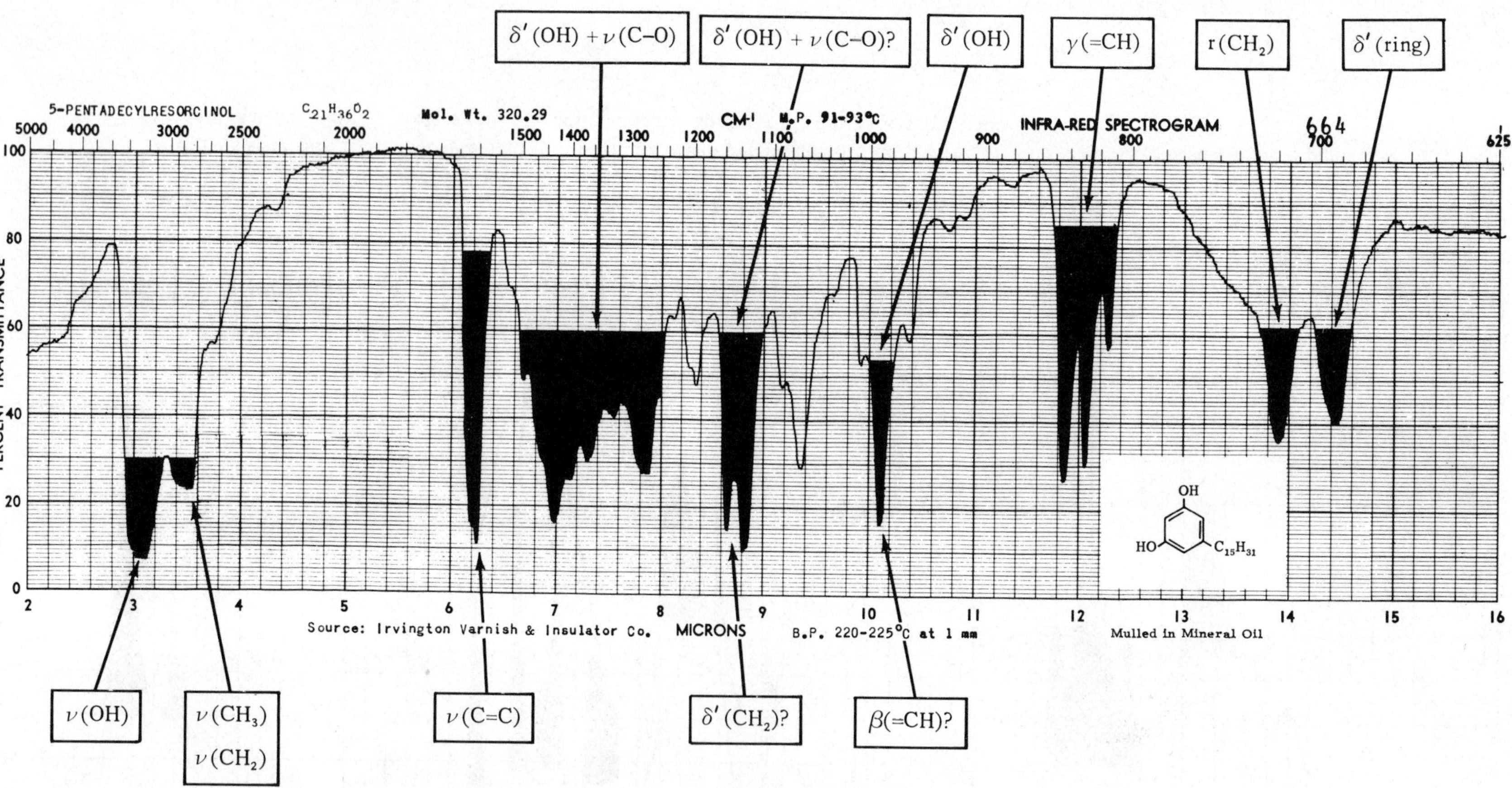

15. This compound is the first example of a phenol where the ring substitution is 1, 3, 5. In addition, this is a dihydroxy compound. There is a strong, very broad band from 1450-1250 cm^{-1} which certainly represents a number of group frequencies. The spectrum at first glance appears confusing until two facts are noted: First, the spectrum was run as a nujol mull. Second, there is a long straight-chain group on the ring. It is therefore to be expected that the 1450 cm^{-1} band, representing CH_3 and CH_2 groups, is the strongest band in the spectrum. Thus the 1250 cm^{-1} band, usually the strongest one in the spectrum of phenols, now is only a medium strong band. The band near 1130 cm^{-1} is also a confusing one, since its large intensity is not expected for this compound. It is probably a deformation of the CH_2 group. 1, 3, 5-substituted aromatic rings should have a band near 710-690 cm^{-1}, and a band near 695 cm^{-1} is assigned as δ′(ring). The bands near 830 cm^{-1} are assigned as γ(=CH), and are in the expected region for the 1, 3, 5-substituted ring.

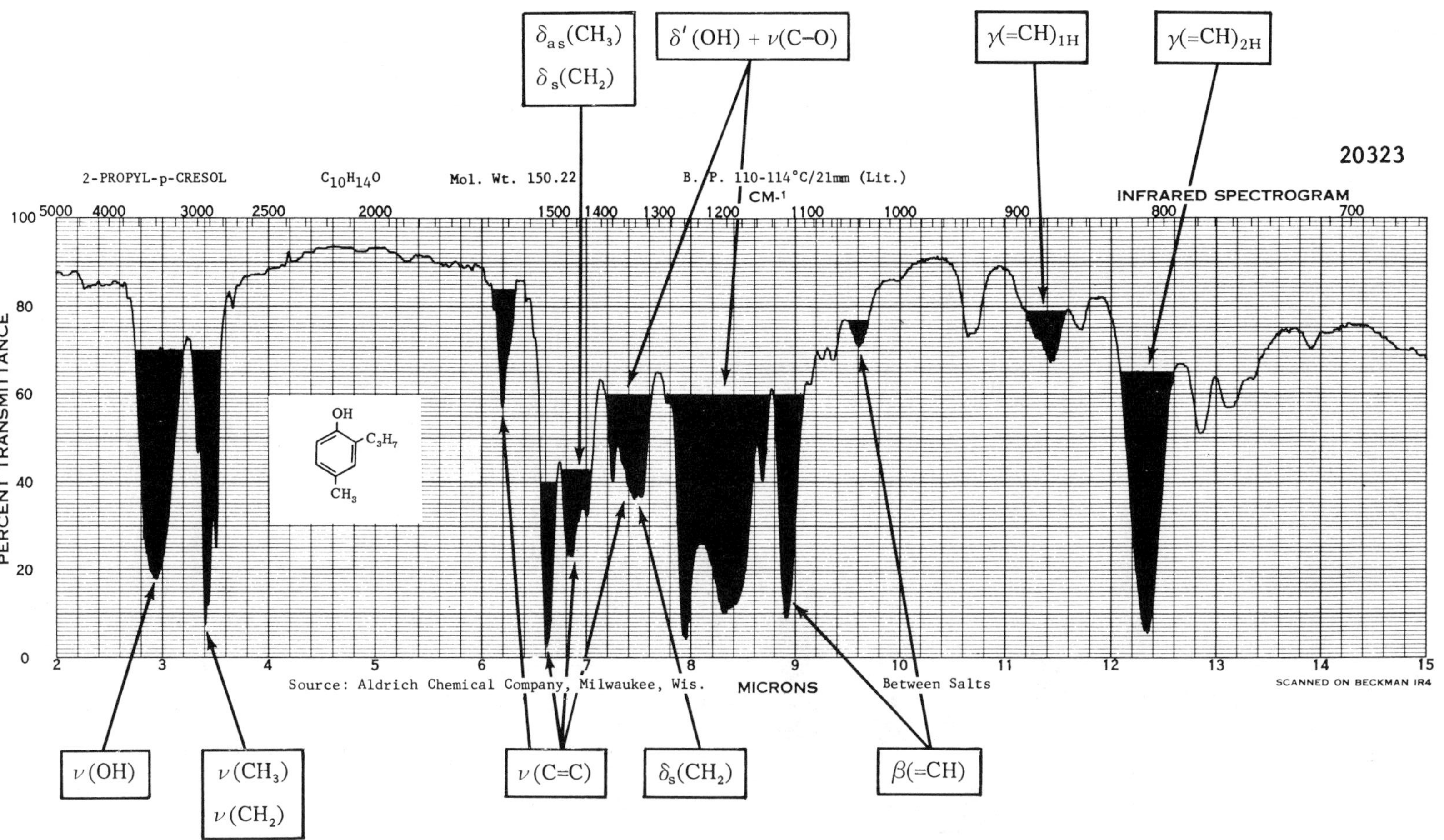

16. The 1, 2, 4-substituted aromatic ring should have bands near 860-800 and 900-860 cm^{-1}. A weak band near 880 cm^{-1} is suggested for one of these assignments, while the strong band near 815 cm^{-1} is assigned as the second. In Volume 1 several 1, 2, 4-substituted rings were examined. In one case the 880 cm^{-1} was much weaker than the 815 cm^{-1}. We therefore feel the assignment of these two bands are correct, and the quite different intensities is not an unusual observation. The strong broad band near 1200 cm^{-1} is typical of the phenolic band we have seen in previous spectra.

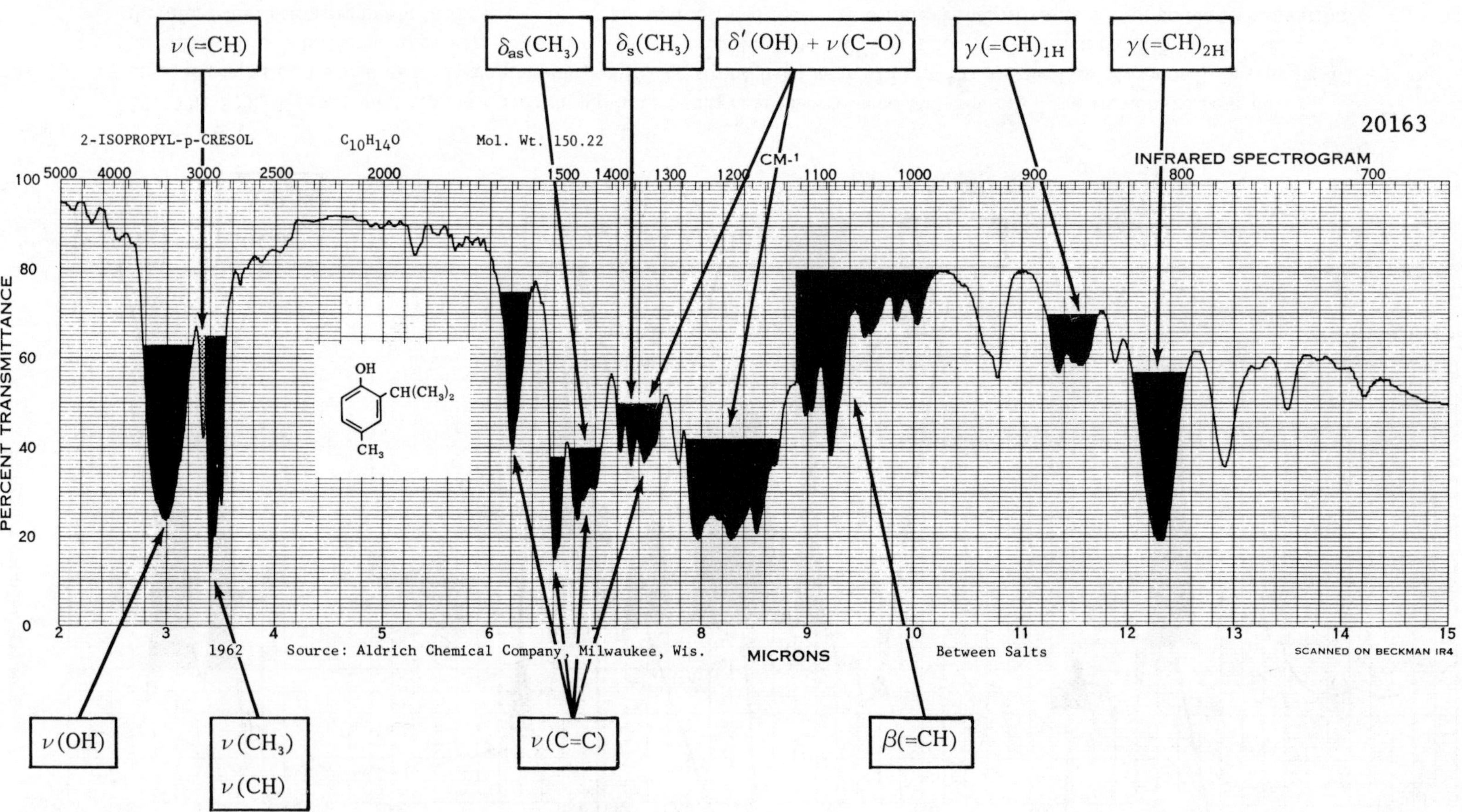

17. This compound also has a 1, 2, 4-substituted ring, and the same bands as for the previous spectrum are observed at 880 and 820 cm^{-1}, with about the same relative intensities. The 1200 cm^{-1} band is very broad. Note how in a compound having this large number of structural groups, the isopropyl splitting of the 1380 cm^{-1} band is not easily assigned (see Volume 1 for this assignment).

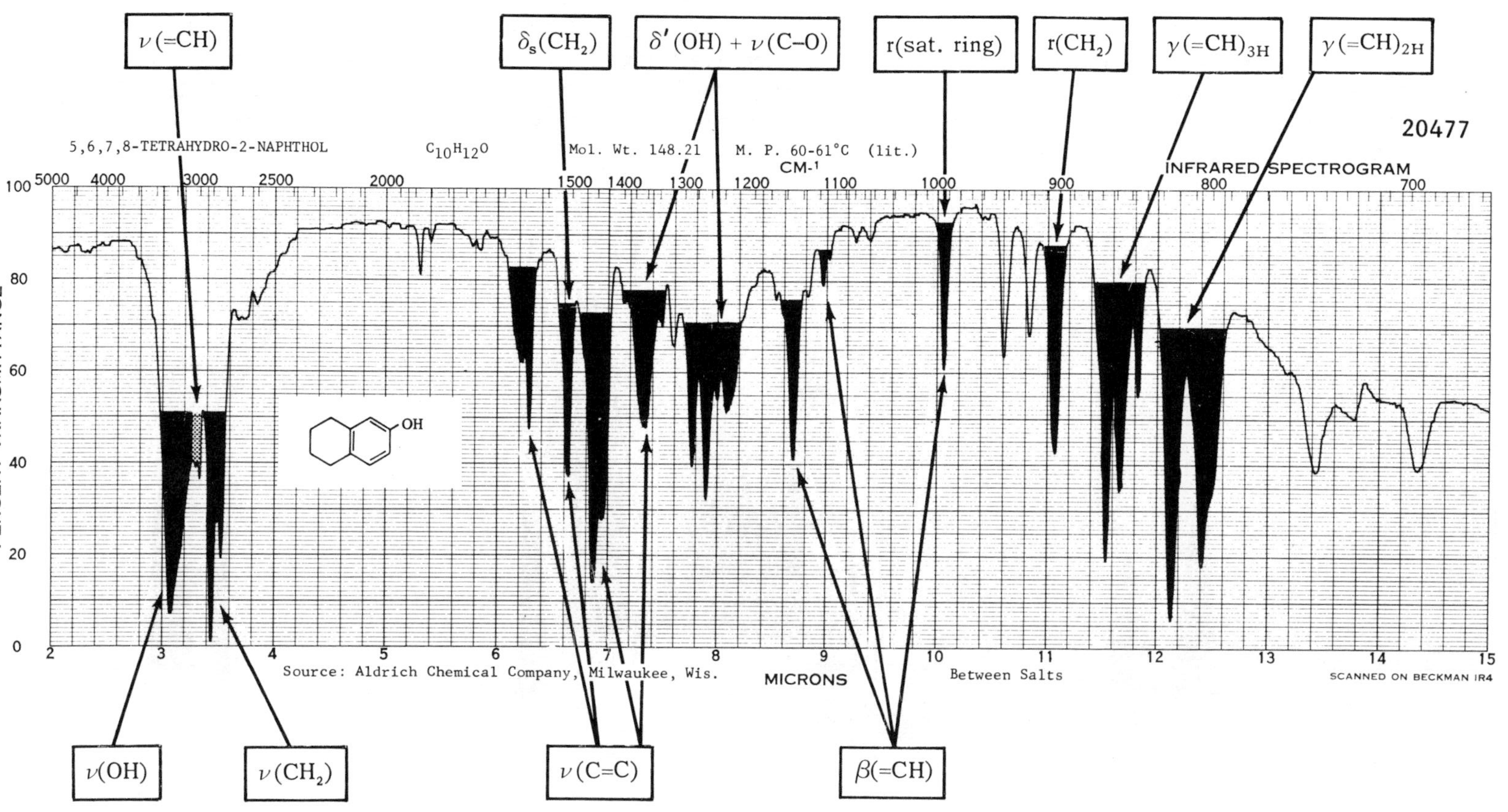

18. This spectrum is also of a 1, 2, 4-substituted ring compound. The 1, 2 substituent is a cyclohexyl ring. The spectrum differs from the previous ones in that there are more bands which appear as doublets. Possibly this is due to the saturated-ring vibrations, which appear in regions similar to the unsaturated ring. In Volume 1 several 1, 2-substituted cyclohexyl spectra were presented, and many strong sharp bands were observed from 1100 to 800 cm^{-1}. Since the assignments of the saturated ring are not as well defined as those for the aromatic ring, it is necessary to guess at the correct assignments for the saturated ring.

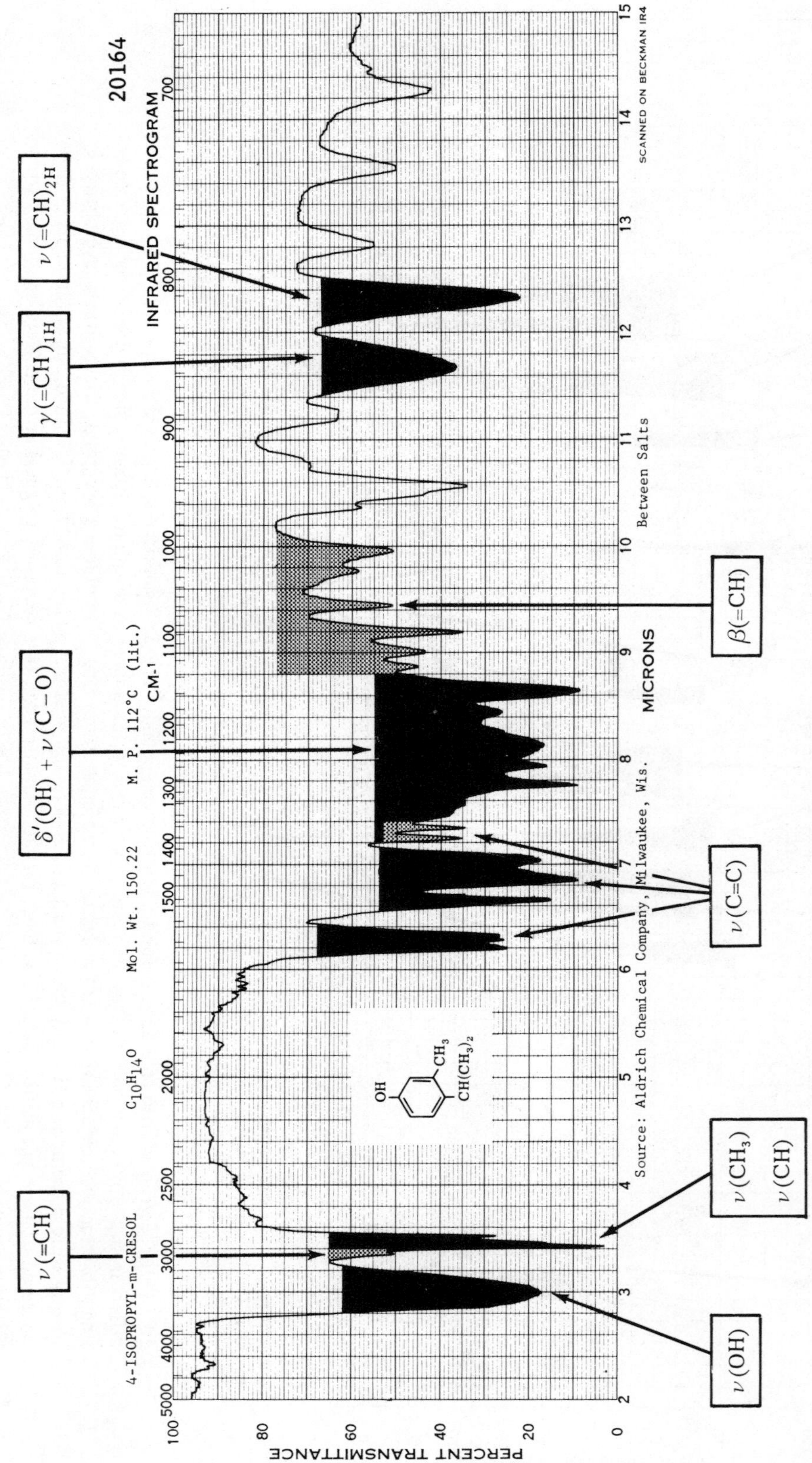

19. The spectrum of 4-isopropyl-m-cresol is still another example of a 1, 2, 4-substituted ring. In this example the 870 and 810 cm^{-1} bands have a more nearly equal intensity rather than the 810 cm^{-1} band being much stronger. The very broad 1200 cm^{-1} band suggests this spectrum might give sharper bands if the sampling method had been changed. The other assignments are similar in previous spectra.

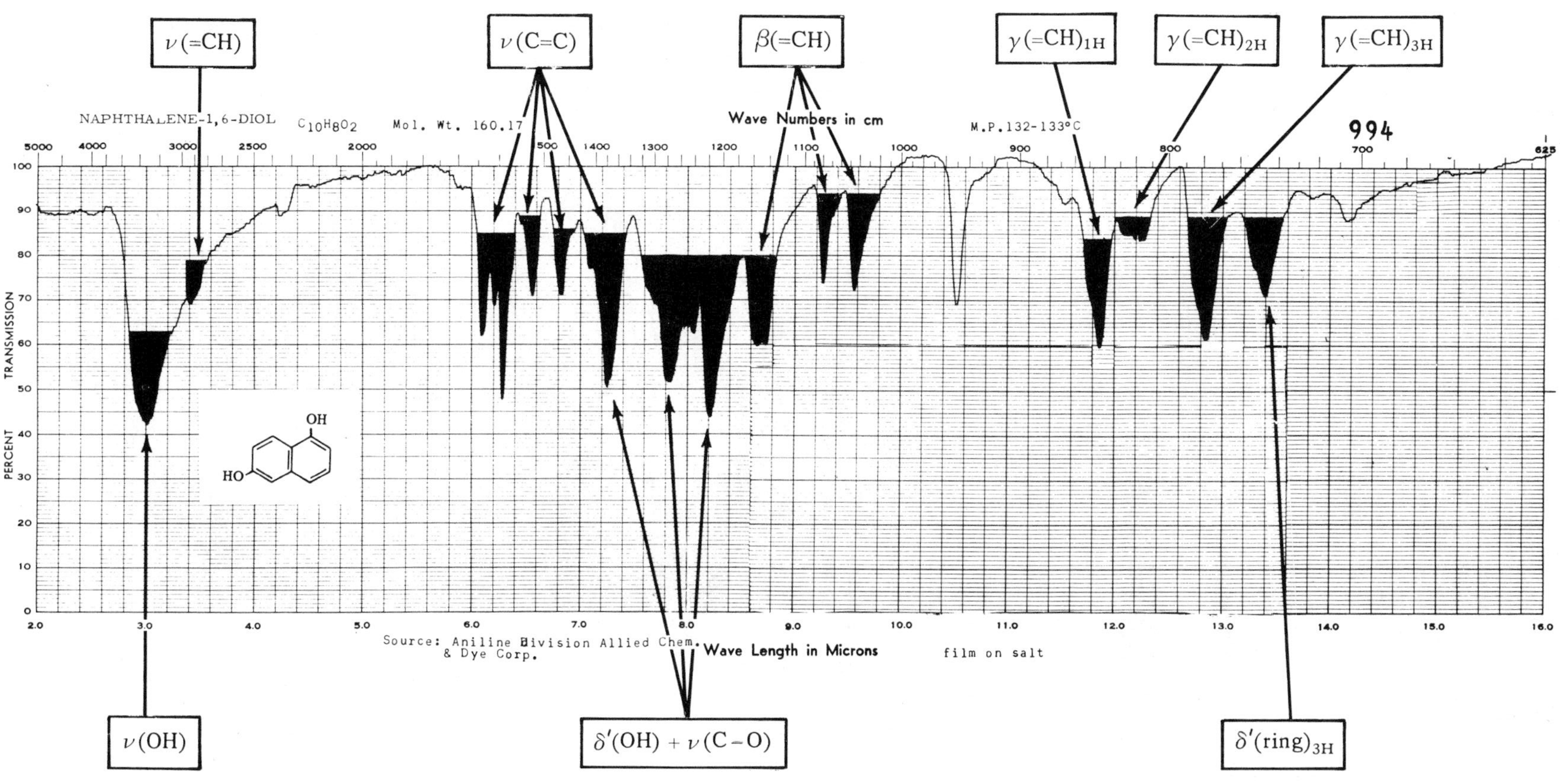

20. This phenol has two OH groups on two different rings. There is no indication of this in the spectrum, except the γ (=CH) bands suggest two kinds of rings. We assign the $\delta'(OH) + \nu(C-O)$ bands as in the previous spectra. Possibly the bands near 1220 cm^{-1} and 1280 cm^{-1} may indicate the presence of the two OH groups.

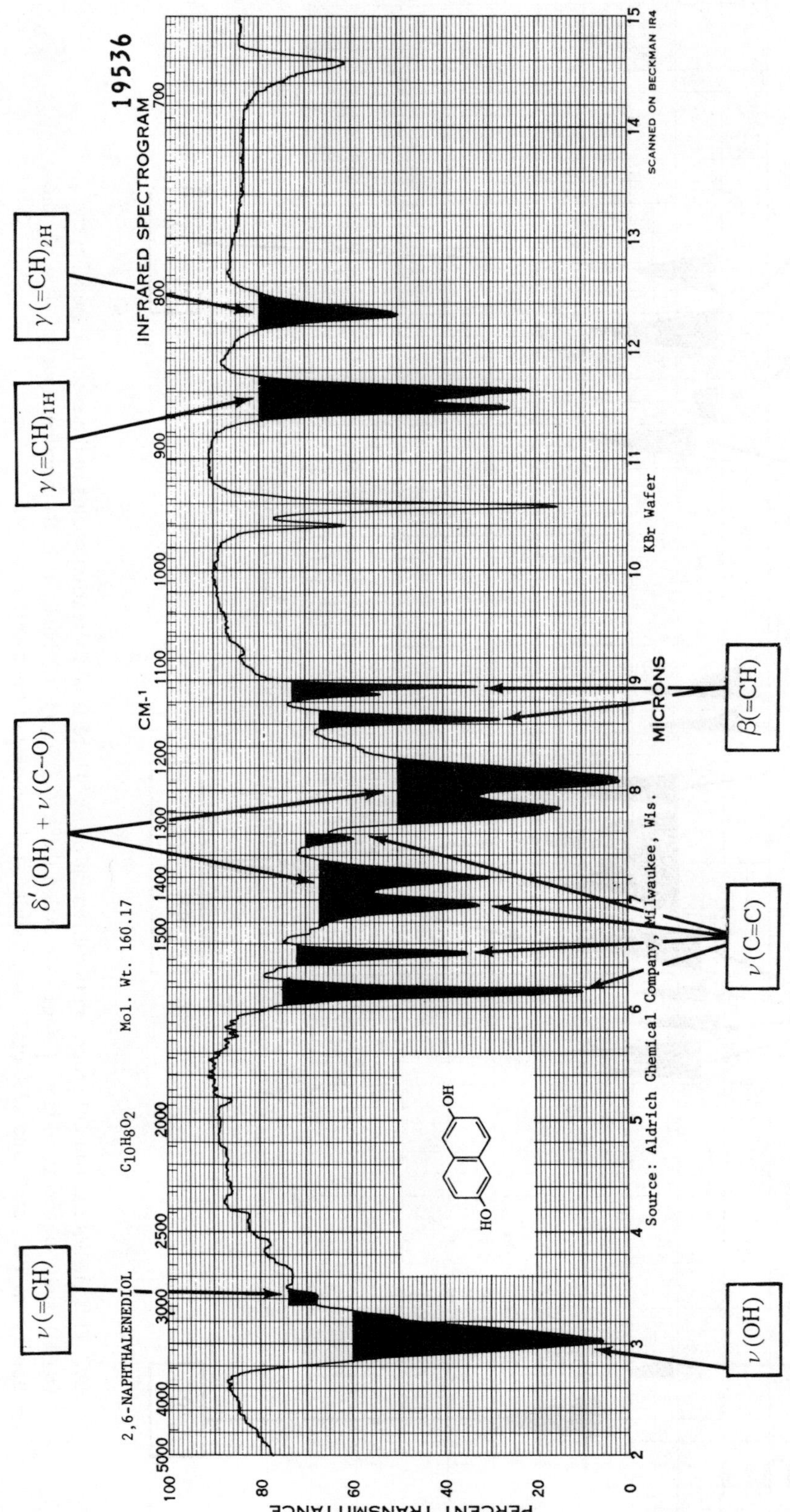

21. This symmetrical phenol has a double band near 1220 cm^{-1} which might be suggestive of the two OH groups; but since we have found no literature studies of dihydric compounds showing doubling of the 1220 cm^{-1} band, we cannot make this a positive suggestion. Other bands are the expected ones.

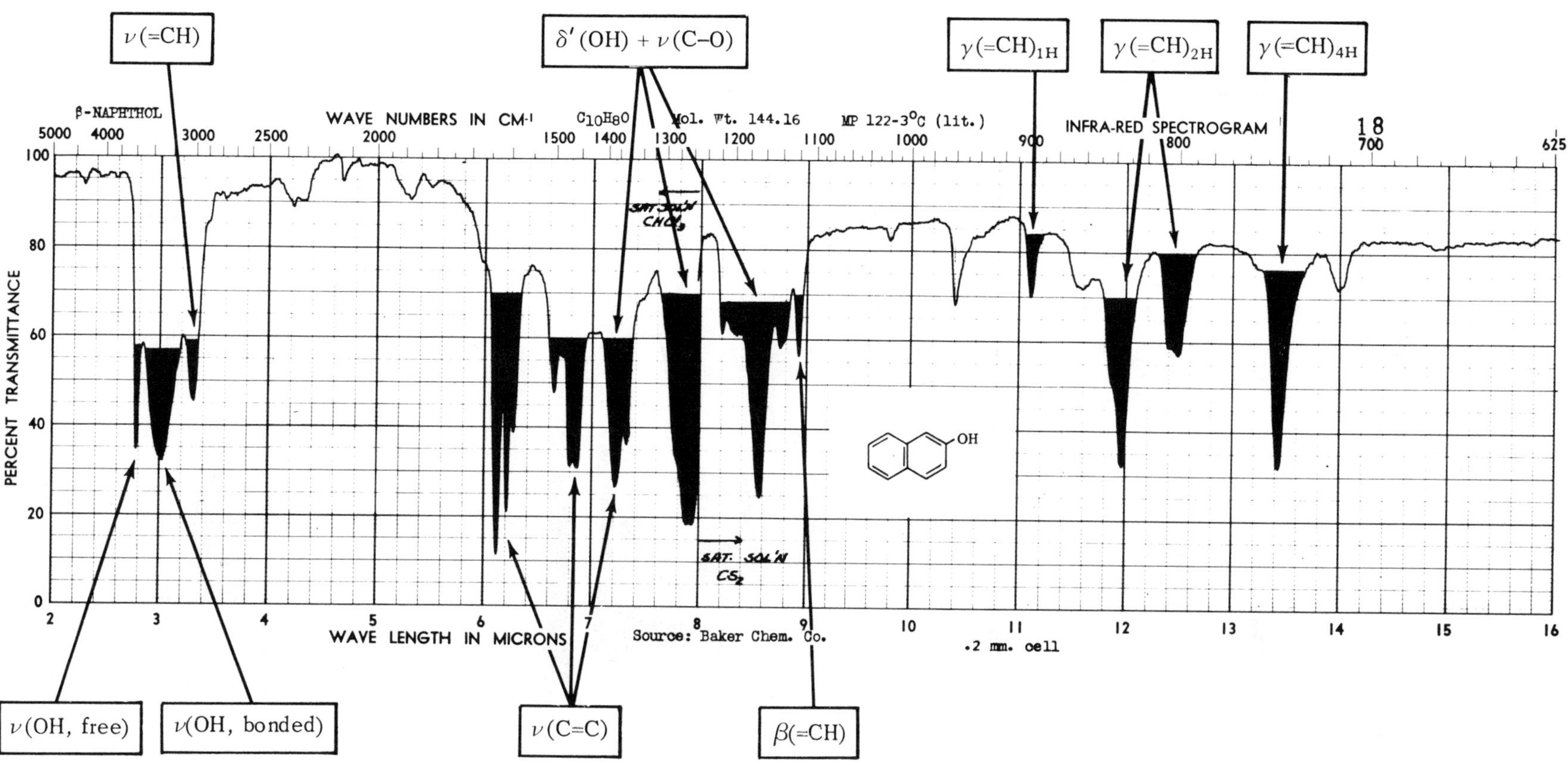

22. This spectrum of β-naphthol was determined as a dilute solution in chloroform and carbon disulfide. The phenol is therefore dissociated and the ν(OH) appears at a high frequency. A lower band in this region is assigned to the bonded OH groups, since presumably an equilibrium occurs between free and bonded species. The CH of the chloroform was probably compensated for by using the solvent in a reference cell. Although this is not noted on the spectrum, the appearance of the spectrum suggests this. For example, the high but irregular base line from 2500 to 2000 cm^{-1} suggests incomplete compensation of two strongly-absorbing solutions.

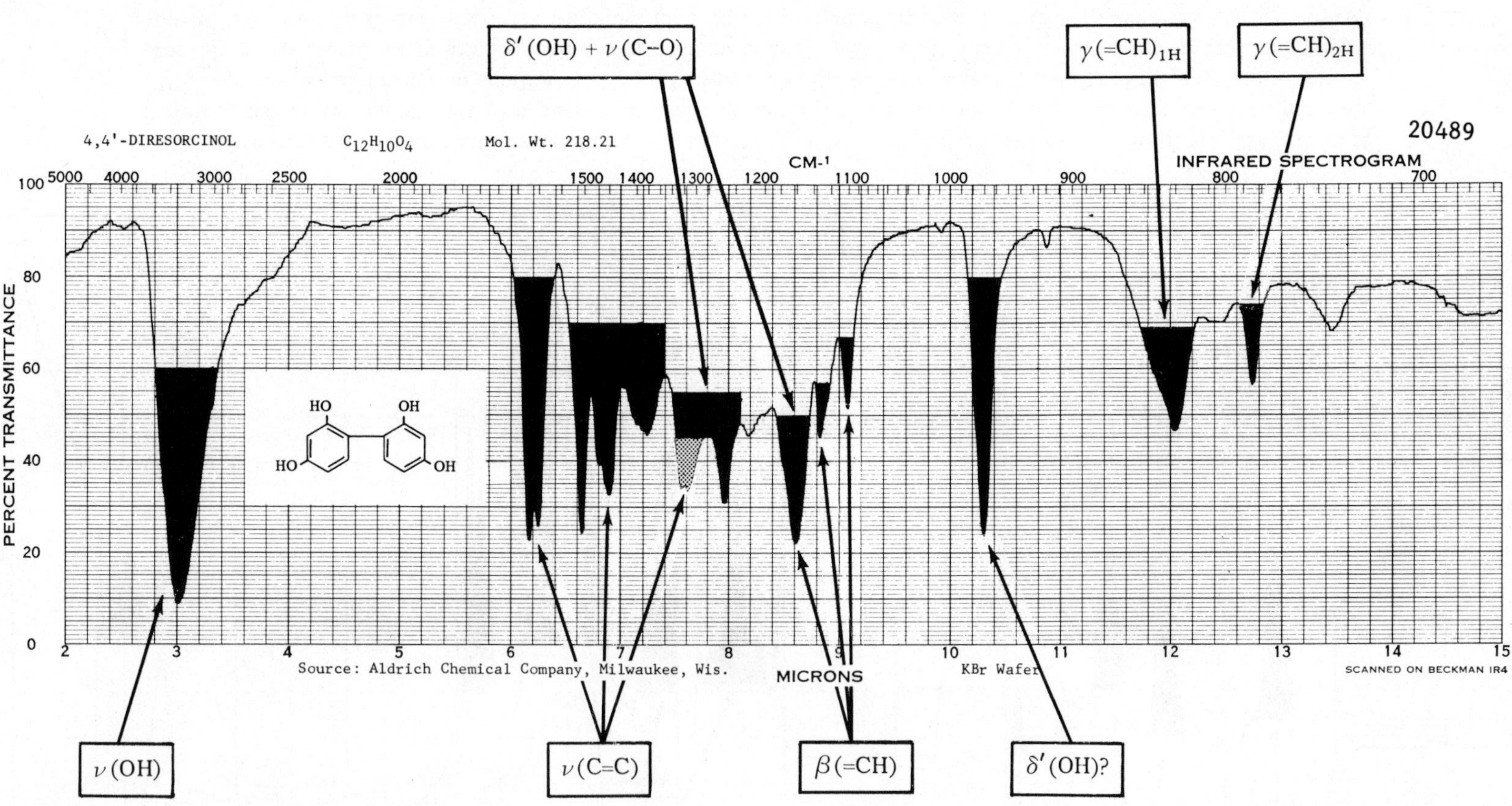

23. The ν(OH) band is quite strong here, but since the compound was run in KBr it is possible some water was present. The 960 cm^{-1} band is tentatively suggested as being a δ'(OH) vibration, since it is strong and not assignable to other structures in the molecule. The spectrum does not have sharply defined peaks, but the expected bands are found.

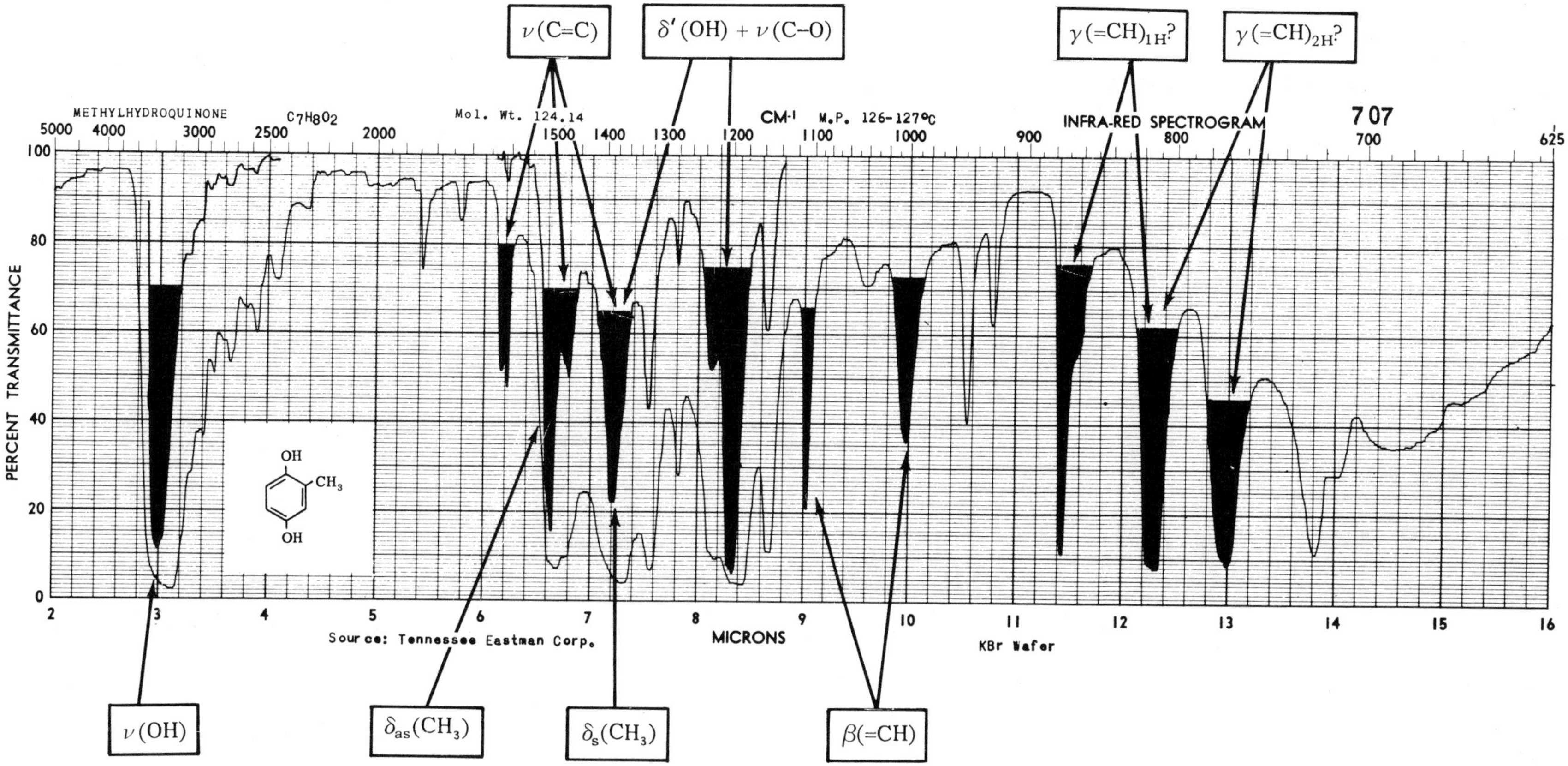

METHYLHYDROQUINONE
$C_7H_8O_2$
Mol. Wt. 124.14
CM-1
M.P. 126-127°C
INFRA-RED SPECTROGRAM
707
PERCENT TRANSMITTANCE
MICRONS
Source: Tennessee Eastman Corp.
KBr Wafer
ν(C=C)
δ'(OH) + ν(C–O)
$\gamma(=CH)_{1H}$?
$\gamma(=CH)_{2H}$?
ν(OH)
$\delta_{as}(CH_3)$
$\delta_s(CH_3)$
β(=CH)

24. Methylhydroquinine has two OH groups attached to the aromatic ring. The very sharp 1200 cm^{-1} band may be due to the sampling technique here, since a KBr pellet of the compound was prepared. There is no indication in the spectrum of the double OH group, unless it is the low position of the 1200 cm^{-1} band. There has been a band near 1000 cm^{-1} in several dihydroxy derivatives, and possibly this band may have diagnostic value. Note spectra 7, 15, and 21, which are dihydroxy compounds, have this strong band near 1000 cm^{-1}.

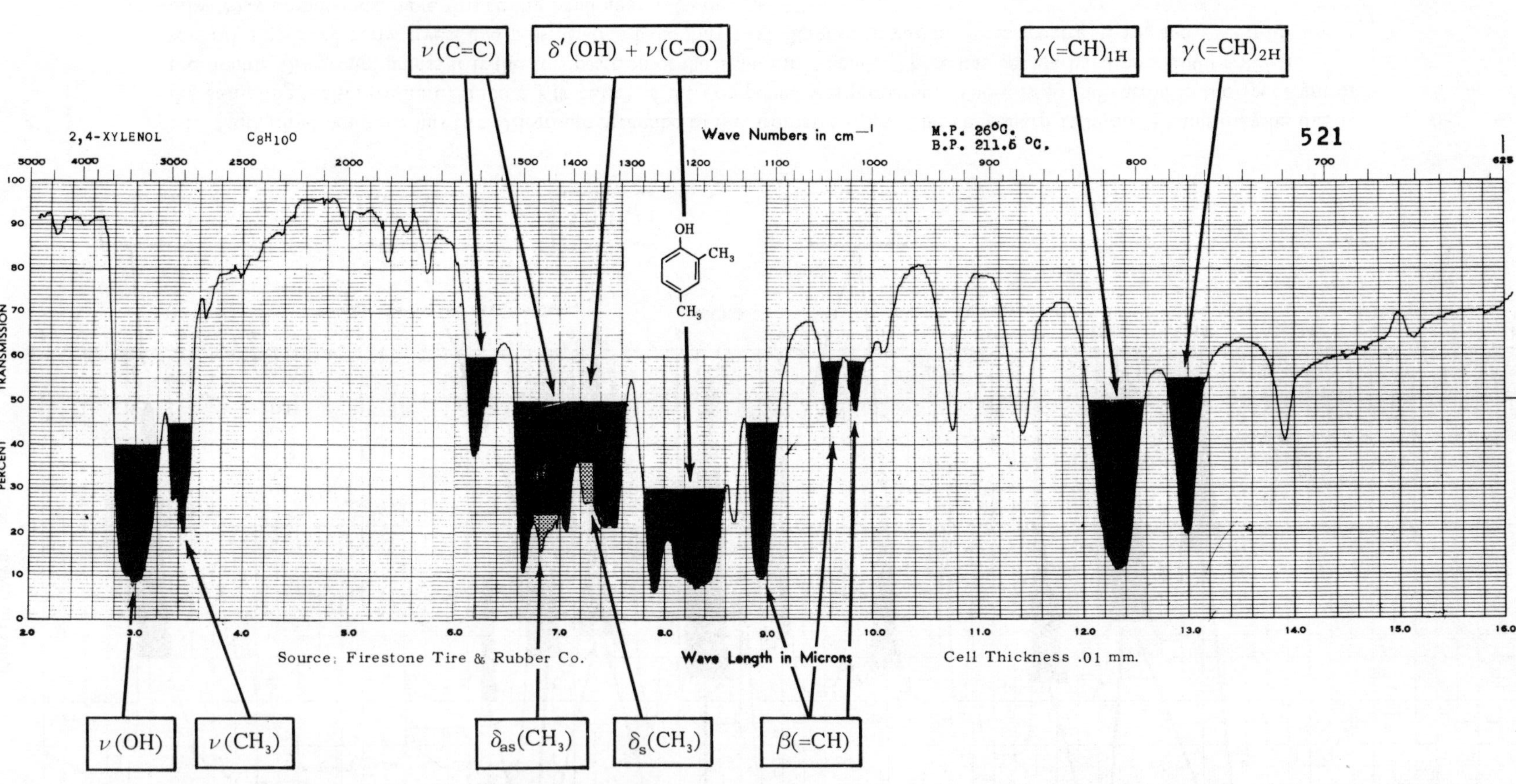

25. The spectrum of 2, 4-xylenol has the broad 1200 cm^{-1} band expected of phenols, but also a broad series of bands in the 1500-1300 cm^{-1} region. This is the spectrum of a liquid phenol, and would give a much sharper series of bands if a dilute solution of it were examined.

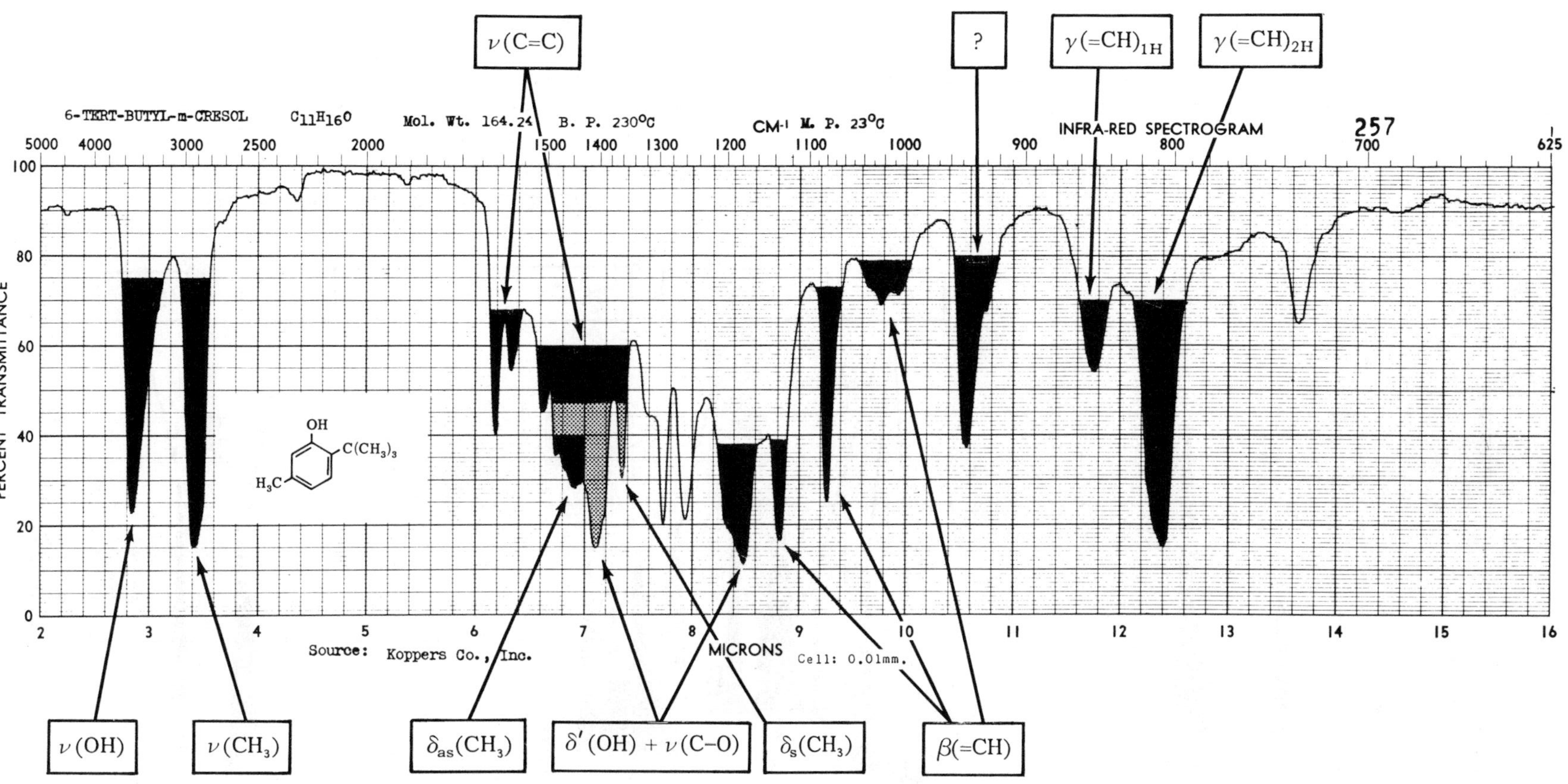

26. The spectrum of 6-tert-butyl-m-cresol shows a high ν(OH), suggesting the self-association of the phenol has been reduced compared to the phenols where the ν(OH) is at 3350 cm^{-1} (see previous spectrum). There is no indication on the spectrum if this dissociation was achieved by diluting the phenol. It is possible the bulky tertiary group in the 2 position is sterically hindering the OH, and that association is lowered. This is not unexpected for this compound.

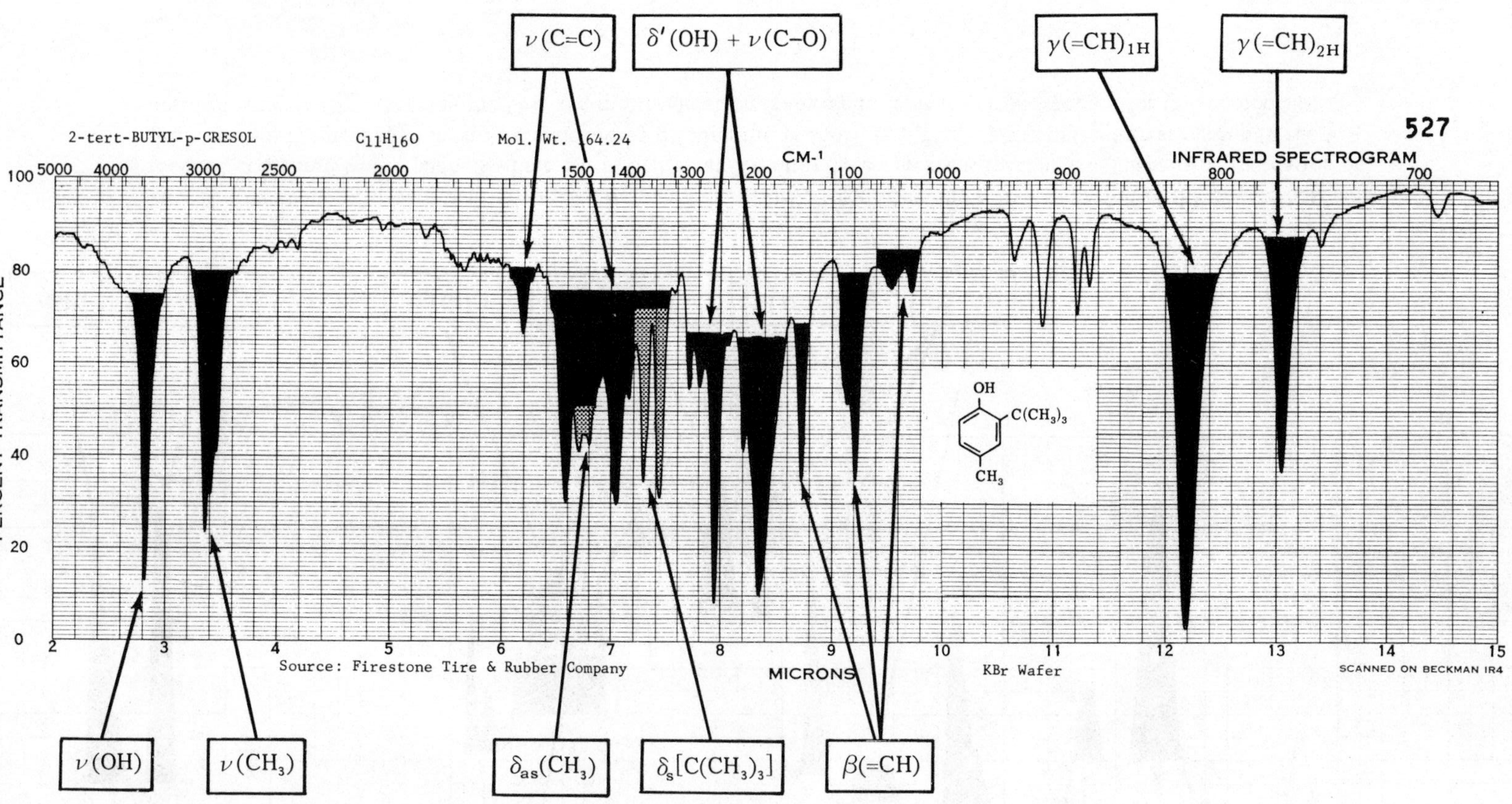

27. The spectrum of this compound should be compared to the previous ones since they differ only in the position of the CH_3 group, both being 1, 2, 4-substituted rings. We again note the high ν(OH), suggesting the steric factor is responsible. The spectrum 16 was of the liquid while this one is of a pellet. We can however, compare them for similarities. It can be noted that many peaks do not coincide. This illustrates how sensitive a tool infrared spectroscopy can be for detecting small structural differences. The spectroscopist unfortunately has no simple way of predicting these differences from the compound structure. It is possible to correlate in some instances the relative intensity of bands with the direction of dipole moment change in a molecule, but for a compound as complex as this one, this is almost an impossible task. We might note both compounds had the 1200 cm^{-1} band in about the same position, while the γ(=CH) bands are at different positions. Perhaps this shift is predictable , since it is the ring hydrogens which may feel the influence of the steric positions of groups greater than the C−O group.

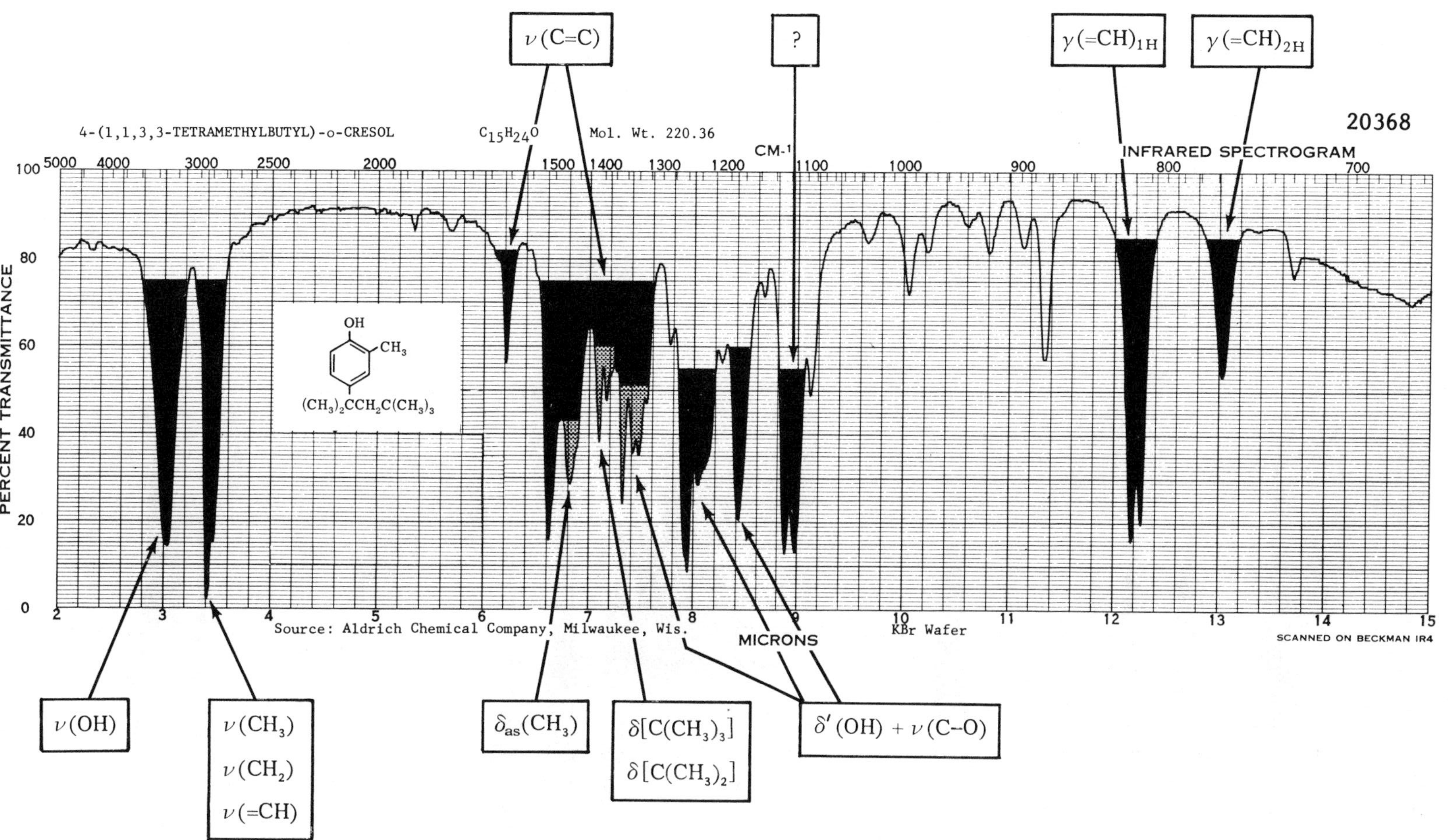

28. As the alkyl substituent groups on the ring are made larger and bulkier, the aromatic ring vibrations are less pronounced. Strong bands may appear in the region from 1500-1100 cm^{-1} which have an intensity near that of the $\gamma(=CH)$ vibrations. This spectrum is an example of such a compound. Note the very strong 1110 cm^{-1} band, which is not easily assignable. Undoubtedly it is due to the alkyl substituent on the ring. The $\gamma(=CH)$ bands have a reversed intensity when compared to some of the previous 1, 2, 4 compounds presented.

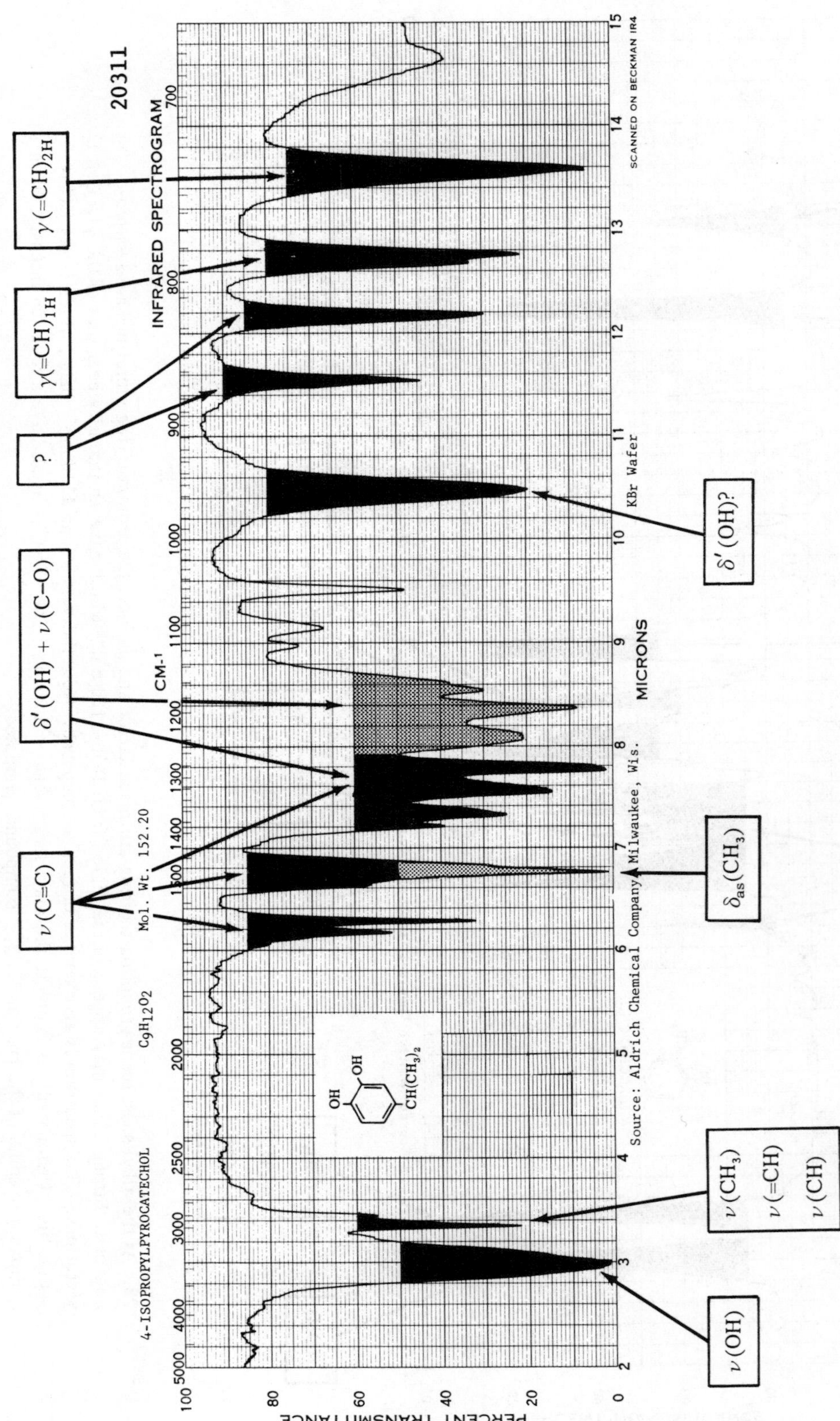

29. Attention is again directed to the strong band in this spectrum near 1000 cm^{-1} which has appeared in a number of these dihydroxy compounds, especially where the two OH groups are ortho in respect to each other. Note the expected isopropyl splitting of the 1380 cm^{-1} band is not easily assigned in the series of maxima in this region. Several strong bands in the 900-800 cm^{-1} region are also not readily assigned.

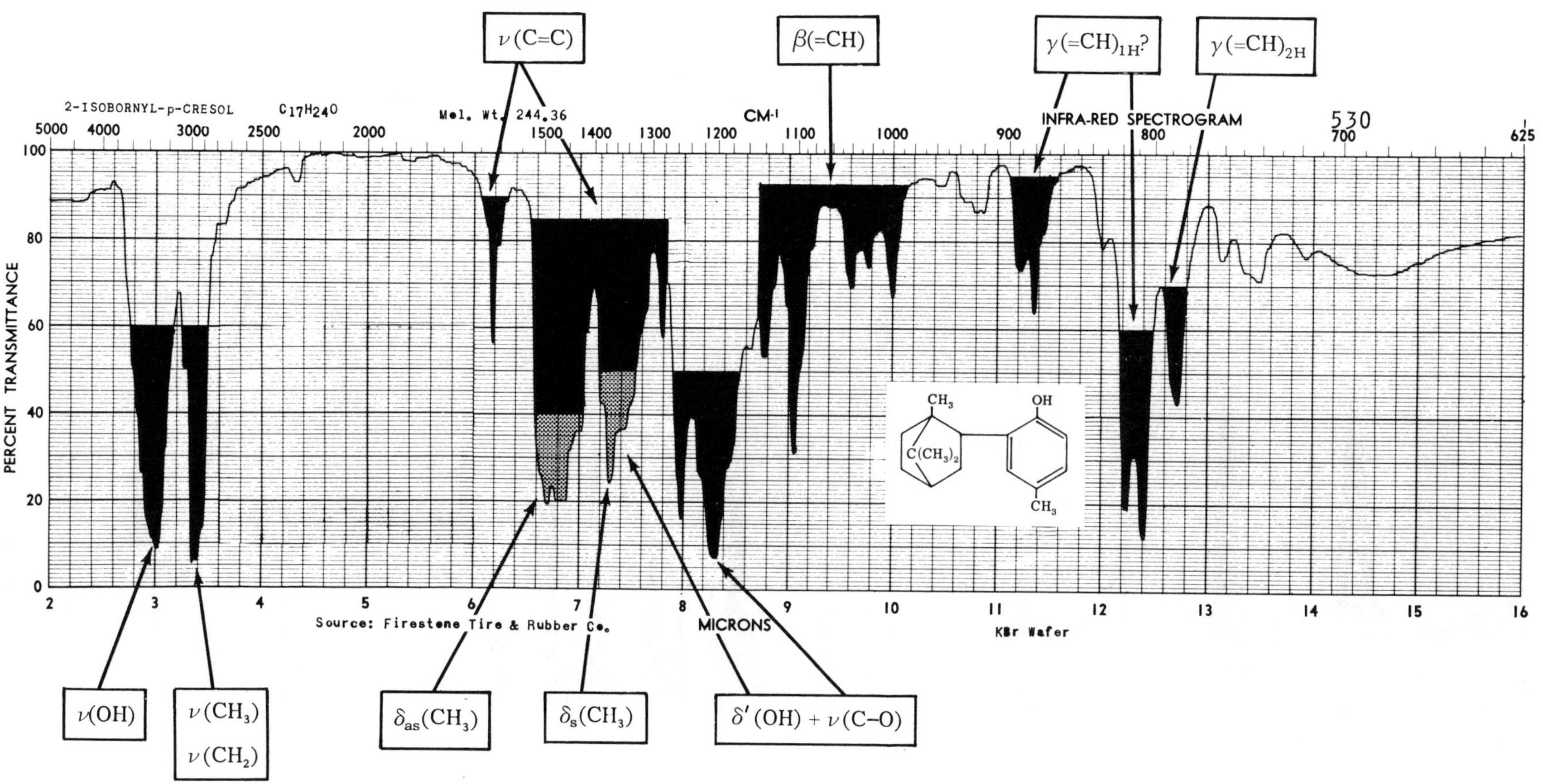

30. This spectrum is of a compound having a bulky group ortho to the OH. But apparently this group does not hinder the OH, as the ν(OH) position is that found for associated phenols. It would be of interest to make a model of this compound to see if this is borne out. The assignments of γ(=CH) are confusing, as three bands appear in the region where two are expected.

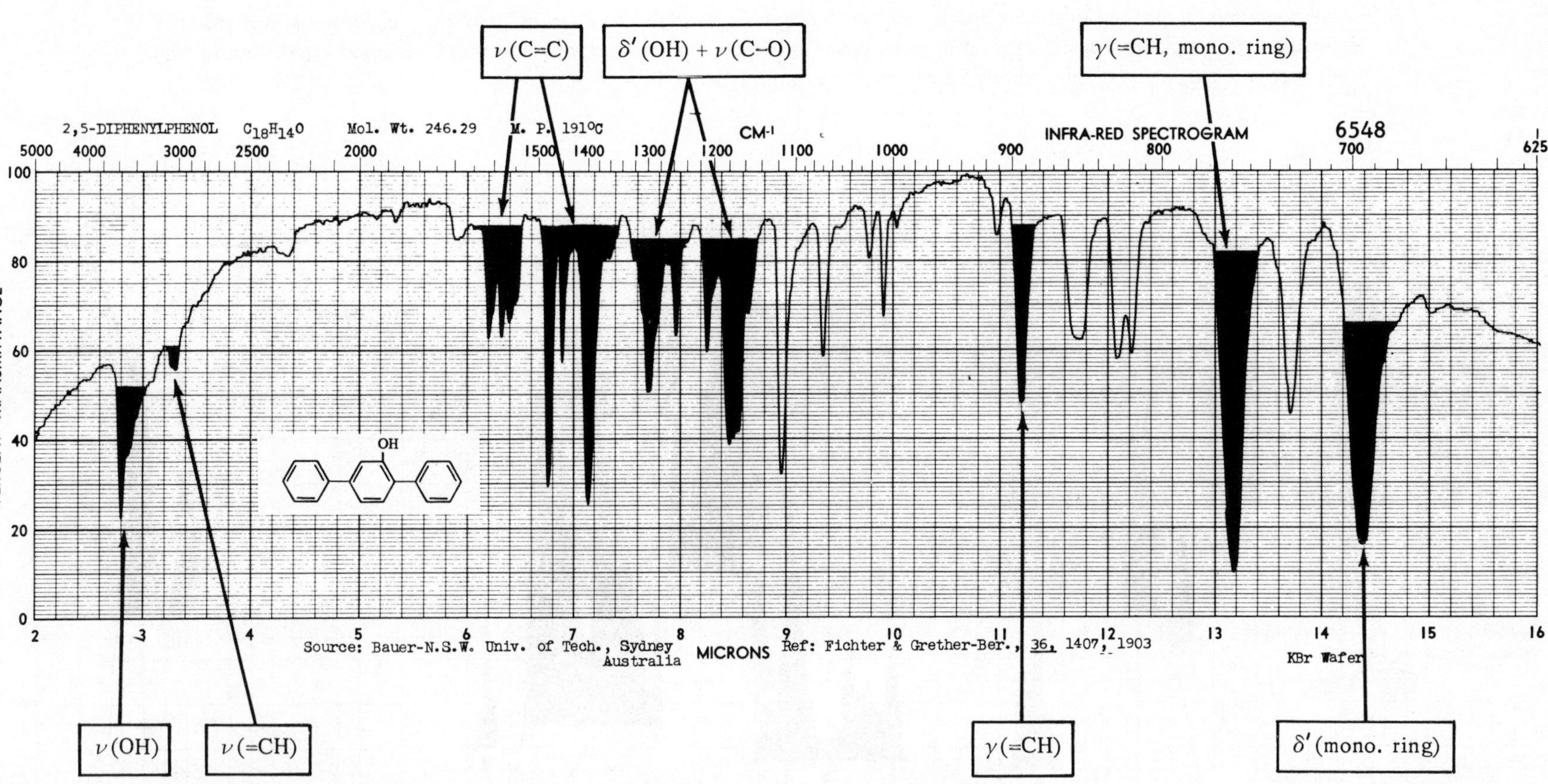

31. This is the final example of the 1, 2, 4-substituted ring, and again it appears the association of this phenol is limited because of steric hindrance. The assignment of δ′(OH) + ν(C–O) is made as in previous spectra. The large number of sharp bands are of course due to the fact that three aromatic rings are present.

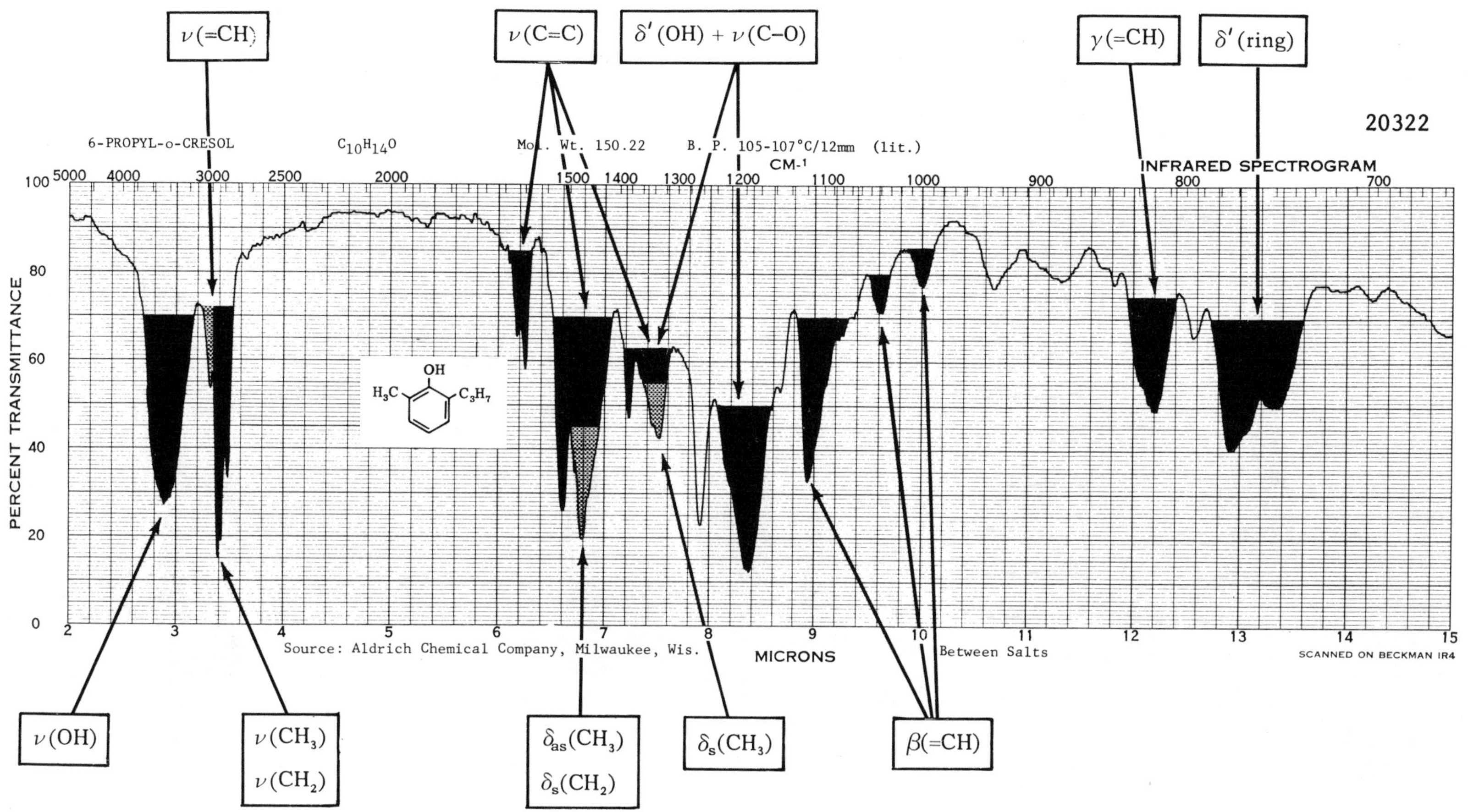

32. This is the first example of a 1, 2, 3-substituted phenol. It is difficult to distinguish it from the previous spectra of the 1, 2, 4 derivatives. The ν(OH) does appear to be shifted to higher frequencies than that observed for the associated phenols, suggesting some dissociation is occuring here. The γ(=CH) bands are rather weak vibrations here when compared to the 1200 cm^{-1} band. In many of the other phenols we have presented this was not always true. The weakness here is due to the fact that only two isolated H atoms occur.

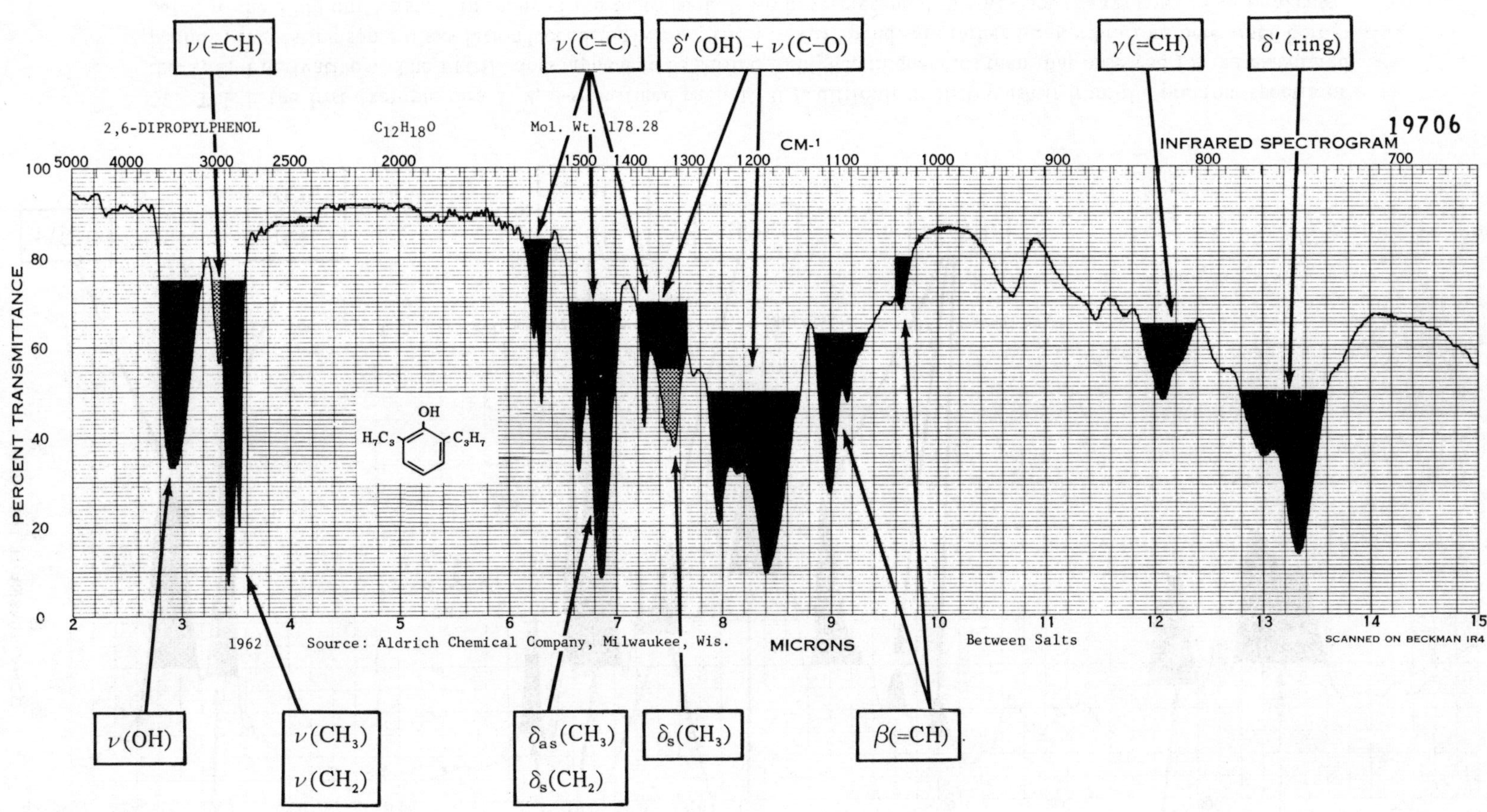

33. This spectrum has several interesting features: The ν(OH) is at slightly higher frequency than for the nondissociated 1, 2, 4 derivatives, even though this is the spectrum of the liquid. This suggests the 1, 2, 3-phenols, where the OH is at the 2 position, are probably partially dissociated due to steric hindrance by the substituents in the 1 and 3 position.

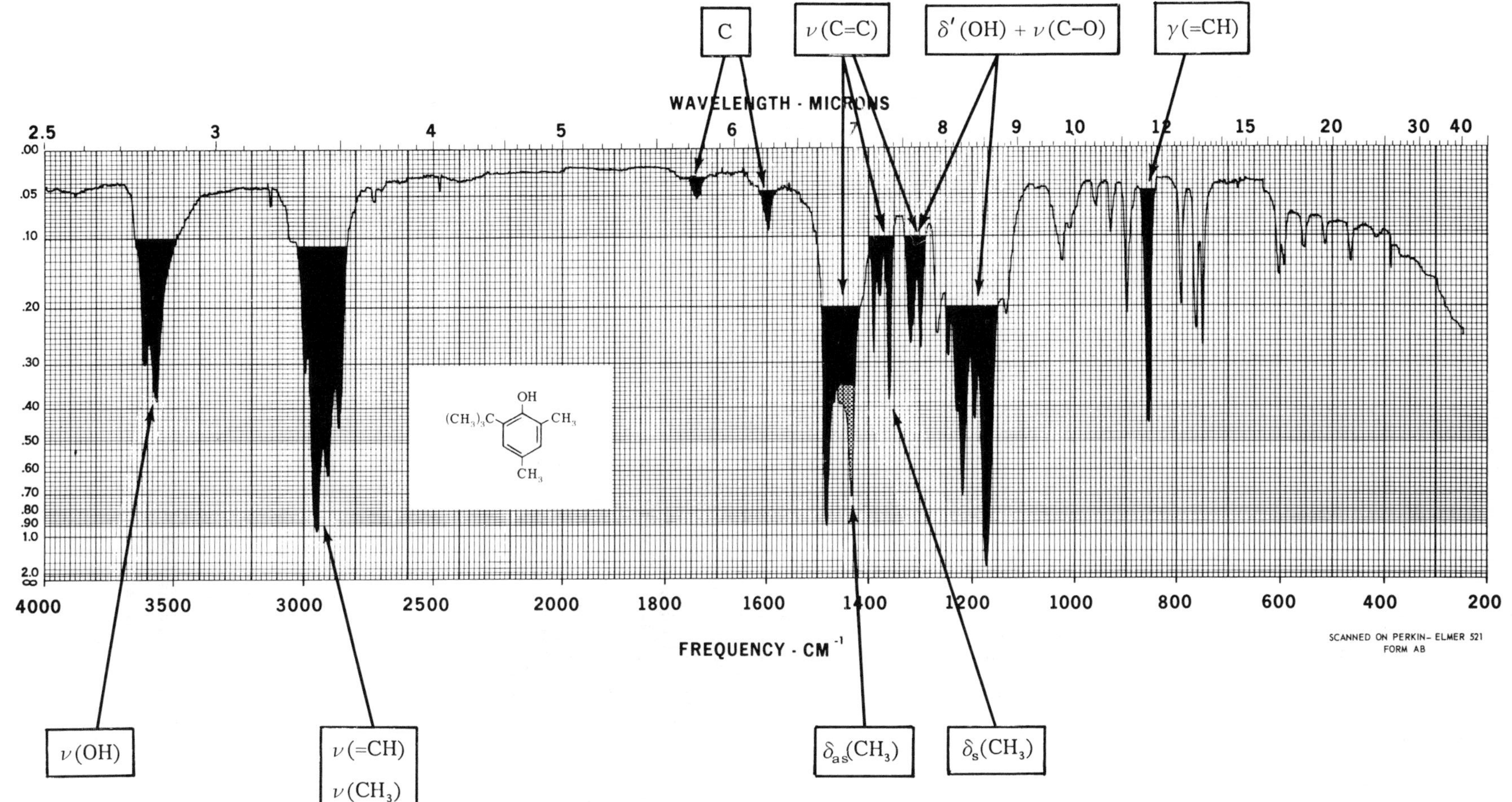

34. This spectrum is an excellent example of the high ν(OH) observed for sterically hindered phenols. Note also the intensity of the γ(=CH) band is now much less than the 1200 cm^{-1} C–O band. This is not unexpected, as there are now only two hydrogens on the ring. The position of the 1200 cm^{-1} band is low compared to the other phenols we have presented, and this might be of diagnostic value in identifying sterically hindered phenols of this type. We shall also suggest the δ'(OH) + ν(C–O) vibration center seems to be nearer 1175 than 1200 cm^{-1}, where it appeared in previous spectra.

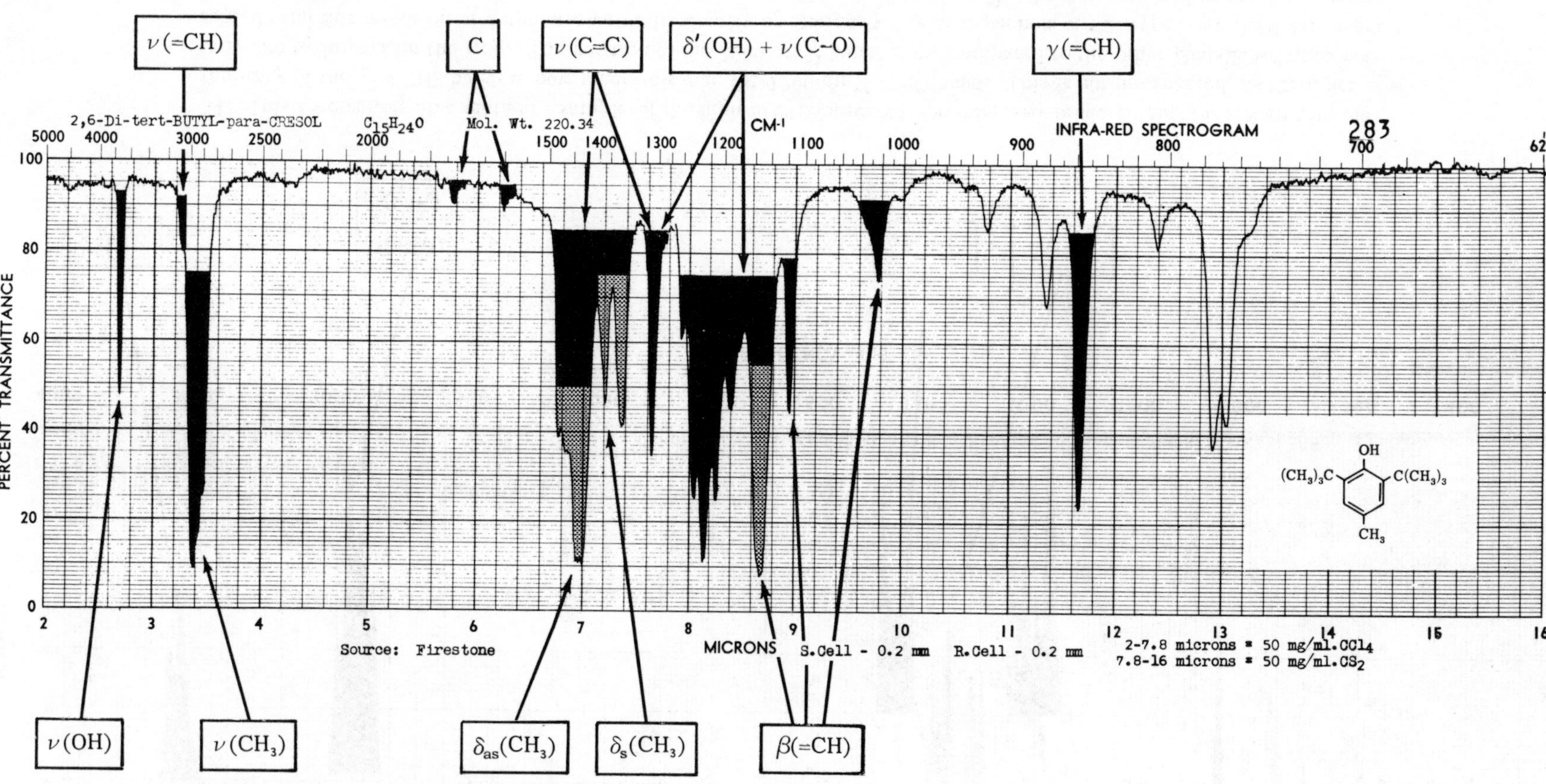

35. This spectrum should be compared to the previous one since both represent hindered phenols. Note the very high position of the ν(OH). In part, this high position is due to the fact that the phenol was run in solution. However, the high concentration of the solute would not result in a great deal of dissociation, and the high position of the ν(OH) must be assigned principally to the steric factor. The spectrum has fairly sharp peaks, and is the type one should strive for in studying phenols. It should be noted there are differences between this and the previous spectrum indicating it would be possible to distinguish between them.

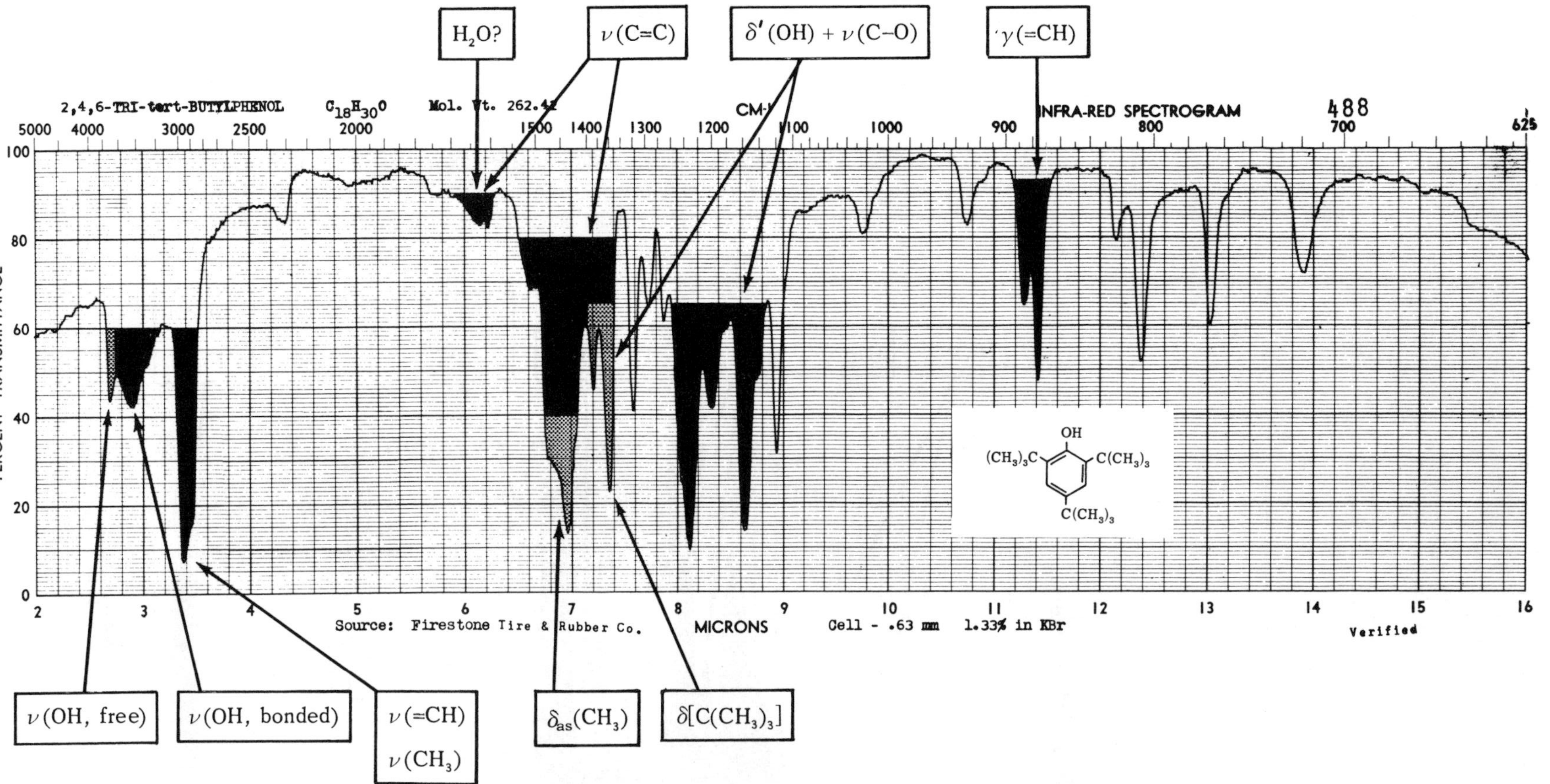

36. This spectrum can be compared to the previous two, since these are all related compounds. Note in this example the three substituents on the phenolic ring are tertiary butyl groups. The previous spectrum had two tertiary groups and a methyl substituted on the ring; however, for spectrum 33, the sampling method was a pellet while for 32, a solution spectrum was presented. We can note for spectrum 33, two ν(OH) bands are observed. One we assigned to the free and the other to the bonded OH. However, there is a suggestion in the spectrum of water (the band near 1600 cm^{-1}), so possibly one of these vibrations has the water OH contributing to it. The likliest position for the water ν(OH) would be near 3300 cm^{-1}.

The author is not happy with the suggestion of others that the band near 1300 cm^{-1} has contributions from the δ'(OH) and ν(C–O) vibrations and should be included in this assignment. It would appear more logical to assign the two strong bands near 1220 and 1150 cm^{-1} as these vibrations. However, to conform with the vibrational assignments presented in this first section of phenols, the 1300 cm^{-1} band is included. That this 1300 cm^{-1} may not have contributions from the COH vibrations is also substantiated by spectra presented in the last part of this section. Compounds such as $C_6(CH_3)_5OH$, which have no aromatic hydrogen, have no band in the 1300 cm^{-1} region.

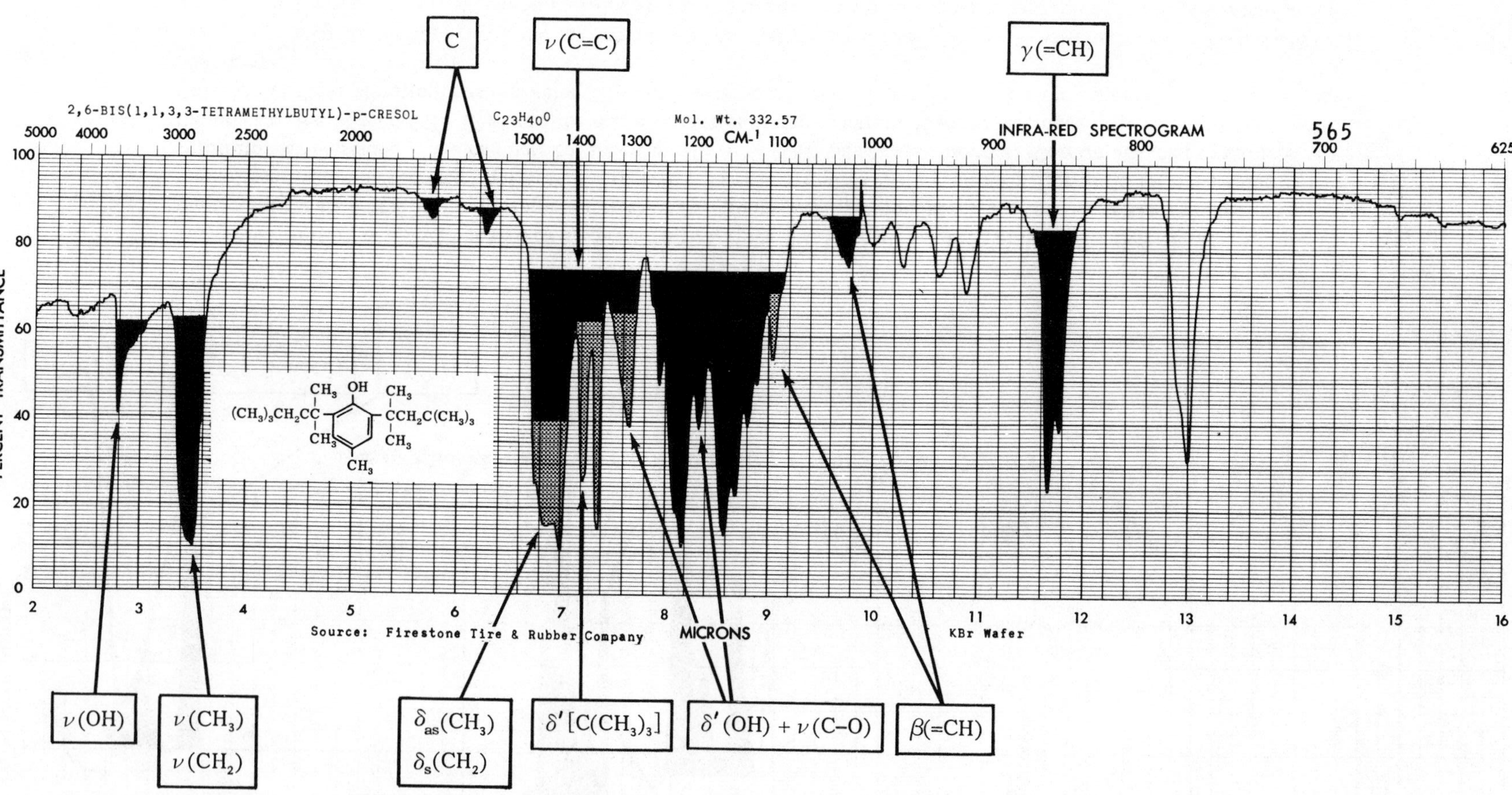

37. This spectrum also is of a compound having a sterically hindered OH group, and again the ν(OH) appears at a high position. Note that a band near 780 cm^{-1} as strong as the γ(= CH) at 850 cm^{-1} is not assignable as a group frequency. This band would mislead one in attempting to decide the substitution pattern on the ring.

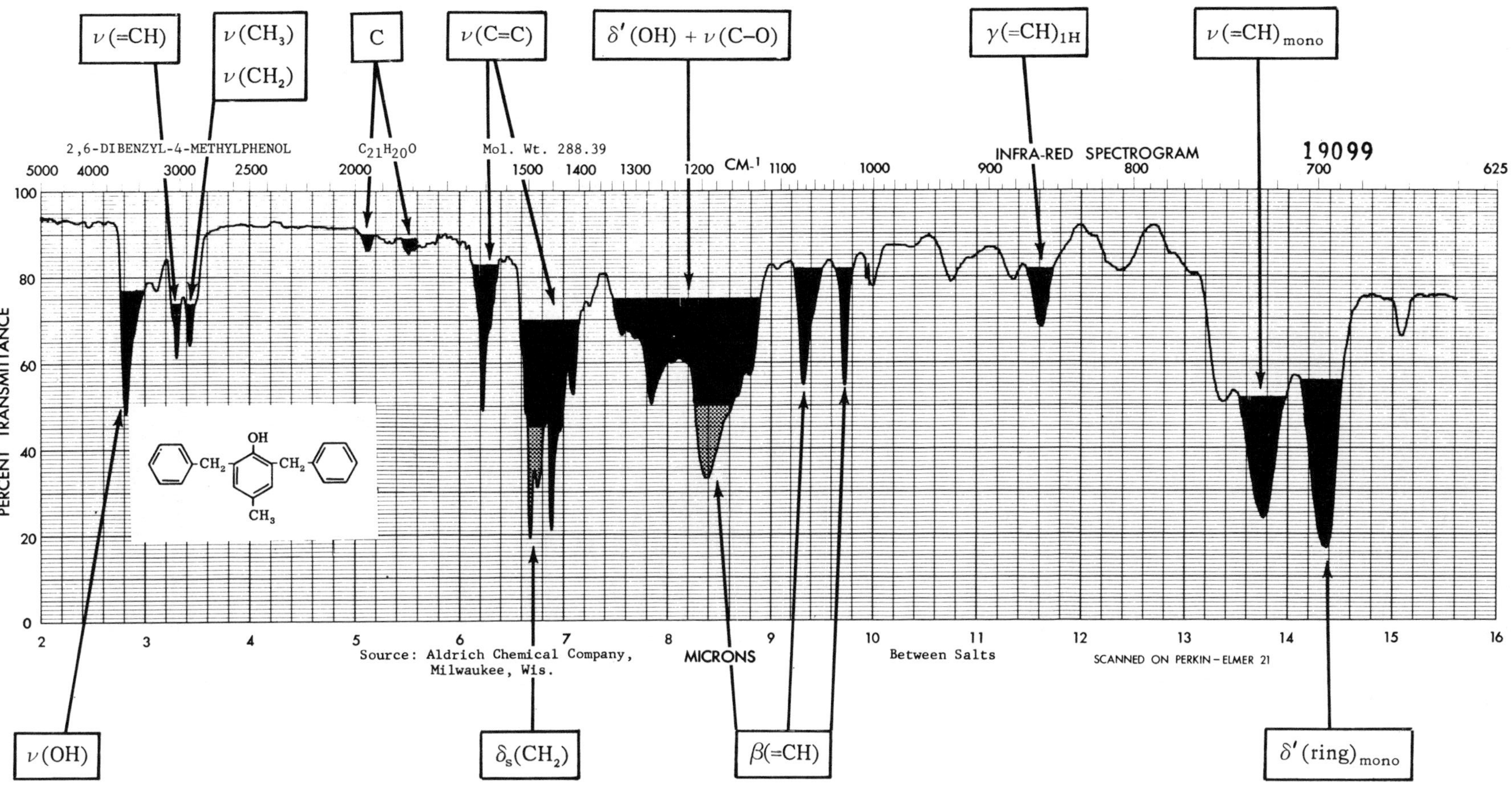

38. In this compound two large substituents are substituted at the ring positions alpha to the OH group. The ν(OH) is at the expected high position. The 1200 cm^{-1} band appears nearer 1150 cm^{-1}, but again the difficulty of correctly assigning the COH vibration in this region makes it difficult to draw any conclusions concerning why it appears at this low position. Note how the assignments of the γ(=CH) of the monosubstituted ring are near the correct regions, but the two bands are much nearer each other than is usually observed.

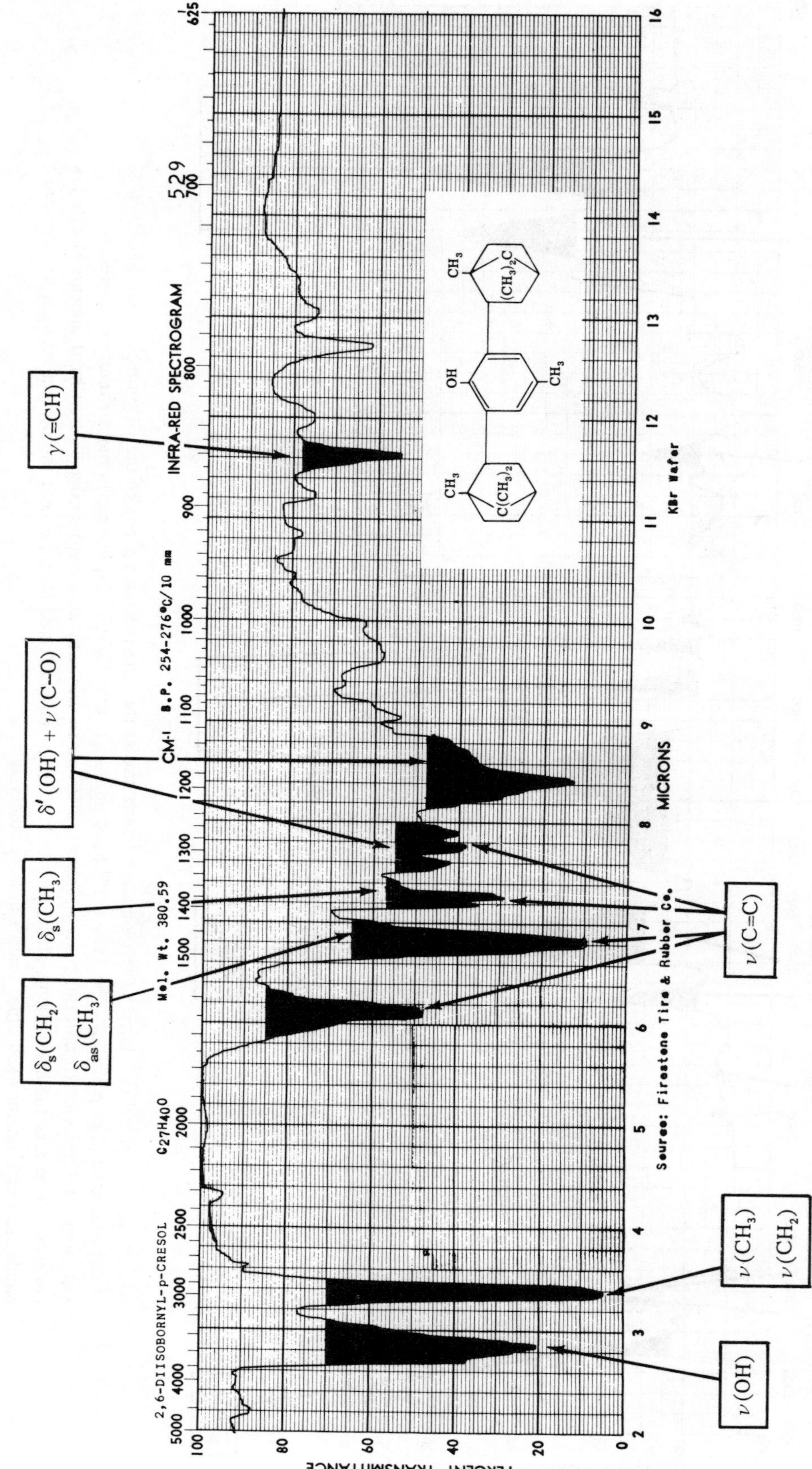

39. This is still another example of the 1, 2, 3, 5-substituted aromatic ring with the OH at the 2 position. As in all the previous examples, the ν(OH) appears nearer the free OH region. Note again the apparent low position of the δ'(OH) + ν(C–O) band.

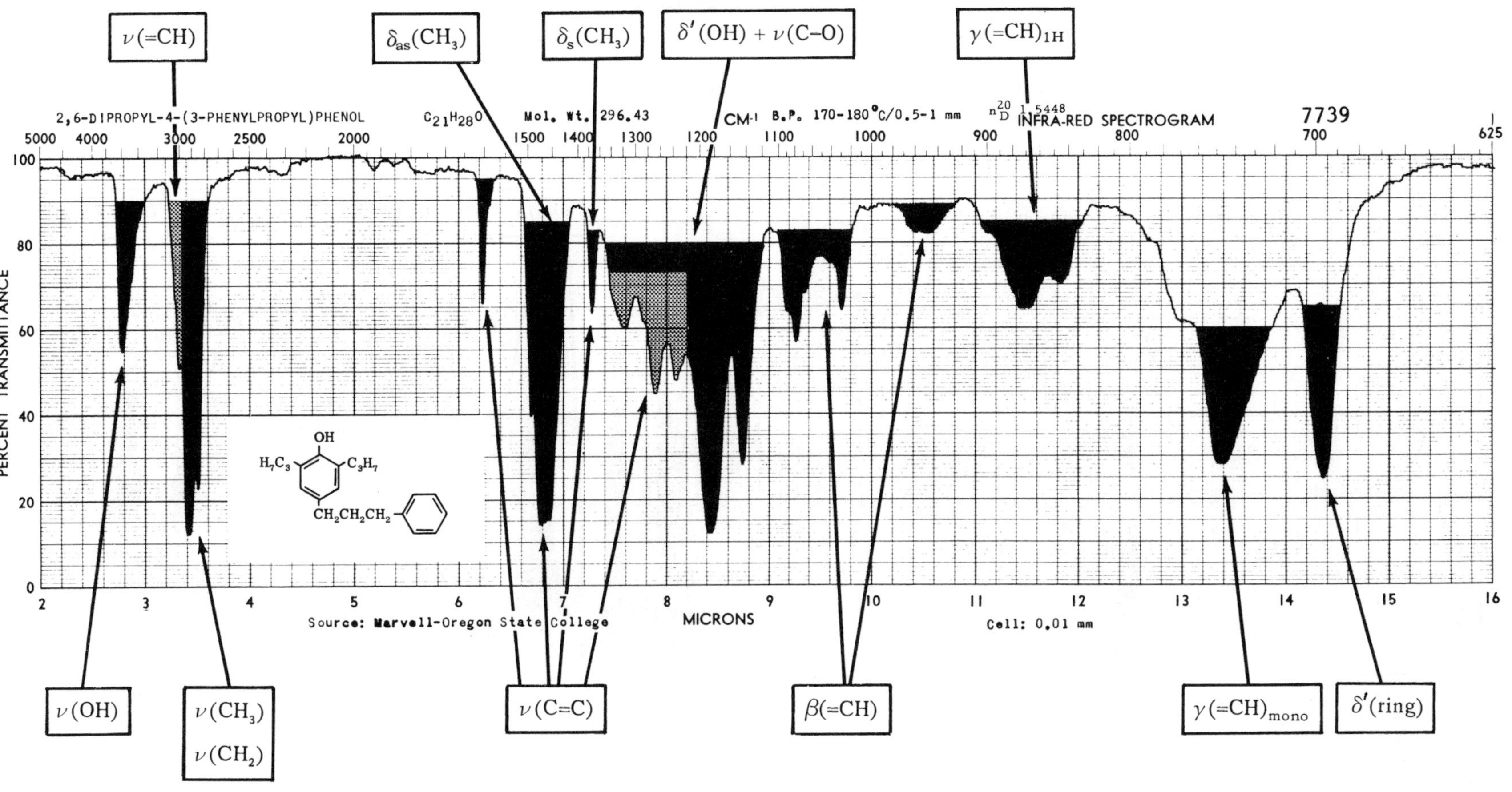

40. This spectrum is apparently of the liquid state. The high ν(OH) position therefore suggests that steric hindrance is occurring even though only a propyl group is attached in the positions adjacent to the OH. Note also the low position of the δ'(OH) + ν(C—O) vibration, as we have found for most of the phenols that are not associated.

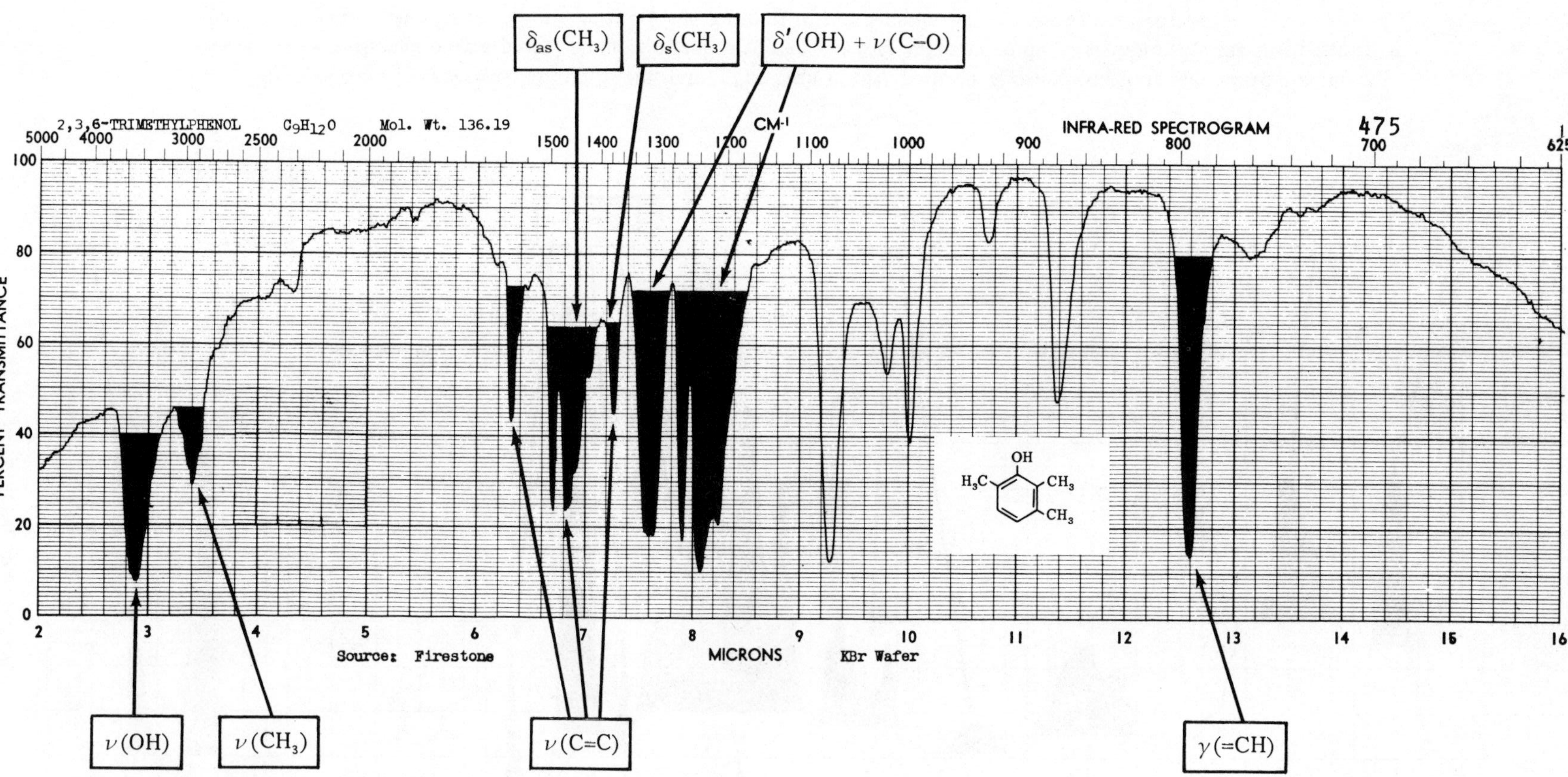

41. This phenol represents a 1, 2, 3, 4-substituted aromatic ring and the γ(=CH) is just in the region expected for this vibration (860-800 cm^{-1}). It can be noted two strong bands at 1320 and 1220 cm^{-1} make a logical assignment for the δ'(OH) + ν(C–O). The ν(OH) appears at a little higher frequency than for those phenols which are highly associated, suggesting some dissociation is occurring. There is a strong band near 1080 cm^{-1} not assignable as a group frequency. A second fairly strong band near 880 cm^{-1} is also not assignable.

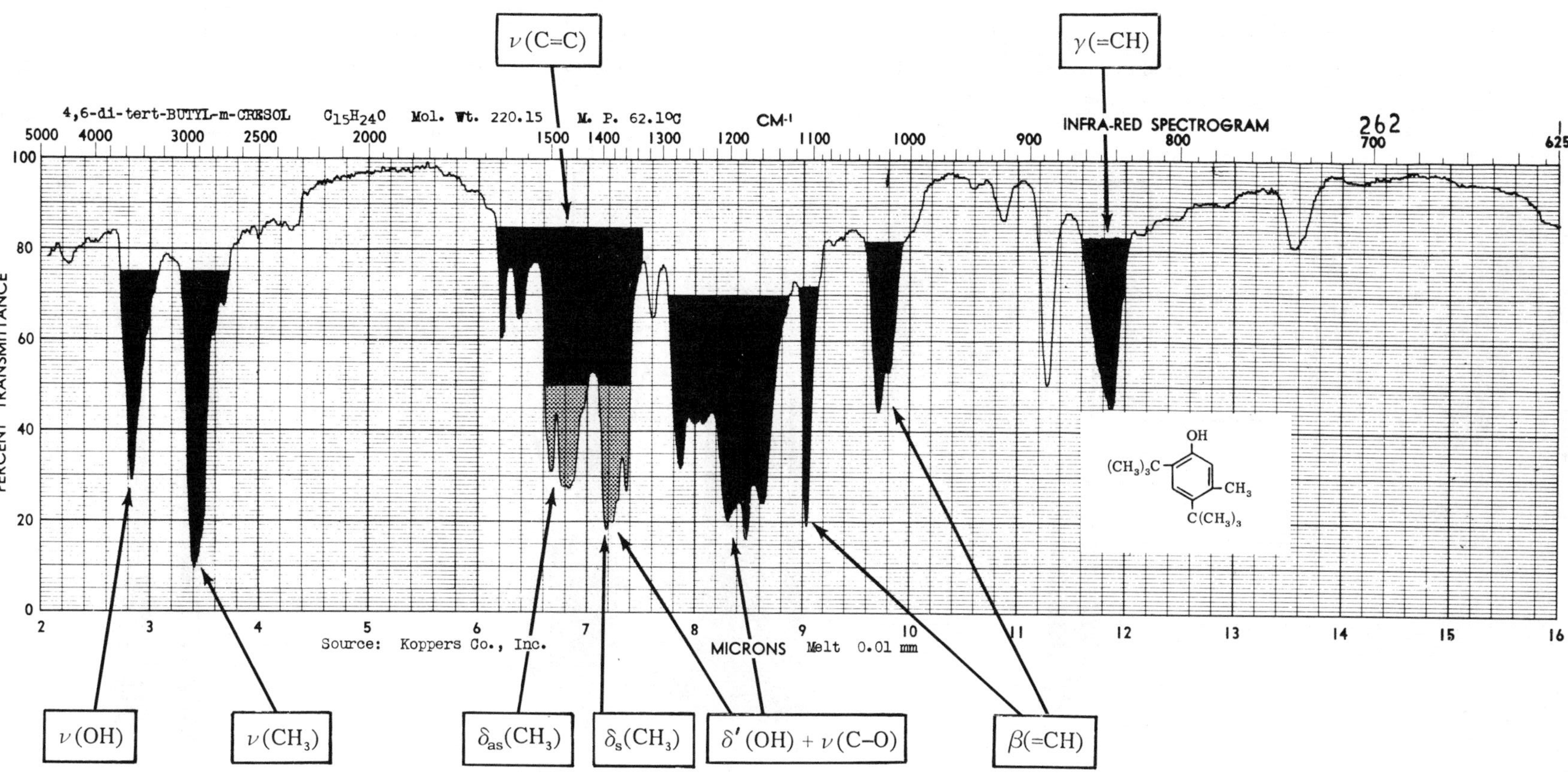

42. The steric hindrance of association of this phenol is evident from the high position of the ν(OH), even though the spectrum is of the solid. Note again the strong band near 1150 cm^{-1}, suggesting the δ'(OH) + ν(C−O) is a lower frequency as the phenol is dissociated. The γ(=CH) assignment could be made to either of two bands in the 900-800 cm^{-1} region. We choose the stronger one for this assignment.

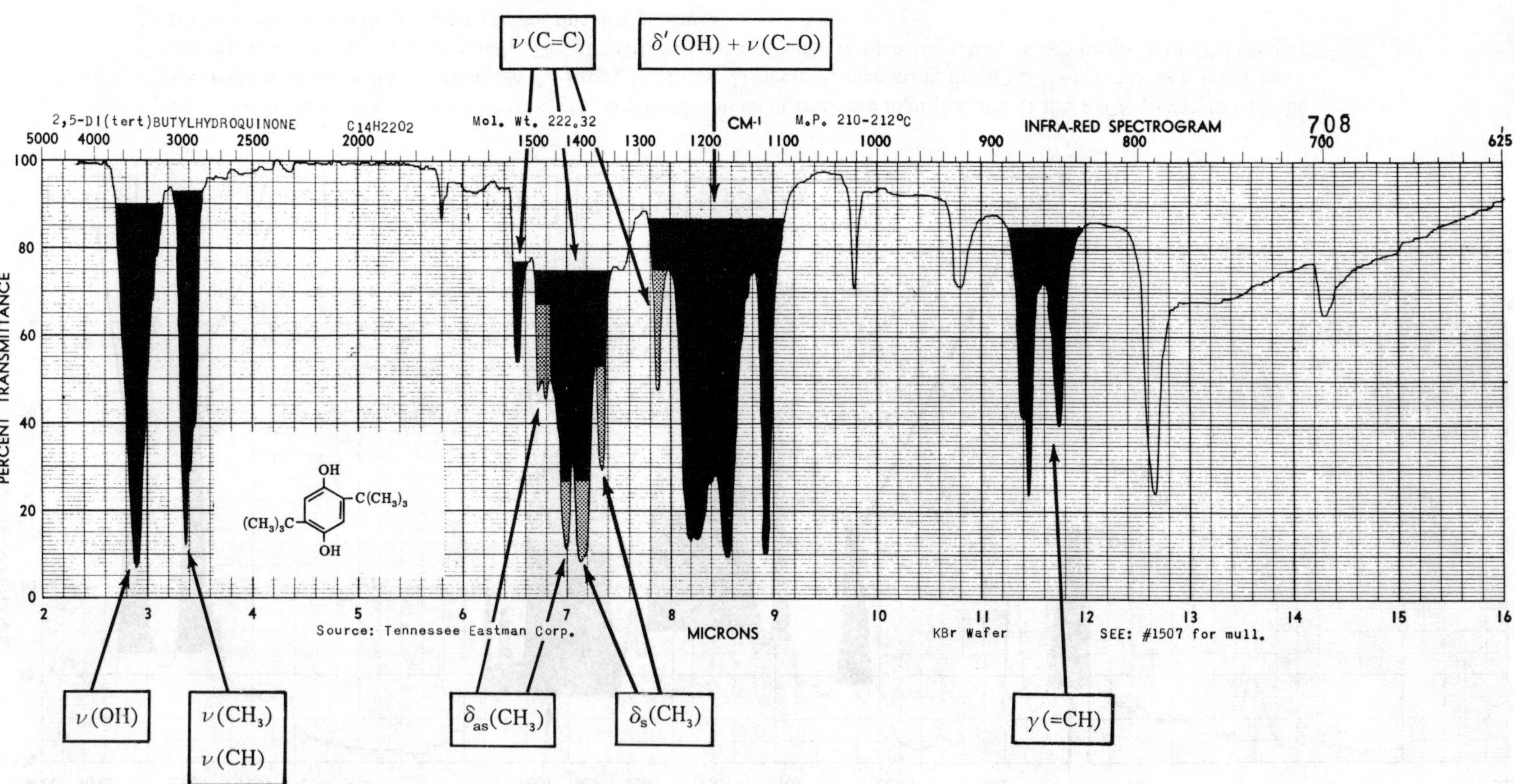

43. This compound has only one ring H, and the assignment of the $\gamma(=CH)$ can be made in the 900-860 cm^{-1} region. A second band, however, near 790 cm^{-1}, is very strong and is probably also $\gamma(=CH)$. The $\delta'(OH)+\nu(C-O)$ is assigned as a strong band centered at 1200 cm^{-1}.

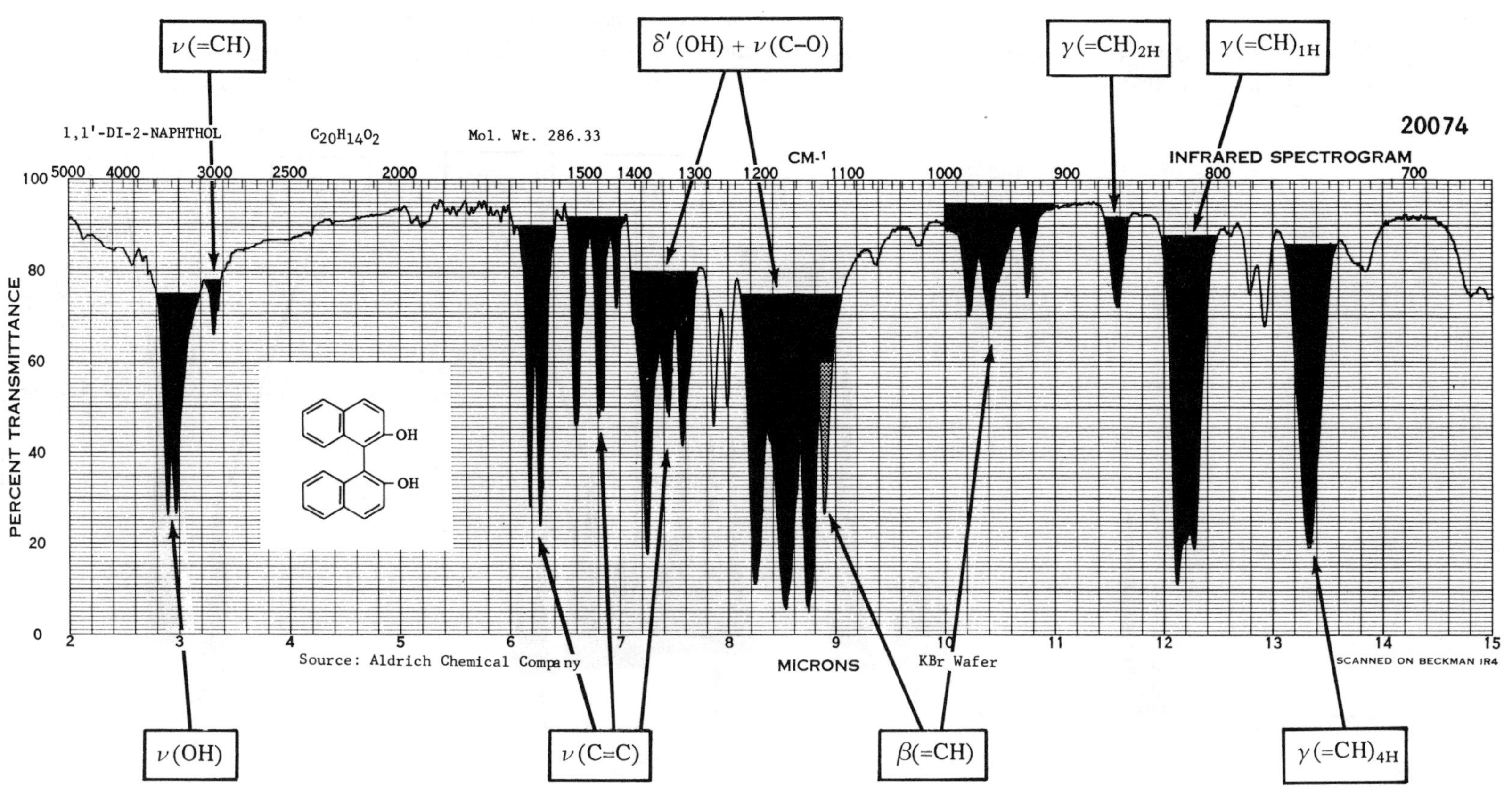

44. This compound has two types of aromatic rings. The $\gamma(=CH)$ assignment for each type can be assigned as they appear in the proper region. The $\delta'(OH) + \nu(C-O)$ is assigned as the series of bands in the 1200-1100 cm^{-1} region. This is low for the band. The doublet for the $\nu(OH)$ is not easily explained.

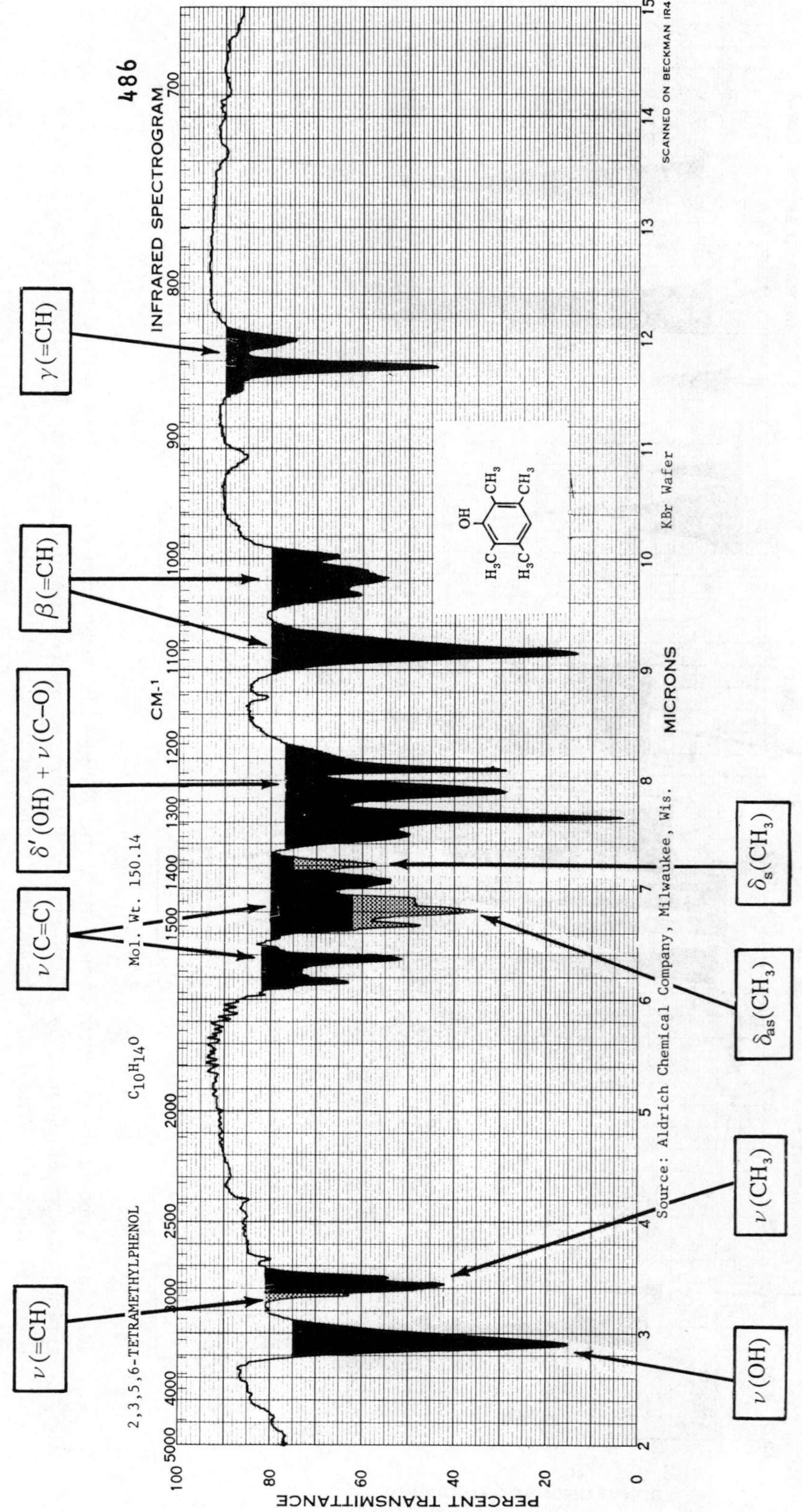

45. This spectrum is of a compound having only one ring H. The γ(=CH) band is therefore weak, but in the correct position. The δ′(OH) + ν(C−O) appears at a higher position than in the previous spectrum. The ν(OH) appears at a position suggesting only very little dissociation is occuring.

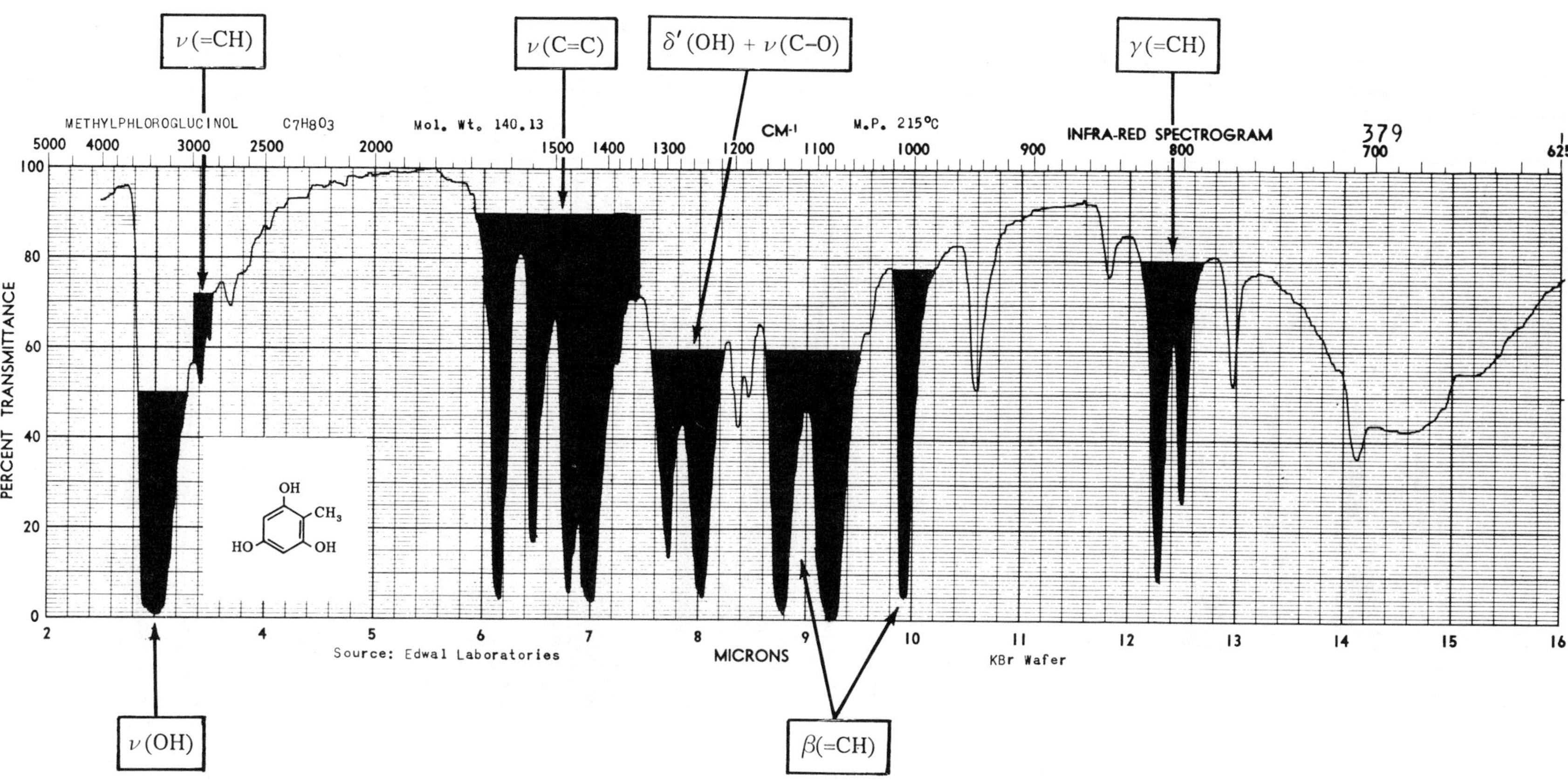

46. This compound has only isolated ring H's. This results in the $\gamma(=CH)$ being near 810 cm^{-1}. The $\delta'(OH)+\nu(C-O)$ is assigned as the doublet near 1250 cm^{-1}. The strong bands near 1100 cm^{-1} are not assignable, however, unless they are also due to the COH group. The strong 1080 cm^{-1} band appears in the next several spectra, and the suggestion is made that the 1080 cm^{-1} may be due to the CH_3 group.

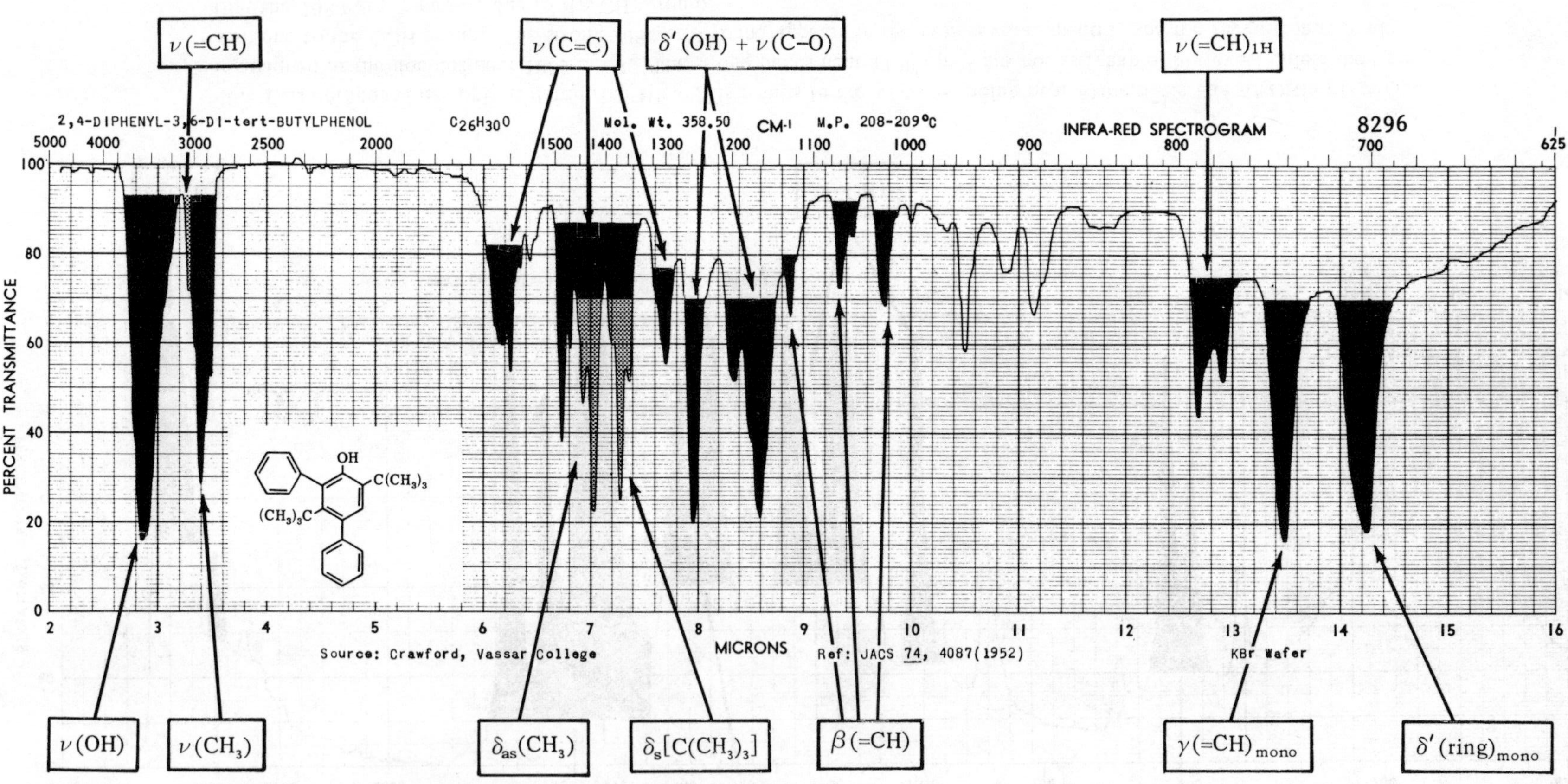

47. This compound, as the other previous two, has only one isolated H on the phenolic ring, but two other rings occur in the molecule. However, this example is presented here to again illustrate that the $\delta'(OH)+\nu(C-O)$ band appears very strong and broad near 1160 cm^{-1}, and also sharp at 1260 cm^{-1}. The other assignments are at the expected positions.

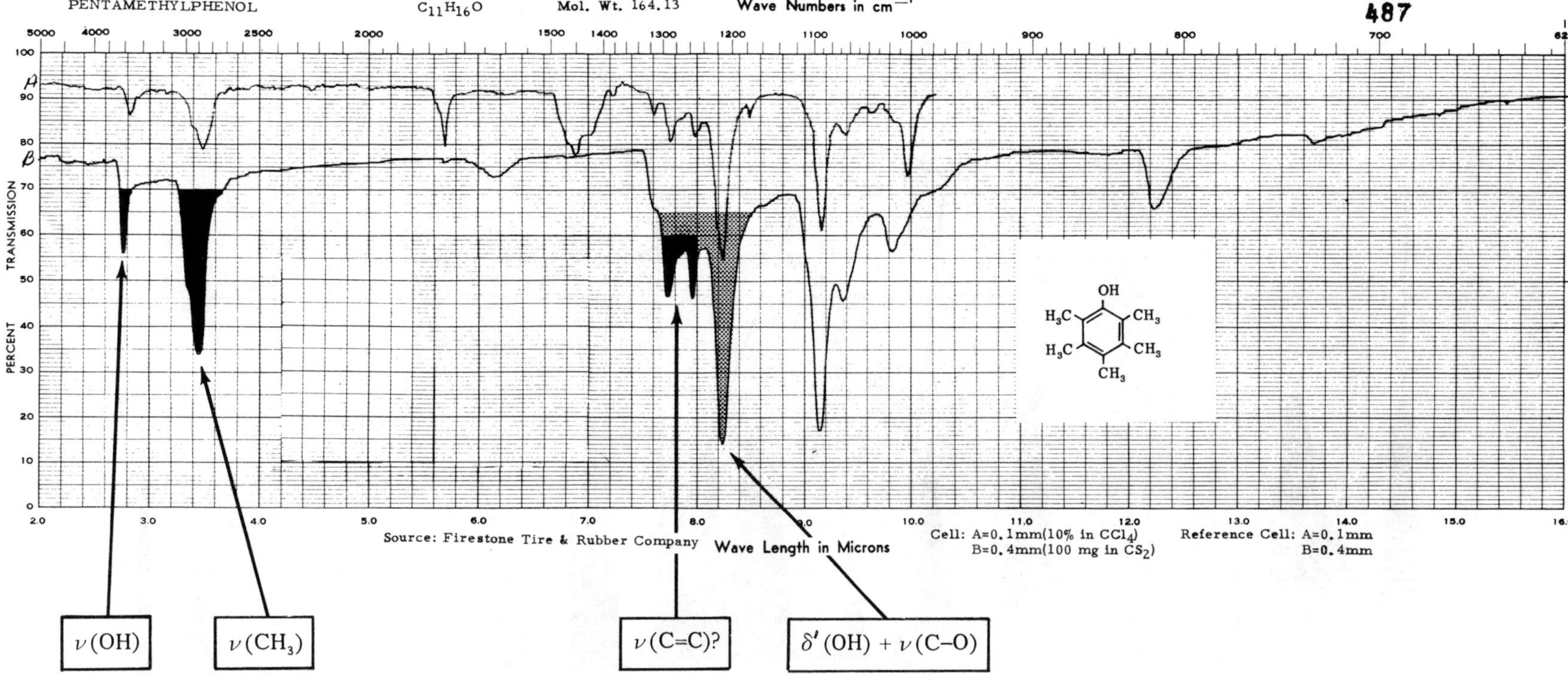

48. This compound has no ring hydrogens. In addition the spectrum is that of a very dilute solution. It is possible therefore, to make several interesting conclusions. First since no ring hydrogens occur, β(=CH) and γ(=CH) vibrations do not interfere with the long wavelength phenolic vibrations. Only two strong bands appear in the 1350-1050 cm^{-1} region. The band near 1210 cm^{-1} must certainly be assigned to the δ'(OH) + ν(C–O) vibration. No 1300 cm^{-1} band appears, agreeing with the previous suggestions this author made that the 1300 cm^{-1} band has very little or no contribution from COH vibrations. The strong 1080 cm^{-1} band could be due to the CH_3 group, as it was strong in the previous spectrum which also had CH_3 groups.

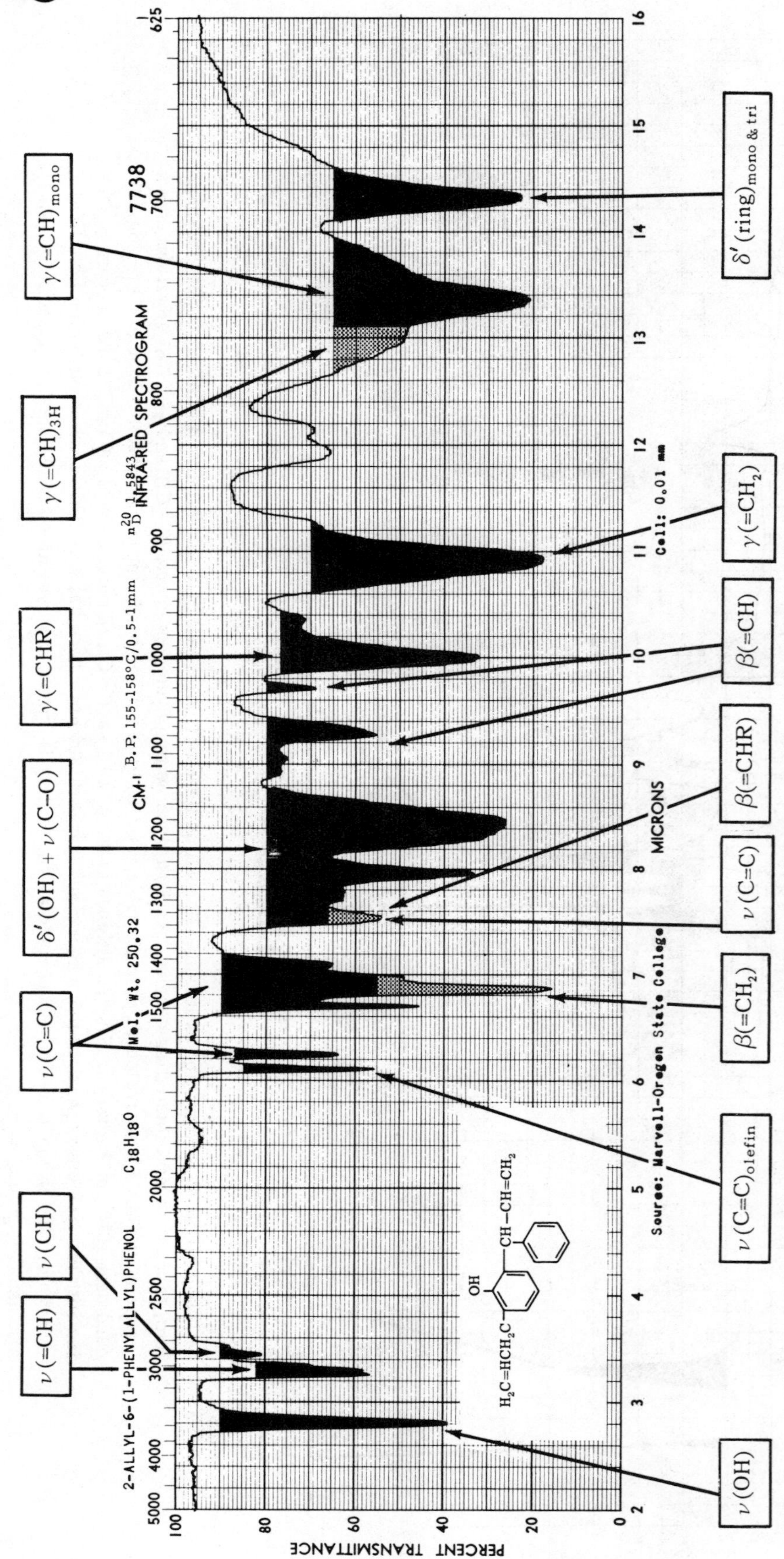

49. This is the first example of a compound having phenolic and olefinic groups. For this compound the olefinic and aromatic out-of-plane vibrations do not coincide, and each can be assigned separately. The δ'(OH) + ν(C–O) vibrations appear in the same positions as in previous spectra.

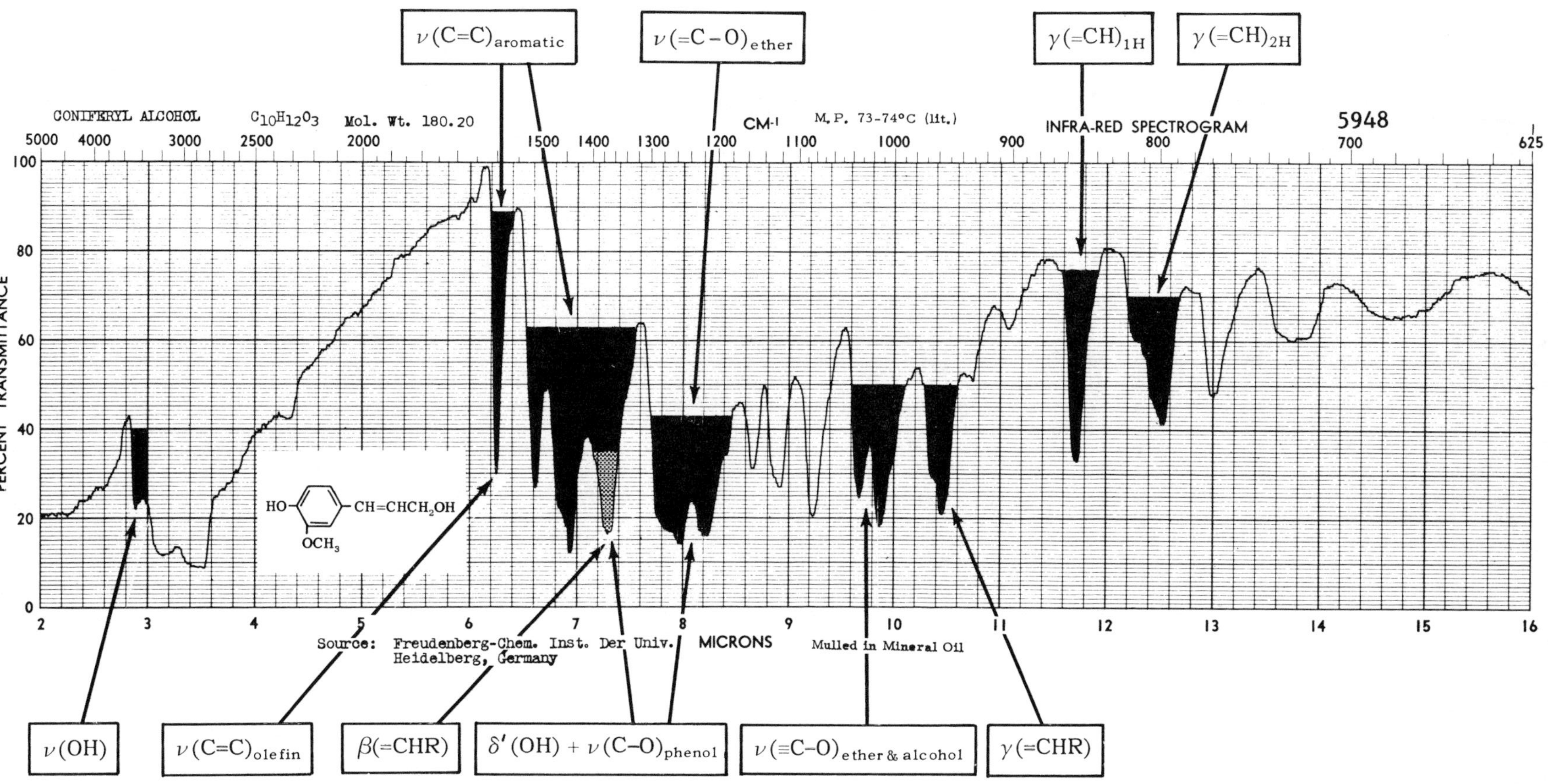

50. This compound has the phenolic, olefinic, and OCH_3 groups. We find it is possible to assign group frequencies to all these units. It is probable, however, that the identification of these groups as being present for an unknown spectrum would, of course, be very difficult.

NONCYCLIC ETHERS

Vibrational Analysis

CH_3OCH_3

Source: G. Herzberg, "Infrared and Raman Spectra of Polyatomic Molecules," Van Nostrand, Princeton, 1945, p. 354.

Band, cm^{-1}		Fundamental and species	Assignment
infrared (gas)	Raman (liquid)		
	2986 S	$\nu_1(a_1)$	$\nu_{as}(CH_3)$
	2950 S	$2\nu_3$?	
2914 VS	2916 S	$\nu_{12}, \nu_{13}, \nu_{18}$	
	2863 VS	$2\nu_4$	
	2812	$\nu_2(a_1)$	$\nu_s(CH_3)$
2399M			
2100S			
2032 M			
1861 M			
1466 VS	1448 S	$\nu_3, \nu_4, \nu_9, \nu_{14}$ ν_{15}, ν_{19}	δ_{as} and $\delta_s(CH_3)$
1180 S		ν_{16}	$r(CH_3)$
1122 M		$\nu_{17}(b_1)$	$\nu_{as}(C-O)$
940 S	918 S	$\nu_6(a_1)$	$\nu_s(C-O)$
920 M			
	414	$\nu_7(a_1)$	δ (COC)

NONCYCLIC ETHERS

CH_3OCH_3

Source: R. C. Taylor, G. L. Vidale, J. Chem. Phys. No. 1, 26:122 (1957).

Band, cm^{-1} (Raman)		Fundamental and species	Assignment
gas	liquid		
2997	2991	$\nu_1(a_1)$?	$\nu_{as}(CH_3)$
–	2889		
2959	2953	overtones,	
2924	2921	$\nu_2(a_1)$?	$\nu_s(CH_3)$
2868	2865		
2821	2814		
1475	1479	ν_3, ν_9, ν_{14}	δ_{as} and
1456	1448	ν_{15}, ν_{19}	$\delta_s(CH_3)$
1440			
1291		ν_{10}, ν_{16}, ν_{20}	$r(CH_3)$
1242	1238	$\nu_4(a_1)$	$\delta_s(CH_3)$
–	1167		
1154	1147	ν_{10}, ν_{16}, ν_{20} ?	$r(CH_3)$
1122	1095	$\nu_{17}(b_1)$	$\nu_{as}(C-O)$
1053	1046	$\nu_5(a_1)$	$r(CH_3)$
929	920	$\nu_6(a_1)$	$\nu_s(C-O)$
478	–	$2\nu_{21}(A_1)$	$t(CH_3)$
448	–	$2\nu_{11}(A_1)$	$t(CH_3)$
413	420	$\nu_7(a_1)$	

X–C₆H₄–O–R (para-substituted)

Source: E. F. Mooney, Spectrochim. Acta 19:877 (1963).

Infrared bands (cm^{-1}), CCl_4 and CS_2 solutions				Assignment
R = Me		R = Et		
X = Cl	X = Br	X = Cl	X = Br	
3092 W	3089 W	3089 W	3091 W	$\nu(=CH)$
3075 W	3074 W	3072 W	3076 W	$\nu(=CH)$
3047 W		3040 W	3039 W	$\nu(=CH)$
3002	3003	2981	2985	$\nu_{as}(CH_3)$
2954	2953	–	–	$\nu_{as}(CH_3)$
		2935	2938	overtone
		2926	2928	$\nu_{as}(CH_3)$
2937	2934			
2904	2903	2899	2901	$\nu_s(CH_3)$
2835	2833			
		2875	2877	$\nu_s(CH_2)$
			1972	
1892	1892	1890	1890	
1860	1869	1869	1867	combinations
1844	1845	1845	1844	
1595		1597	1592	
1581	1579	1578	1577	$\nu(C=C)$
1490	1487	1488	1487	
1462	1460	1474	1474	$\delta_{as}(CH_3)$
1452 Sh		1445 W	1456 W	
1442 W	1440 W	1441 W	1442 W	
1403 W	1404 W		1404 W	
		1392	1391	$\delta_s(CH_2)$
1288 Sh	1288 Sh	1284 Sh	1288 Sh	
1295	1295	1295	1295	$\delta_s(CH_3)$
1244	1245	1243	1241	$\nu(C-O)$
1180	1181			
1167	1170	1168	1170	$\beta(=CH)$
1114 VW	1111 W	1117	1115	$\beta(=CH)$
1100 W	1099 W	1101 W	1100 W	
1093	1073	1092	1072	$\nu(C-X)$
1037	1036	1047	1049	$\nu(C-O)$
1006 W	1002 W	1006	1002	$\beta(=CH)$
		925	925	$\nu(C-C)$
		902	902	
825	824	825	830	$\gamma(=CH)$
800	801	799	799	
698	696	698	696	$(C-C)_{ring}$
640	602	666	639	$\delta'(C-X)$
		638	600	
627	629	625	625	$\alpha(CCC)$
508	506	509	506	$\gamma(=CH)$

NONCYCLIC ETHERS

(Structure: benzene ring bearing X and OR on adjacent carbons)

Source: E. F. Mooney, Spectrochim. Acta 19:877 (1963).

Infrared bands (cm^{-1}), CCl_4 and CS_2 solutions				Assignment
R = Me		R = Et		
X = Cl	X = Br	X = Cl	X = Br	
3091 Sh	3090 Sh	3092 Sh	3080	$\nu(=CH)$
3067	3068	3067	3060	
	3058 Sh	3032 VW		
		3017 VW		
3008	3008	2986	2985	$\nu_{as}(CH_3)$
2957	2959			
	2915 Sh	2938	2933	overtone
		2926	2920	$\nu_{as}(CH_2)$
2938	2938 }			
2902	2906 }	2903	2899	$\nu_s(CH_3)$
2831	2835 }			
2888 VW	2885 VW			
		2884	2882	$\nu_s(CH_2)$
		2851 W		
		1969		
1926	1931	1929	1925 }	
1888	1890	1890	1885 }	combination
1847	1852	1848	1848 }	and
1816	1802	1817	1808 }	overtones
1759	1763	1767	1764 }	
1667	1670	1667	1667	
1587	1590	1590	1580 }	
1575	1575	1580	1574 }	$\nu(C=C)$
1504				
1485	1481	1483	1483 }	
1460	1463	1471	1470	$\delta_{as}(CH_3)$
		1458 W	1456 W	
1446	1447	1443	1442	$\nu(C=C)$
1433	1434			
1401 VW		1395	1391	$\delta_s(CH_2)$
		1367 VW	1365 VW	
1299	1297	1288	1292 Sh }	$\delta_s(CH_3)$
		1298	1301 }	
1270	1271	1276	1275	$\beta(=CH)$
1247	1252	1245	1247	$\nu(C-O)$
		1241 Sh		
1194 VW		1197 VW		
1182 W	1183 W			
1159	1161	1160	1160 }	$\beta(=CH)$
1129	1125	1134	1127 }	
		1111	1109	
		1091	1089	
1064	1057	1063	1053	$\nu(C-X)$

CH_3-O in Heteroaromatic Systems

Source: A. R. Katritzky, B. J. Ridgewell, Spectrochim. Acta 20:589 (1964).

It was found that the $\nu(CH_3-O)$ band can be used to distinguish between the two general types of compounds given below:

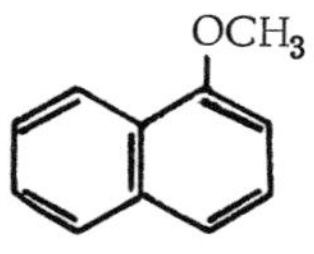

OCH_3

I

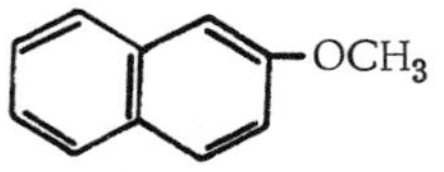

$-OCH_3$

II

The following table summarizes the results. The data is based on 0.2 M $CHCl_3$ solutions in 0.1 mm cells.

We expect two ν(C–O) vibrations. The first is ν(=C–O) for the vibrations of the O against the ring, and this is expected near 1250 cm^{-1}. The O stretch against the CH_3 is expected near 1030 cm^{-1}. If we examine the following table most compounds have two strong bands near 1300 cm^{-1}. These are assigned to the ν(=C–O) and a ring vibration coupling together. For compounds of type II a well defined $\nu(CH_3-O)$ occurs in the 1025-1040 cm^{-1} range. This vibration is found in this same region in many monocyclic methoxy compounds, including anisole itself. However the compounds of type I show no strong band here, but one near 1100 cm^{-1}. This is puzzling, as examining 58 orthosubstituted anisoles reveals that almost all have a strong band in the 1040-1020 cm^{-1} region. If the 2, 6 derivatives are examined, however, no strong bands appear here. It is concluded that steric hindrance is causing the band to disappear from this region.

Compound	ν(CH)	$\delta_{as}(CH_3)$	$\delta_s(CH_3)$	ν(C–O) + ring		$\nu(CH_3-O)$
Quinolines						
2-		1465 M	1442 MS	1318 VS	{1281 VS, 1243 VS}	1024 S
5-		1461 MSh	1447 MWSh		1267 VS	
Quinazolines						
2-		1465 M	1443 S	1320 S	1293 VS	1040 S
4-		1468 S*	1451 S	1380 VS	1302 M	1100 VS
5-	2830 W	1467 S*	1443 M	1312 S	1275 VS	1058 MS
6-	2850 W	1460 MSh	1447 MS	1323 S	1272 S	1027 S
7-	2850 W	1462 MS		1323 VS	1271 S	1026 S
8-	2830 W	1471 S*	1443 MS	1310 VS	1262 S	1062 W
Quinoxalines						
2-		1465 M		1315 VS	1275 MS	1025 S
5-	2835 W		1443 MS	1298 S	1262 VS	1025 VW
6-	2850 W	1461 M	1435 S	1307 VS	1260 MS	1027 VS*
Naphthalenes						
1-	2830 W	1453 M	1445 M	1270 VS	1242 S	1104 VS
2-	2830 W	1459 M	1446 S	1276 S	1263 VS	1033 S

*Peak is superposition of two bands.

NONCYCLIC ETHERS

$CH_3OC_6H_5$

Source: J. H. S. Green, Spectrochim. Acta 18: 39 (1962).

Band, cm^{-1}		Fundamental and species	Assignment
infrared (liquid)	Raman (liquid)		
3098 W	3079 M	(a")	$\nu(=CH)$
3068 M	3063 S	(a')	$\nu(=CH)$
3037 M		(a')	$\nu(=CH)$
3007 M	3014 M	(a")	$\nu(=CH)$
2957 M	2946 S	(a' + a")	$\nu_{as}(CH_3)$
2905 M			overtone and combinations
2835 M	2840 S	(a')	$\nu_s(CH_3)$
1958 W			overtone
1940 W			combination
1862 Sh			"
1884 W			"
1800 Sh			"
1778 W			"
1699 W			"
1603	1598 VS	(a')	$\nu(C=C)$
1593		(a")	$\nu(C=C)$
1497 S	1501 W	(a')	$\nu(C=C)$
1471 M			combination
1456 M	1457 M	(a' + a")	$\delta_{as}(CH_3)$
1443 M		(a")	$\nu(C=C)$
1392 W	1393 VW		overtone
1338 M		(a')	$\nu(C=C)$
1326 Sh			combination
1304 M	1300 S		$\delta_s(CH_3)$

table continued.

$CH_3OC_6H_5$, J. H. S. Green, (continued)

Band, cm^{-1}		Fundamental and species	Assignment
infrared liquid	Raman (liquid)		
1296 M		(a")	β(=CH)
1246 S	1248 S	(a')	X-sensitive
1204 VW			combination
1182 M		(a')	β(=CH)
1172 M	1176 S	(a')	$\nu(CH_3-O)$
1153 M	1148 M	(a")	β(=CH)
1076 M	1073 W	(a")	$r(CH_3)$
1039 S*	1044 W	(a')	$r(CH_3)$
1019	1026 S	(a')	β(=CH)
994 M	995 VS	(a')	Ring
975 Sh		(a')	γ(=CH)
957 W		(a")	γ(=CH)
882 M	891 W	(a')	γ(=CH)
829 Sh			combination
819 W	820 M	(a")	γ(=CH)
783 S	785 S	(a')	X-sensitive
754 S	759 W	(a')	γ(=CH)
692 S	686 VW	(a')	$(C=C)_{ring}$†
664 W			combination
613 W	616 M	(a")	α(CC)
553 M	554 M		combination
510 M	512 M	(a')	X-sensitive
439 W	444 S	(a')	X-sensitive
352		(a')	δ(C−O−C)
259	258 M	(a")	X-sensitive
221	209 M	(a')	X-sensitive

*This band is assigned as ν(C−O) by other authors.
†In this author's notation this is listed as δ' (ring).

NONCYCLIC ETHERS

$CBr_3CH(OH)OCH_3$

Source: A. Novak, E. Whalley, Spectrochim. Acta 16:521 (1960).

Infrared band, cm^{-1}		Assignment
solution, CCl_4	solid	
3602		$\nu(OH)_{free}$
3545	3340	$\nu(OH)_{bonded}$
	1460 S	$\delta_{as}(CH_3)$
	1450 S	
	1403 S	$\delta(=CH+OH)$
	1352 S	$\delta_s(CH_3)$
	1295 S	$\delta(=CH+OH)$
	1195 M	$r(CH_3)$
	1102 VS	$\nu(C-O)$
	1080 VS	
	1001 S	$\nu(CH_3-O)$
	955 M	$\delta(CH)$
	760 VS	$\nu(C-CBr_3)$
	735 VS	

$CCl_3CH(OH)OCH_3$

Source: A. Novak, E. Whalley, Spectrochim. Acta 16:521 (1960).

Infrared band, cm^{-1}		Assignment
solution, CCl_4	solid	
3605		$\nu(OH)_{free}$
3558	3350	$\nu(OH)_{bonded}$
	1462 S }	$\delta_{as}(CH_3)$
	1455 S }	
	1407 S }	$\delta(=CH+OH)$
	1390 S }	
	1358 S	$\delta_s(CH_3)$
	1302 S	$\delta(=CH+OH)$
	1198 M	$r(CH_3)$
	1115 VS }	$\nu(C-O)$
	1087 VS }	
	1025 S	$\nu(CH_3-O)$
	967 M	$\delta(CH)$
	830 VS }	$\nu(C-CBr_3)$
	815 VS }	
	662 S	
	580 M	

$$\begin{matrix} Cl \diagdown \\ H \diagup \end{matrix} C{=}N{-}O{-}CH_3$$

Source: A. E. Parsons, J. Mol. Spectr. 3:73 (1959).

Infrared band, cm^{-1}		Assignment
vapor	liquid	
3093	3083 MW	$\nu(CH)$
2993	2976 W	$2\nu(CCl) + \delta_s(CH_3)$
2954	2941 M	$2\delta_{as}(CH_3)$
2887	2904 W	$2\nu_{as}(NOC) + \nu(CCl)$
2830	2825 W	$2\delta_s(CH_3)$
	1961 VVW	$\nu_{as}(NOC) + \nu_s(NOC)$
	1835 VVW	$\nu_{as}(NOC) + \nu(CCl)$
	1806 VW	$2\nu_s(NOC)$
1613	1597 MW	$\nu(CN)$
1572 1563	1555 MW	$2\nu(CCl)$
1464	1466 MW	$\delta_{as}(CH_3)$
	1443 MW	$\delta_s(CH_3)$
1276	1274 M	$\delta(CH)$
1182	1190 W	$r_\gamma(CH_3)$
1155	1156 VW	$r_\beta(CH_3)$
1084 1080* 1072	1063 VS	$\nu_{as}(NOC)$
917 911 905	905 VS	$\nu_s(NOC)$
813	806 W	$\delta(CNO)$
802 789	784 VS	$\nu(CCl)$

*author reports lack of amide bands as due to hydroxy-imino configuration.

For: The infrared spectra of chloro- and bromobenzene derivatives—I. anisoles and phenetoles.
See: E. F. Mooney, Spectrochim. Acta 19:877 (1963).

NONCYCLIC ETHERS

Cyclopropylphenylcarbinol and Cyclopropylphenycarbinyl Ether

Source: Private communication.

$\triangleright$–C(H)(–OH)–C_6H_5	$\triangleright$–C(H)(C_6H_5)–O–C(H)(C_6H_5)–$\triangleleft$	Assignment
3448 S		ν(OH)
3079 S	3079 S	$\nu(\Delta\text{–H})$
3064 S	3064 S	ν(CH)
3027 S	3027 S	ν(CH)
3007 S	3007 S	$\nu(\Delta\text{–H})$
2870 S	2871 S	ν(CH)
1969 W	1969 W	aromatic
1898 W	1894 W	"
1828 W	1825 W	"
1613 W	1616 M	"
1502 S	1502 S	"
1460 S	1460 S	"
1435 W	1435 M	
1410 W	1385 M	
1337 W	1342 W	
1285 W	1290 W	
1264 W	1264 M	
1200 M	1199 M	
1176 W	1168 M	β(=CH)
1139 M	1139 M, 1156 M	
1080 M*	1079 S	ν_{as}(C–O)
1030 S	1053 VS }	$\delta'(\Delta)$
973 W	1020 S }	
950 M	952 M	
923 M	910 M	
863 W	870 W	$\delta'(\Delta)$
837 M	838 M }	ν_s(C–O)?
771 M	769 S }	
746 M	748	γ(=CH)
700 S	700 VS	γ(=CH)

*Note the non-shifting of the ν(C–O) band near 1080 cm^{-1}. This illustrates the independence of the C–O band of the groups attached to oxygen.

Diphenylether and Related Compounds

Source: J. E. Katon, W. R. Feairheller, Jr., E. R. Lippincott, J. Mol. Spectr. 13:72 (1964).

The infrared and Raman spectra of diphenylether are reported. The symmetry of the molecule is assigned as C_s. The C_{2v} structure is ruled out. They suggest the two phenyl rings are nonequivalent and are at an angle with respect to each other. The angle between normals to the rings probably does not equal 90°. Bands at 1236 and 1198 cm^{-1} are assigned as ring–oxygen stretching modes [ν(C–O)]. These suggest the angle is 90°, since, as we have discussed earlier, the coupling would be zero at 90°, and ν_{as}(C–O) and ν_s(C–O) would coincide. The authors compare the vibrations of diphenylether to a number of related molecules, and their comparison follows.

Diphenylether		Anisole	Phenetole	Phenol	Toluene	Ethyl benzene	Assignment
ring I	ring II						
3089	3089	3079	3096	3085	3090	3080	ν(CH)
3075	3075	3068	3068	3076	3067	3064	ν(CH)
3068	3040	3037	3068	3044	3061	3053	ν(CH)
1600	1593	1603	1603	1604	1599	1613	ν(CC)
1487	1487	1497	1498	1497	1492	1499	ν(CC)
1174	1164	1182	1175	1167	1178	1179	β(CH)
1023	1023	1019	1026	1026	1041	1031	β(CH)
1003	1003	995	998	999	1002	1003	ring
979	979	975	975	978	966	985	γ(CH)
894	904	882	901	881	895	904	γ(CH)
749	749	754	755	749	729	745	γ(CH)
690	698*	692	690	688	695	696	$(CH)_{ring}$
3089	3089	3098	3096	3091	3090	3080	ν(CH)
3015	3027	3007	3040	3030	3032	3040	ν(CH)
1591	1585	1593	1592	1596	1599	1587	ν(CC)
1455	1455	1443	1448	1465	1460	1464	ν(CC)
1335*	1330*	1338	1335	1333	1330	1330	ν(CC)
						(1310 ?)	
1284	1294*	1296	1293	1313	1313	1330	β(CH)
1153	1153	1153	1155	1145	1155	1156	β(CH)
1072	1072	1076	1080	1071	1029	1064	β(CH)
961	961	957	953	958	981	964	γ(CH)
824	866	819	829	825	842	840	γ(CH)
602	616	613	614	617	623	624	α(CCC)
396	478	–	–	408	465	404	$(CC)_{ring}$
1236	1198	1248	1246	1259	1209	1291	X-sensitive
798	798	783	797	810	786	771	X-sensitive
498	563	511	508	526	521	556	X-sensitive
412	481	444	427	500	464	487	X-sensitive
228	215	209	180	241	216	158	X-sensitive
245	312	258	238	408	344	314	X-sensitive

*Raman.

NONCYCLIC ETHERS

Correlation Table

Group frequency	Symbol	Position (cm^{-1})	Intensity
A. Aliphatic Ethers			
≡C−O asymmetric stretch	ν_{as}(≡C−O)	1120± 20	S
−O−CH_2 stretching	$\nu(OCH_2)$*	2955-2922 2878-2835	S
−O−CH_3 stretching	$\nu(OCH_3)$	2992-2955 2897-2867	S S
−O−CH_2 symmetric bend	$\delta_s(-OCH_2)$	1420	M-S
−O−CH_3 bending	$\delta_s(-OCH_3)$	1450	M-S
B. Aliphatic-Aromatic Ethers Aromatic-Aromatic Ethers			
=C−O− stretch	ν(=C−O−)	1300-1200	S
≡C−O− stretch	ν(−O−C≡), aliphatic—aromatic only	1060-1010	M
O−CH_3 rock	$r(OCH_3)$, anisoles	1100-1000	M-S
O−CH_3 bend	$\delta_s(OCH_3)$	1450	M-S
C. Aliphatic-Olefinic Ethers Olefinic-Olefinic Ethers			
=C−O− stretch	ν(=C−O−)	1225-1200	S
≡C−O− stretch	ν(−O−C≡), aliphatic—olefinic only	1060-1010	M
−OCH_3 rock	$r(OCH_3)$		
=CH stretch	ν(=CH)	3125-3098	M-S
C=C stretch	ν(C=C),* gauche	1660-1635	
C=C stretch	ν(C=C),* trans	1620-1610	M-S
=CH in-plane bend	β(=CH)	1323-1320	M-S
=CH out-of-plane bend	γ(=CH)	970-960	M-S
=CH_2 out-of-plane bend	$\gamma(=CH_2)$	820-810	M-S

*Both gauche and trans forms can exist together, so vinylic ethers have a double ν(C=C).

The preceding correlation may appear to be more complex than is necessary for the reader to utilize it in predicting group frequencies. It was prepared, however, to emphasize that we must examine both groups attached to the oxygen atom. For example, the group frequency associated with the ν(C−O) vibration will appear in a position determined by both groups. We could, for example, prepare a simple listing of group frequencies for ethers as follows. We list the ν_{as}(C−O) and the ν_s(C−O) for these ethers, noting the ν_{as}(C−O) as ν(=C−O) to indicate it is the unsaturated group bonding to the oxygen that results in the high position of the ν_{as}(C−O):

	ν_{as}(C−O), cm^{-1}	ν_s(C−O), cm^{-1}
$R-CH_2-O-CH_2R$	1110 VS	925 VW
R_2CHOR_2CH	1110 VS	925 VW
$C_6H_5OCH_2R$	1200 VS	1050 M
$C_6H_5OC_6H_5$	1225 VS	*
$H_2C=CH-O-CH_2R$	1200 VS	1050 M
$H_2C=CH-O-CH=CH_2$	1200 VS	*

*No assignment has been suggested.

Attention should be directed to the previous discussion concerning the CH_3O group in heterocyclic systems. Here the ν(C−O) of this group was either at 1100 or 1050 cm^{-1}, depending on the steric factor near the CH_3O group. If we examine a large number of ethers often we see 1100 or 1050 cm^{-1} bands, and often both appear.

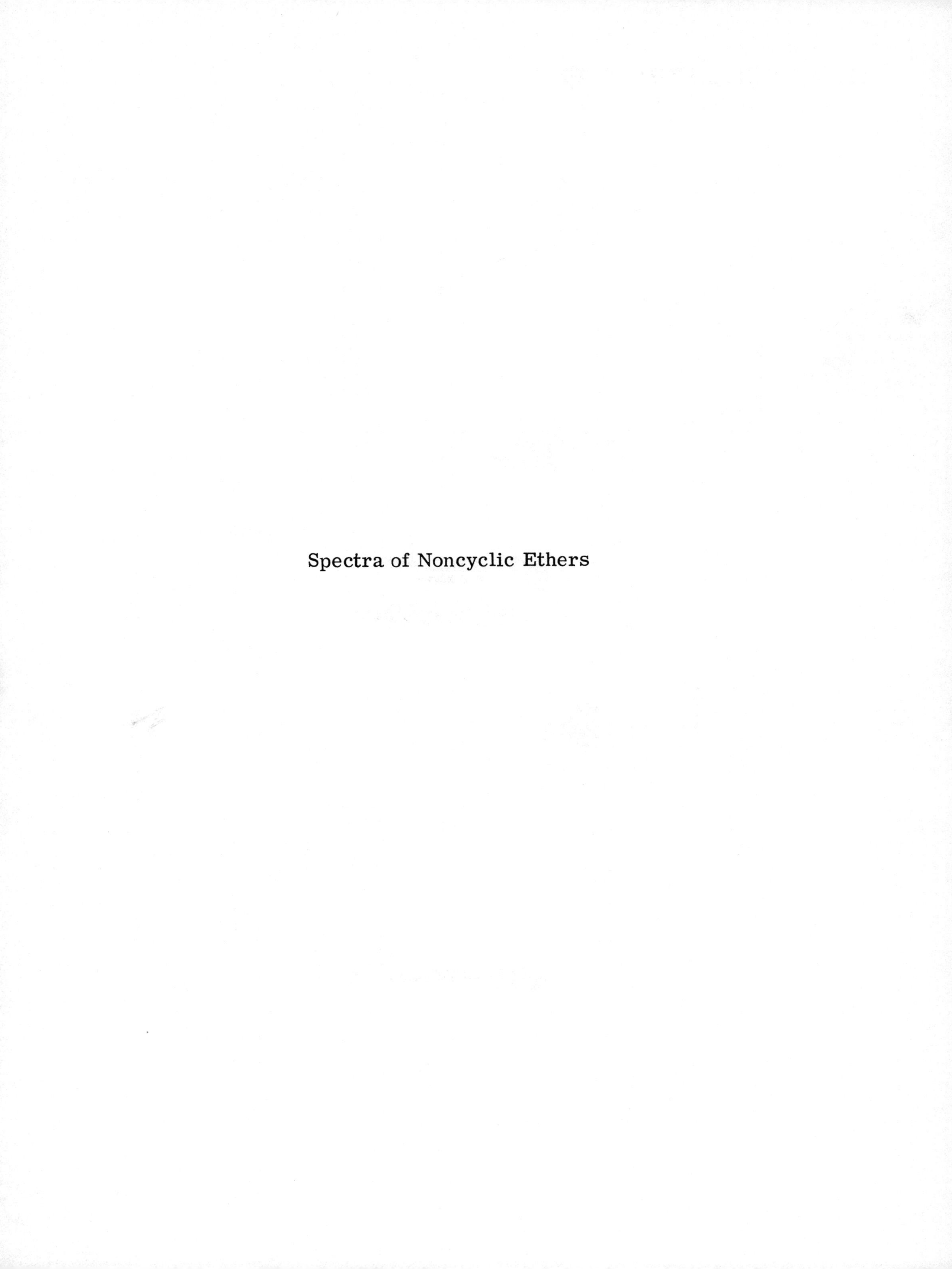

Spectra of Noncyclic Ethers

NONCYCLIC ETHERS ❶

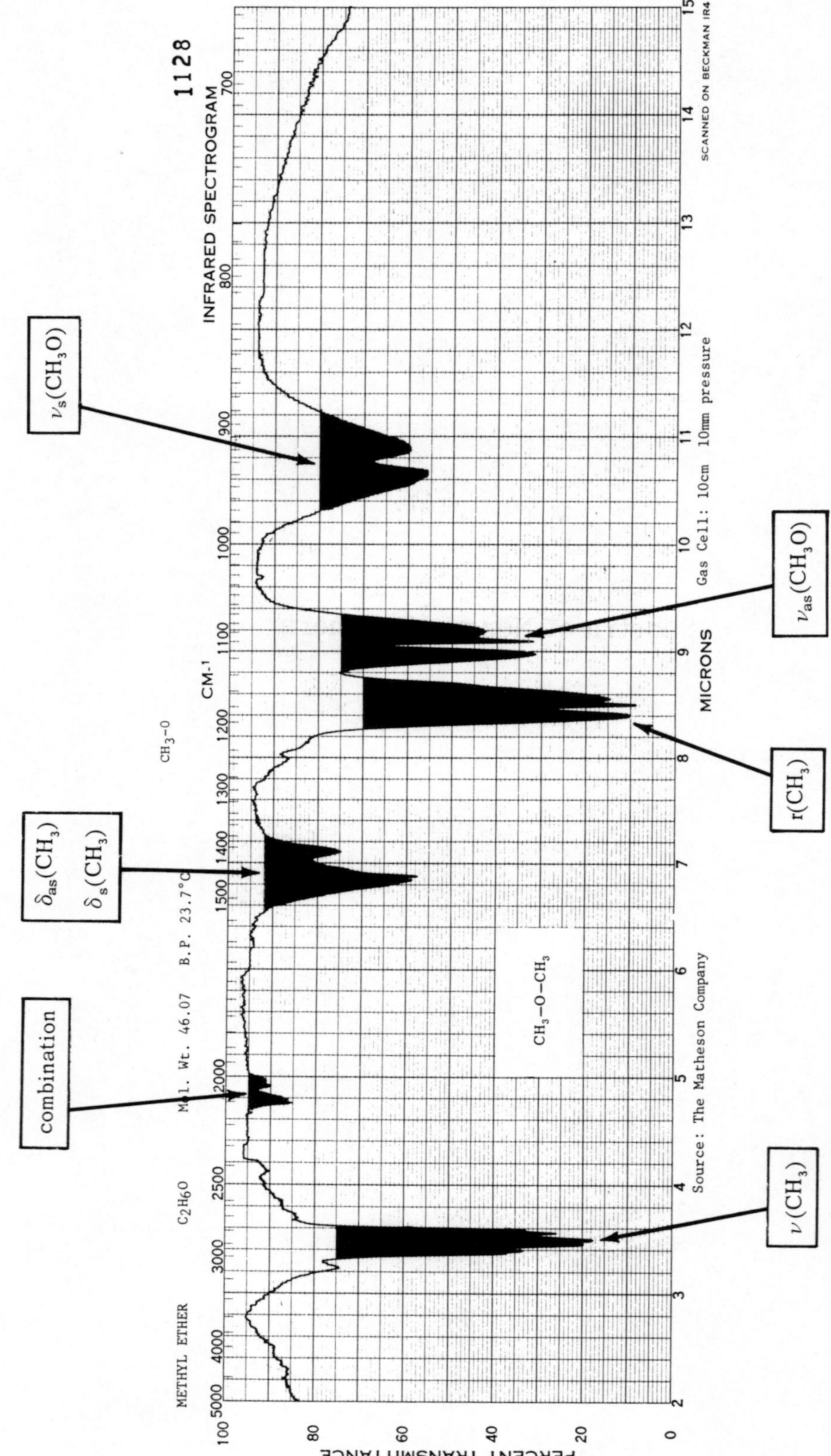

1. The assignments for dimethyl ether are based on the vibrational analysis presented earlier. It should be noted both the ν_{as}(C–O) and ν_s(C–O) vibration give strong bands. This will not be true of all ethers. The r(CH_3) vibration is unusually strong in this spectrum, probably because of the high symmetry and few atoms present.

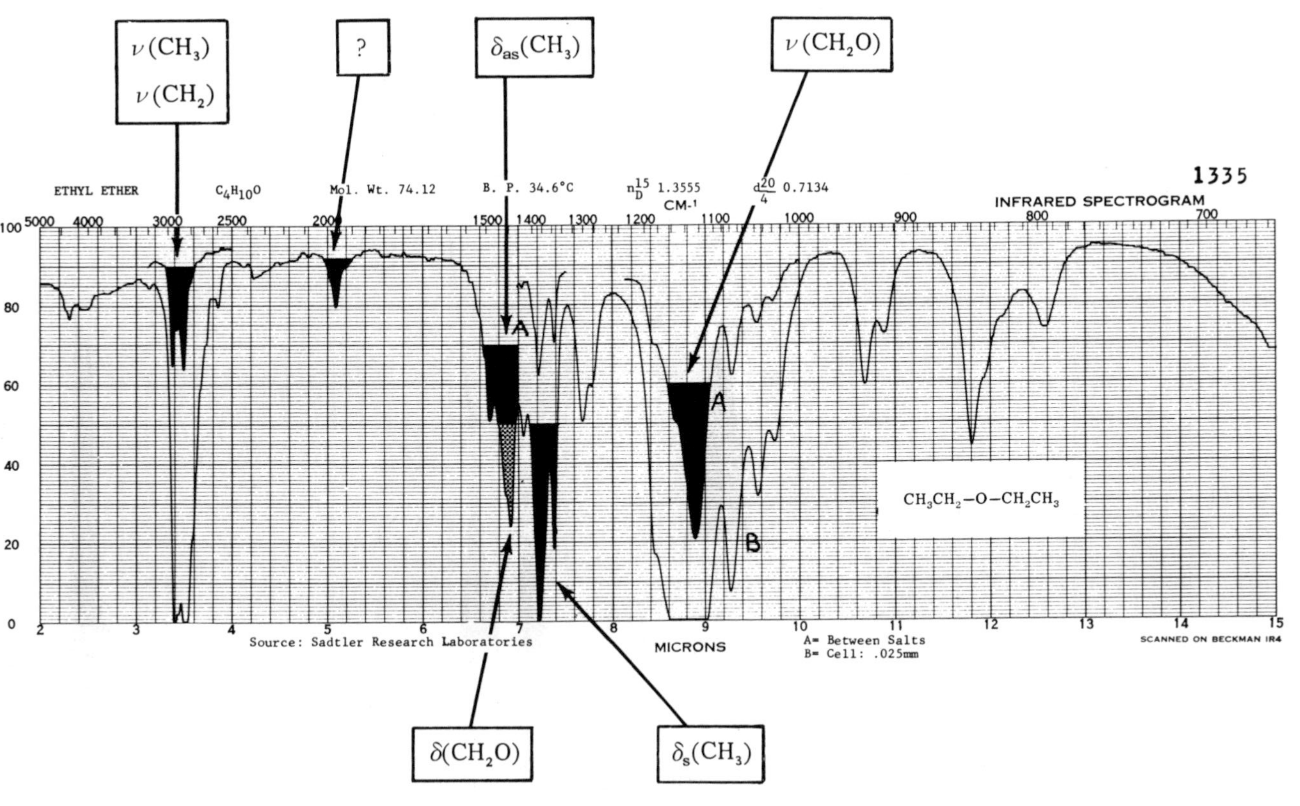

2. This spectrum is typical of an aliphatic straight-chain ether. The only strong band below 1200 cm^{-1} being the ν(C−O). The CH_2 group adjacent to the oxygen should have its scissor vibration shifted from the 1465 cm^{-1} position. The strong band near 1450 cm^{-1} is therefore assigned to it. The broadness of the ν(C−O) band is expected for the ethers.

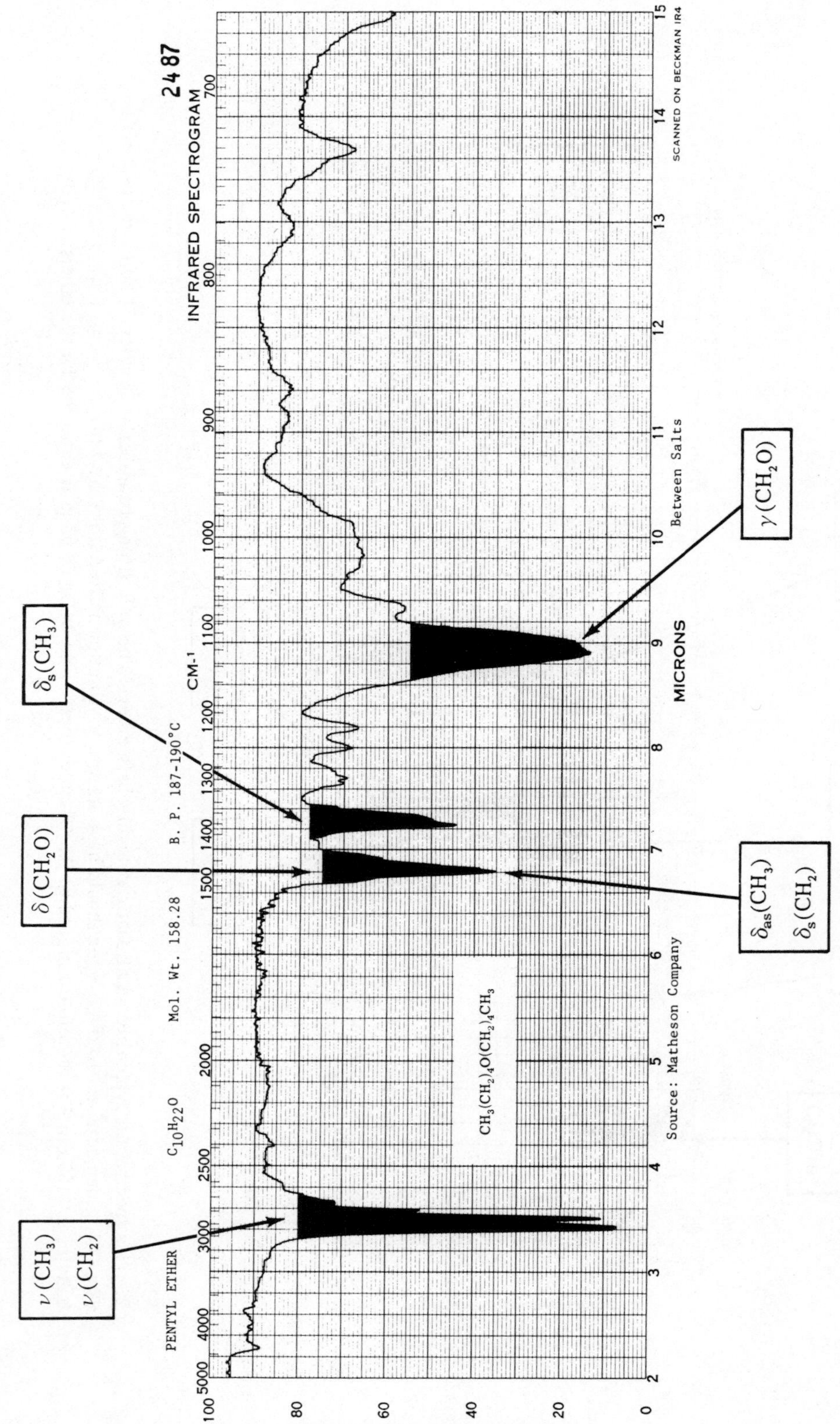

3. n-Amyl ether's spectrum resembles that of diethyl ethers, the only differences appearing in the CH_3 and CH_2 vibrations below 1000 cm^{-1}.

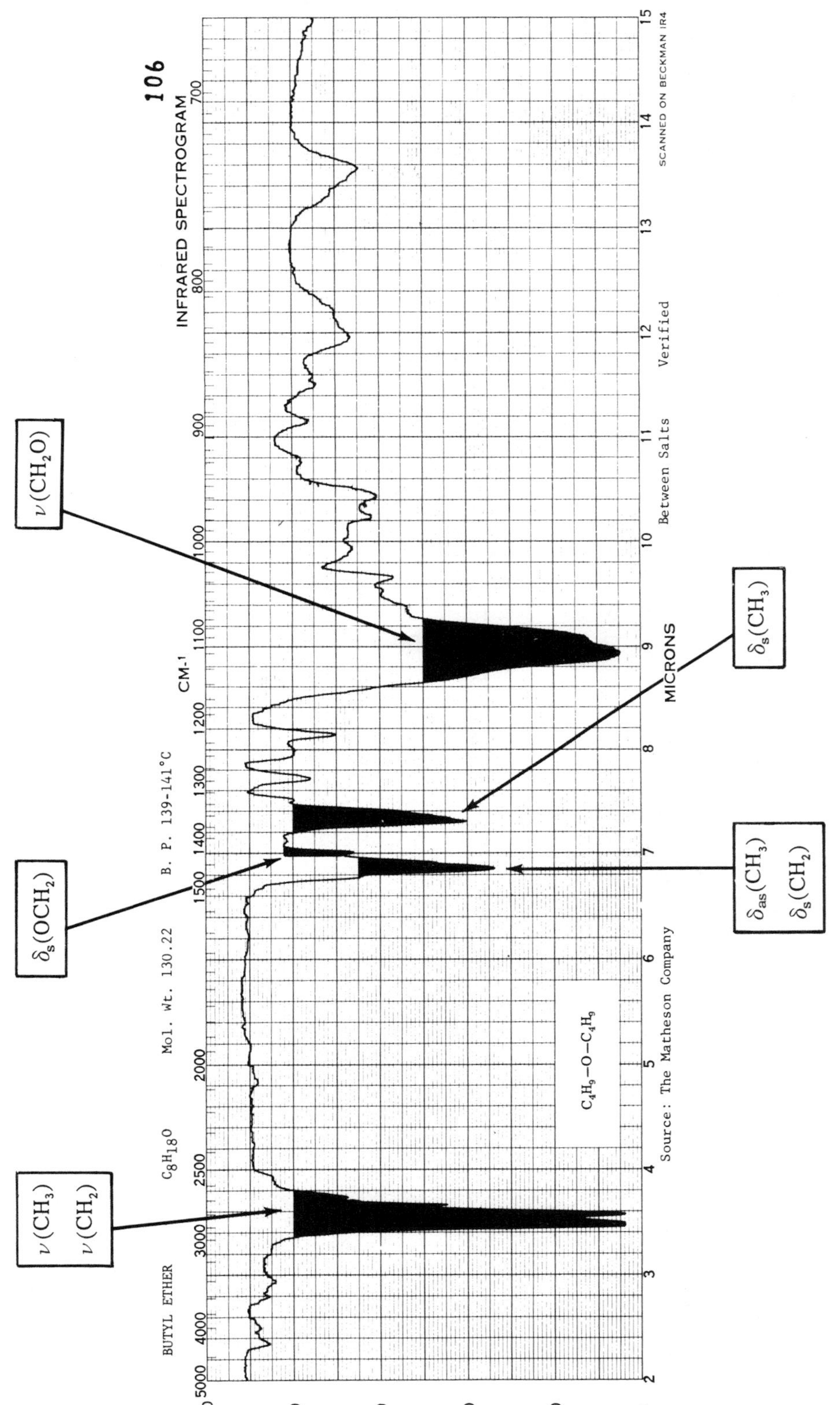

4. Butyl ether's spectrum again illustrates the typical straight-chain aliphatic ether. The only strong band below 1200 cm^{-1} being the $\nu(C-O)$.

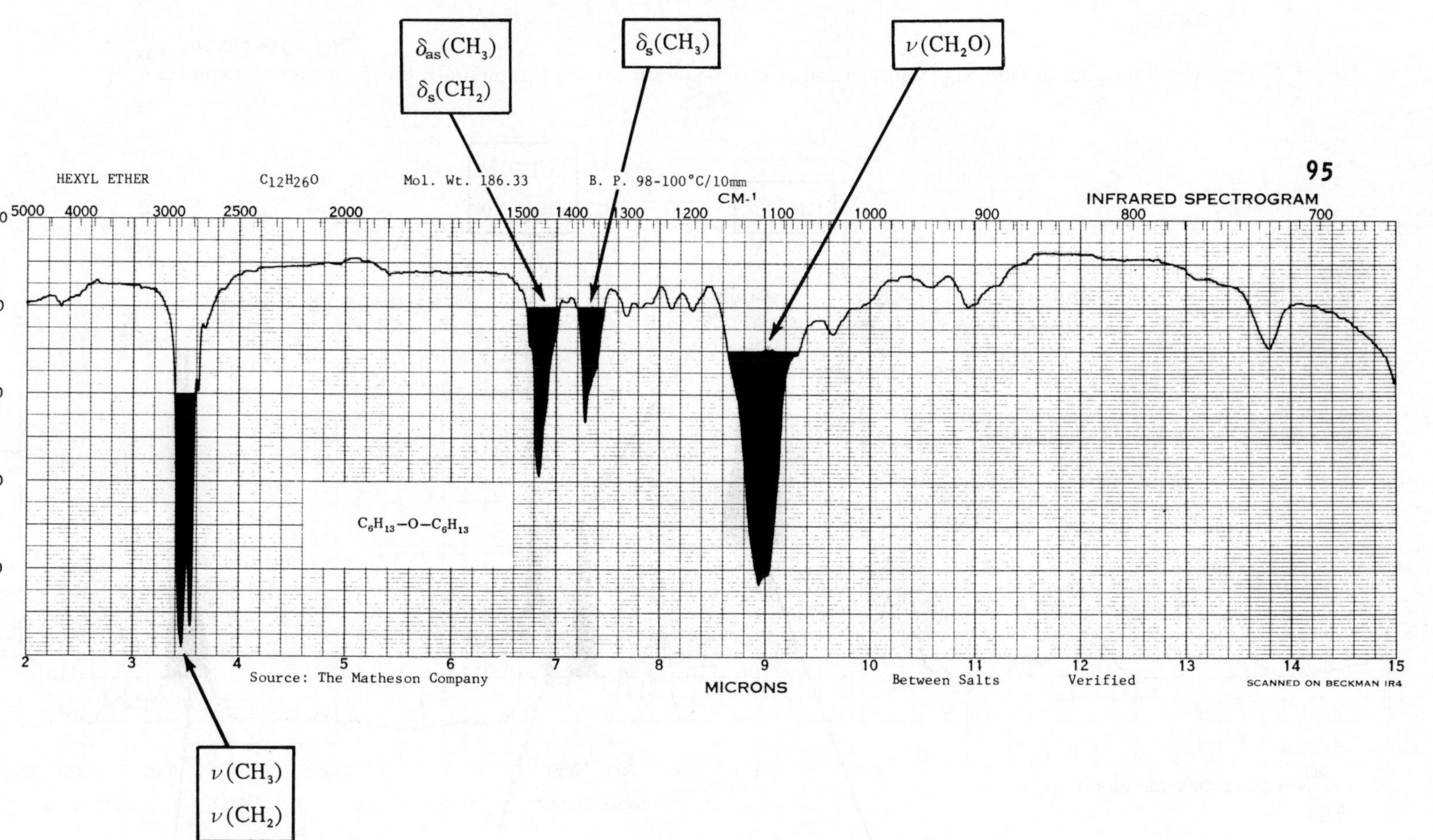

5. The hexyl ether spectrum is illustrative of how the intensity of the $\nu(C-O)$ relative to the 1450 cm^{-1} CH_3, CH_2 band changes as the number of CH_2 groups increases. The intensity of the 1450 cm^{-1} band approaches that of the $\nu(C-O)$ but remains lower.

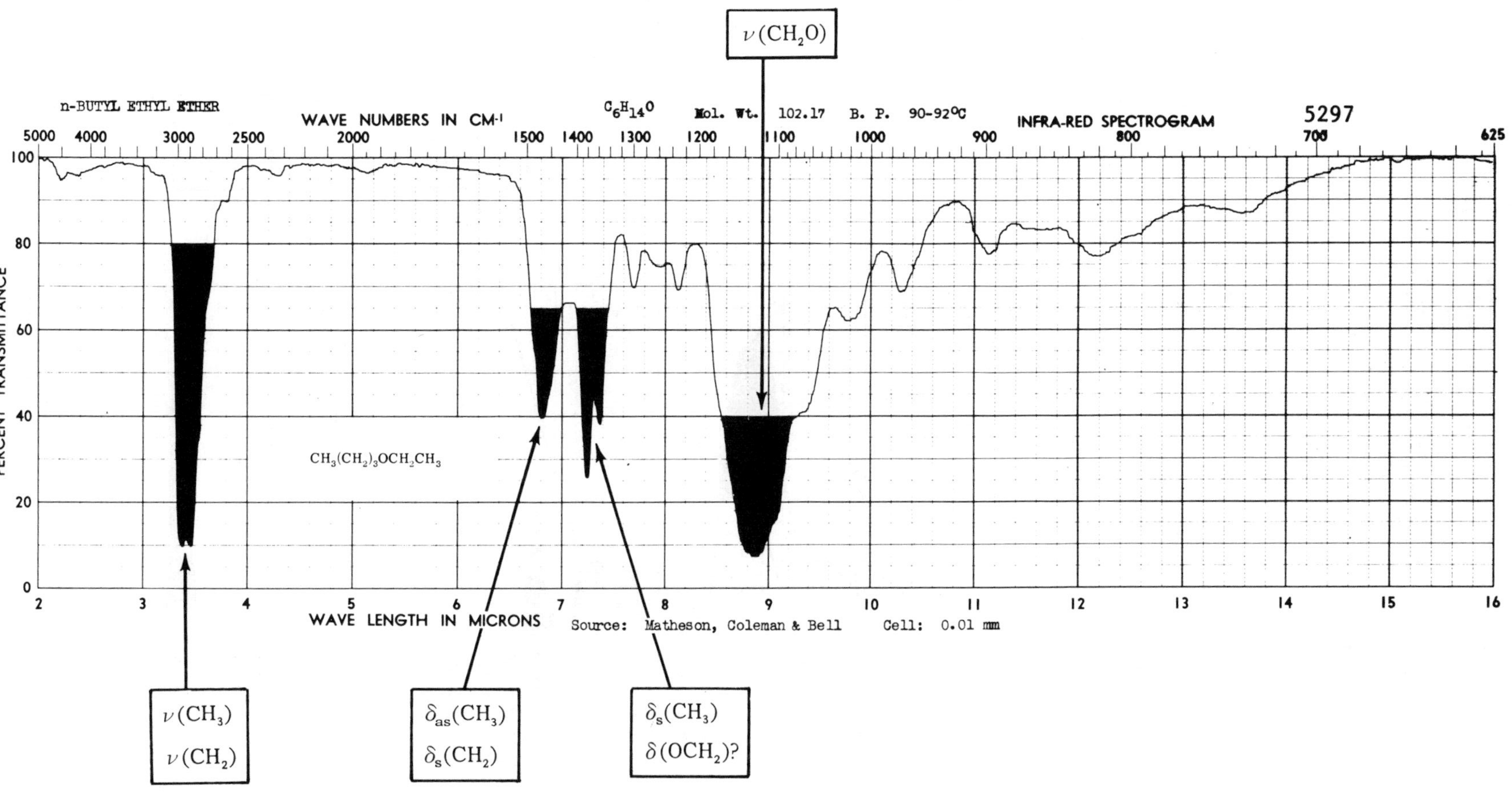

6. n-Butyl ethyl ether's spectrum is the first example of an aliphatic ether having two different chains on the oxygen atom. This difference does not change the position of the $\nu(C-O)$ or the general appearance of the spectrum when it is compared to the previous ones.

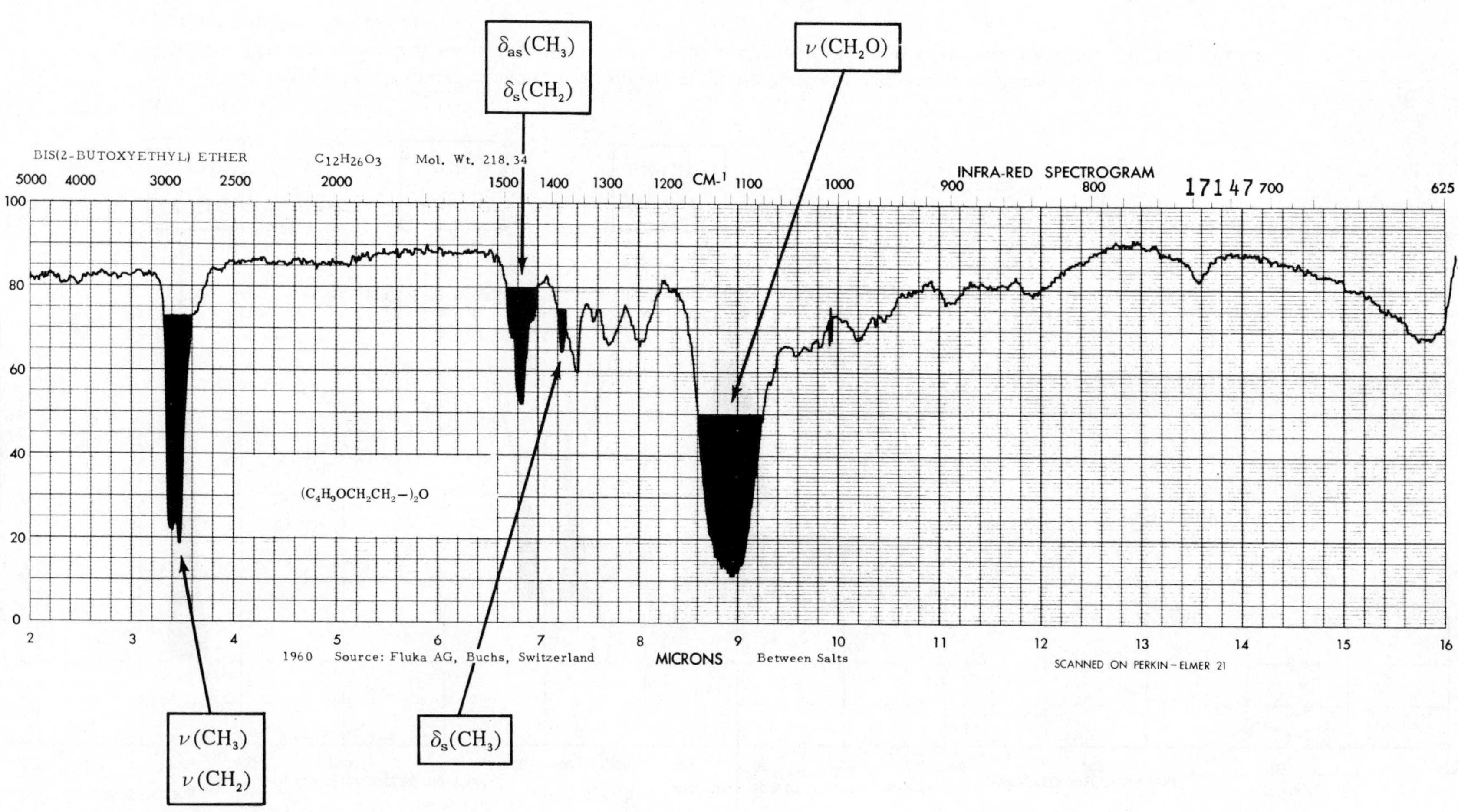

7. Bis (2-butoxyethyl) ether is an example of an aliphatic ether having three oxygen atoms. As for the previous aliphatic ethers, the $\nu(C-O)$ is near 1110 cm^{-1}, and the spectrum is quite similar to the simple ethers.

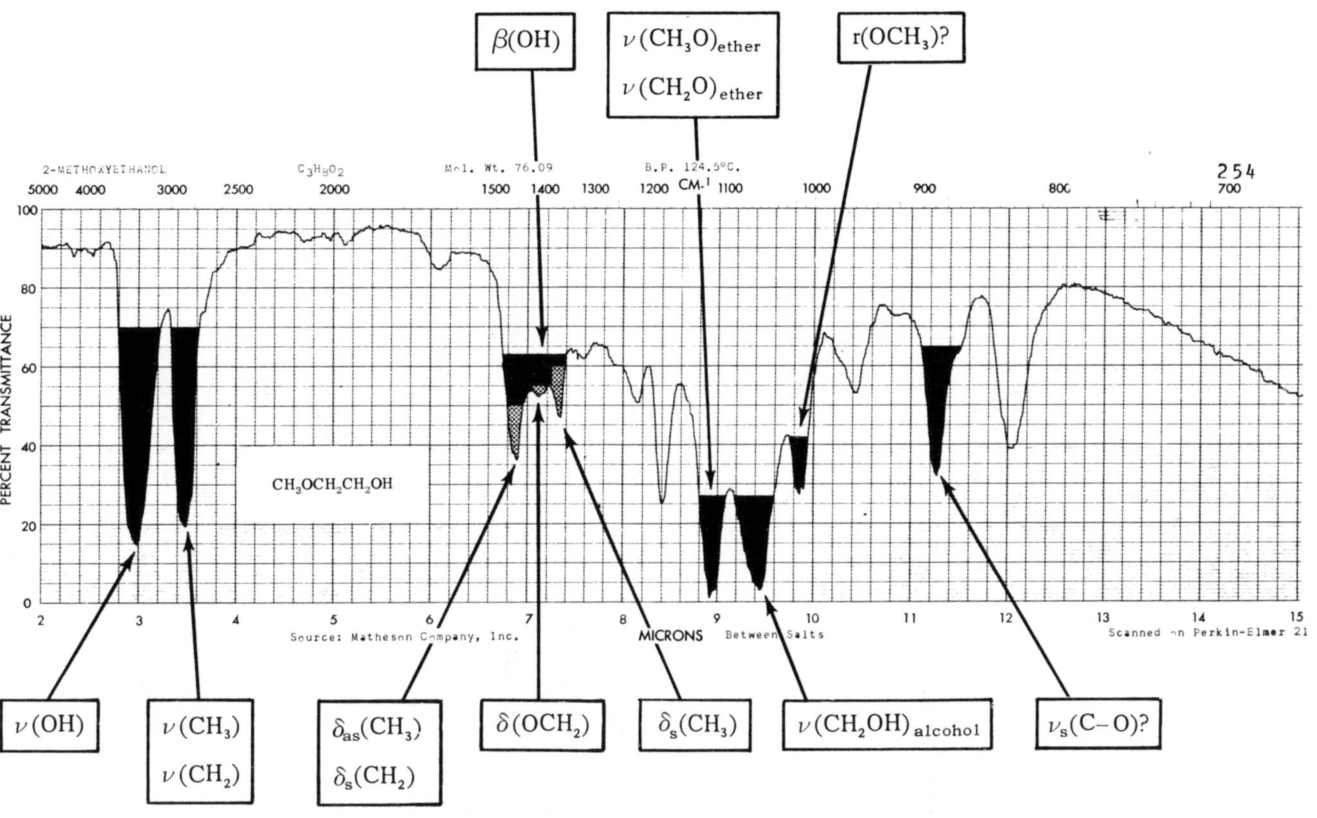

8. A simple combination of alcohol and ether linkages is illustrated in the compound whose spectrum is presented here. The ν(C$-$O) of ether is near 1110 cm^{-1} and of the alcohol near 1055 cm^{-1}, as expected from assignments of the alcohol spectra of volume 2 and the ether assigments just discussed. Note again the broadening of the 1500-1300 cm^{-1} region by the β(OH). The group $-OCH_3$ occurs in anisoles as well as other ethers, and often has a quite strong r(CH_3) vibration near the ν(C$-$O) vibration (see for example dimethyl ether and anisole spectra). This vibration can therefore make it difficult to assign the ν(C$-$O).

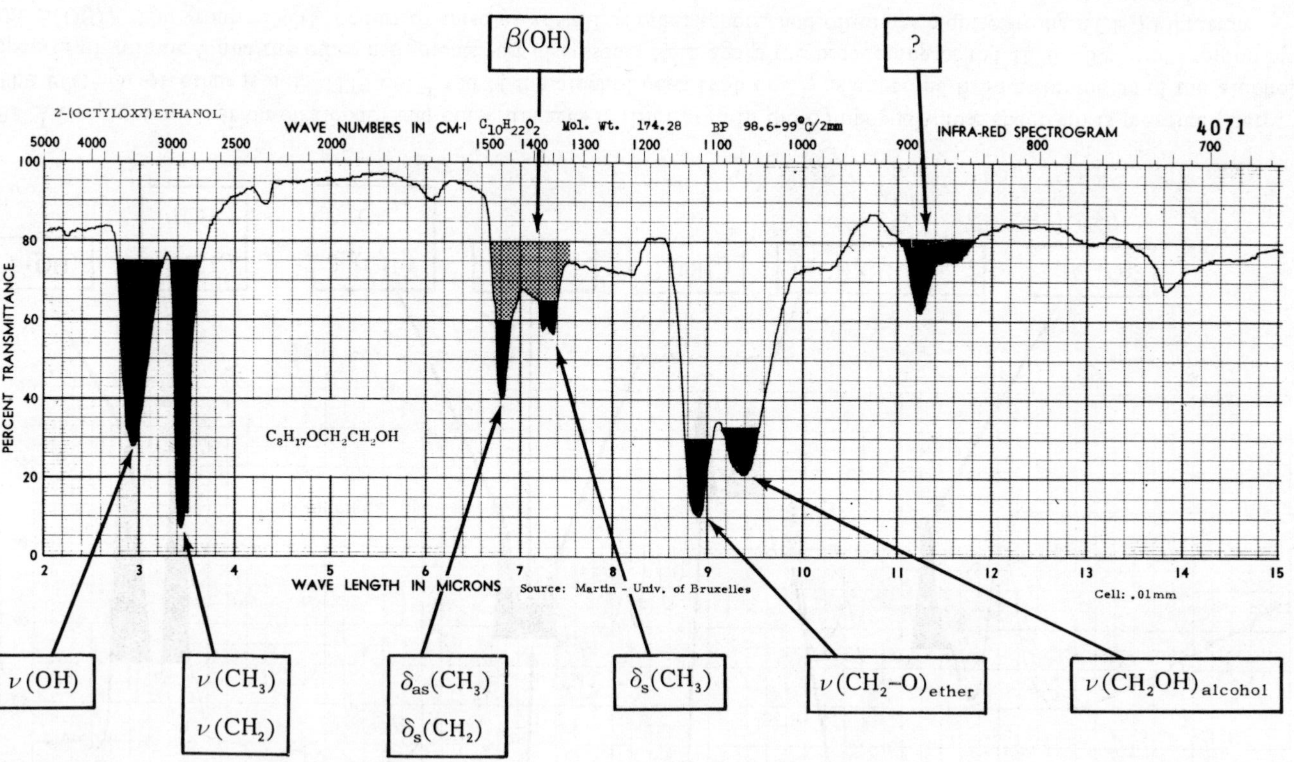

9. Attention is directed to a band near 900 cm^{-1}. This could be $\nu_s(C-O)$. The combination of alcohol and ether groupings in this compound result in $\nu(C-O)$ bands which are distinct for each. All the strong bands can be assigned as group frequencies and this spectrum has the appearance of a typical aliphatic alcohol plus ether. Note the band near 900 cm^{-1} again.

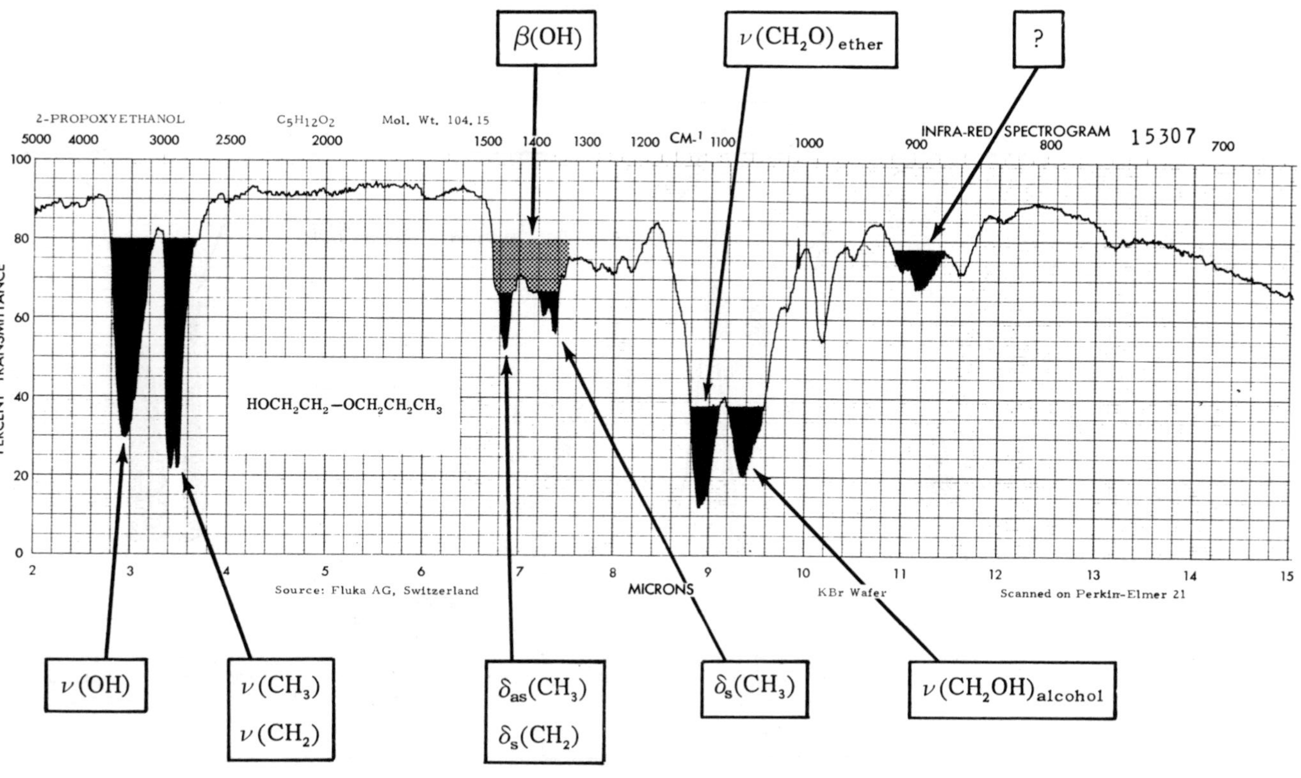

10. The 2-propoxyethanol spectrum is quite similar to the previous one. Only the weaker bands lower than 1000 cm^{-1} can be used to distinguish between these two spectra.

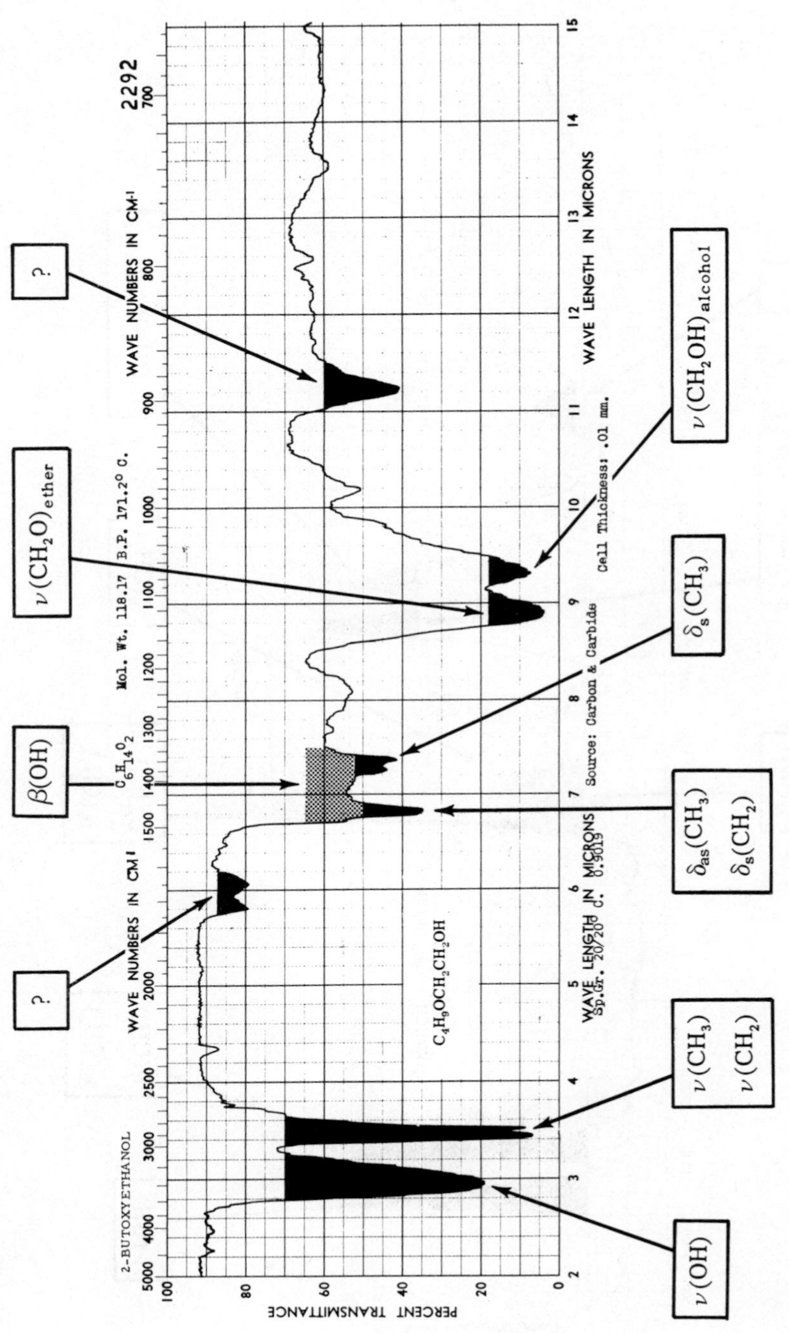

11. The 2-butoxyethanol spectrum completes the three examples of alcohol-ether compounds having one grouping of each. Its spectrum is similar to the previous members of the series, except the ν(C−O) alcohol is shifted to a slightly higher position. Note the band near 900 cm^{-1} again, which we find with OCH_2CH_2OH.

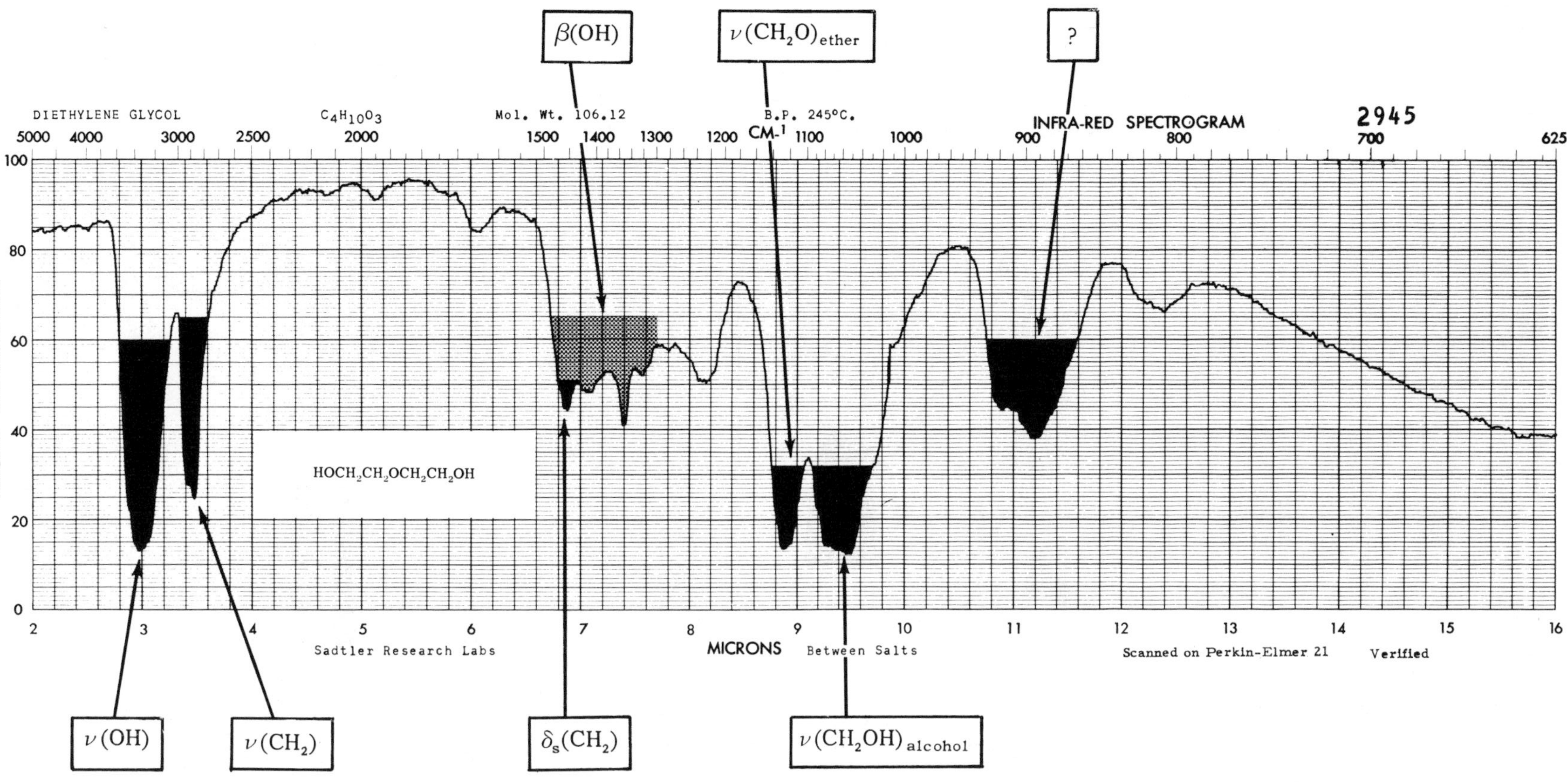

12. The spectrum of diethylene gylcol is an interesting one, since it verifies a general rule this author presented in Volume 2. In that volume it was pointed out that monohydric alcohols in the associated state show similar spectra, since they essentially represent long chains of $(CH_2)_x$–OH groups held together by hydrogen bonding. Only if diluted solutions are studied will the spectra differ in bands associated with the COH group. This spectrum illustrates this, since it is quite similar to the previous three monohydric-alcohol spectra.

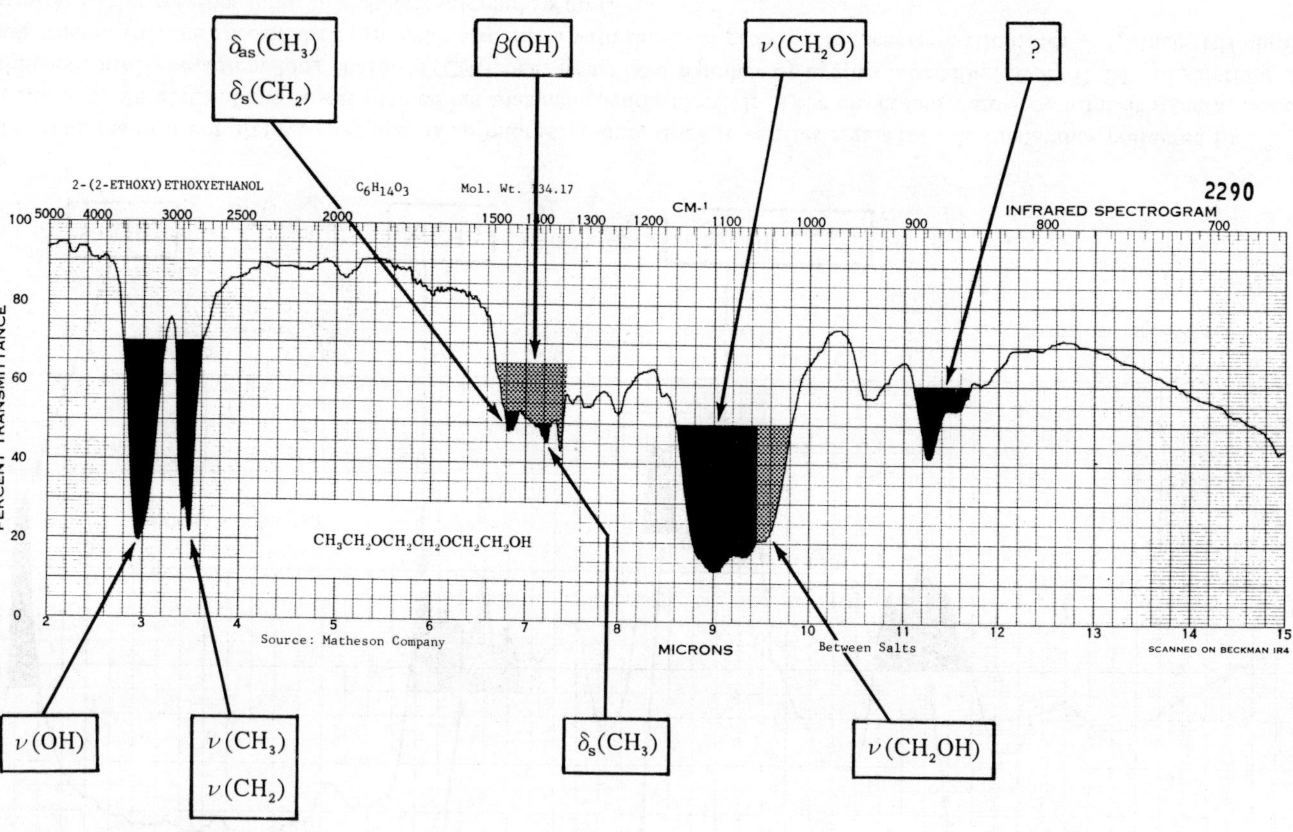

13. The compound 2-(2-ethoxy)-ethoxyethanol has two ether and one alcohol group. This results in the ν(C—O) vibration appearing as a very broad band. Three maxima are observed which could possibly be due to the three environments for the C—O group. It should be noted that a spectrum such as this would be difficult to utilize in identifying a compound of this type, as it does not differ in much detail from many of the previous spectra.

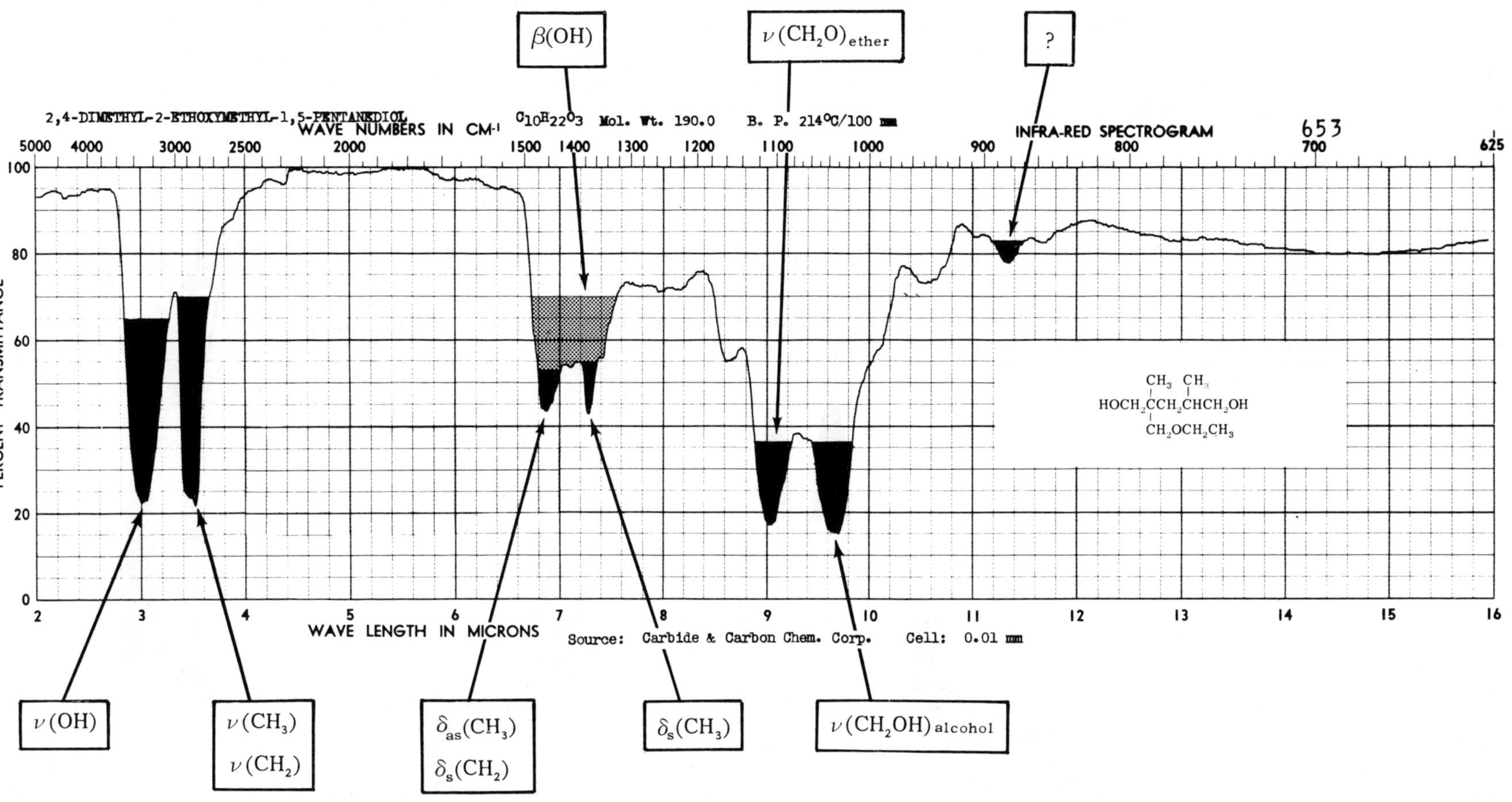

14. This spectrum is of a compound having branched hydrocarbon chains, but still having primary alcohol groups and a CH_2OCH_2 ether link. The two ν(C–O) bands are quite distinct here. There are no other bands which might be used to distinguish this from the straight-chain derivatives we have previously examined.

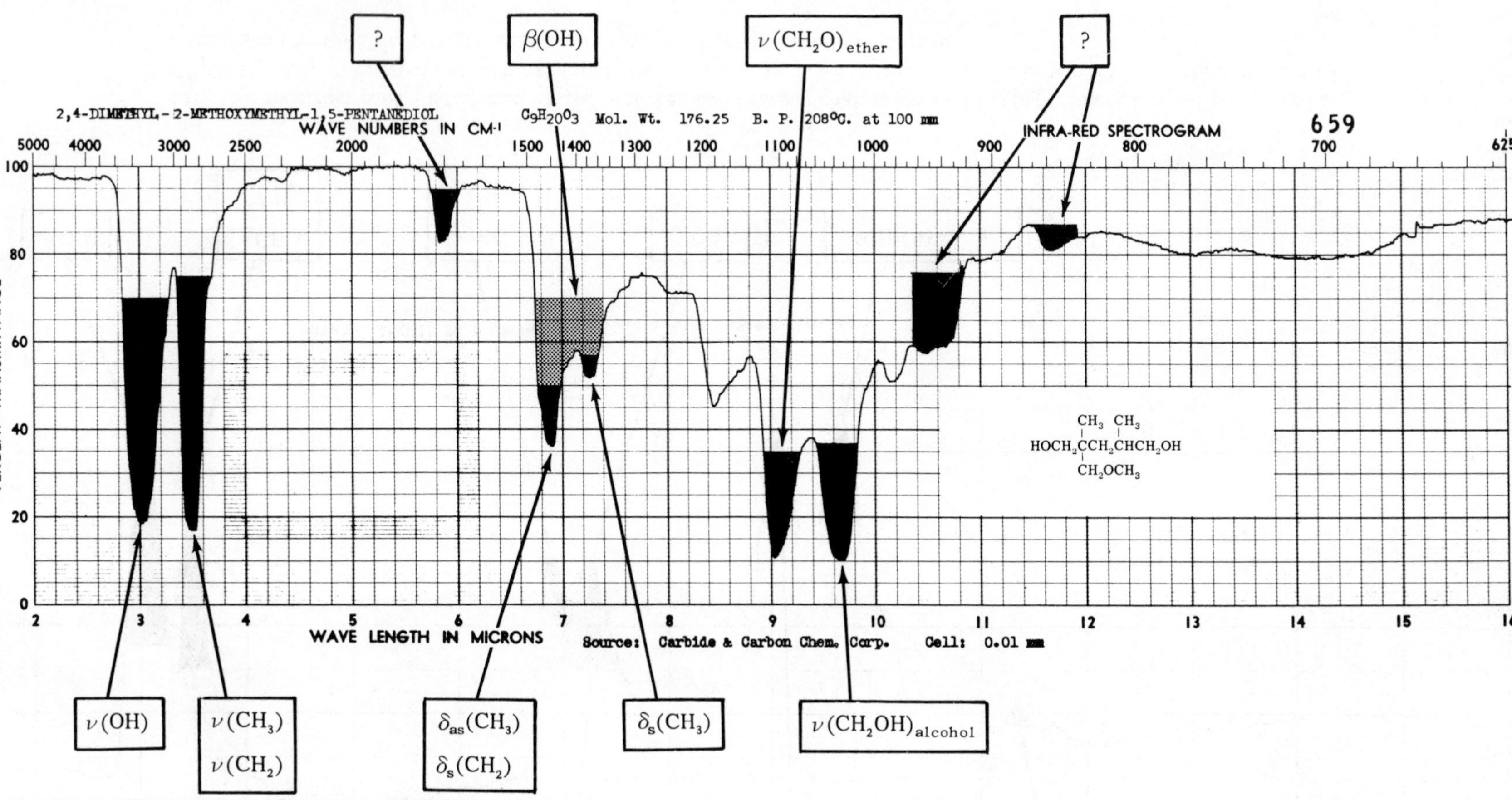

15 This spectrum is of a compound having the grouping CH_3-O-CH_2 in addition to $-CH_2OH$. We again assign the ν(C−O) of the alcohol as the lower frequency peak near 1035 cm^{-1}, and the ether as the peak near 1110 cm^{-1}. The spectrum is quite similar to the previous one, and this is of interest since the $r(CH_3O)$ vibration often interferes with the ν(C−O) assignment (see for example anisole). Apparently in this compound the $r(CH_3O)$ vibration is not strong in the ν(C−O) region, or is shifted to another position.

⓰ NONCYCLIC ETHERS

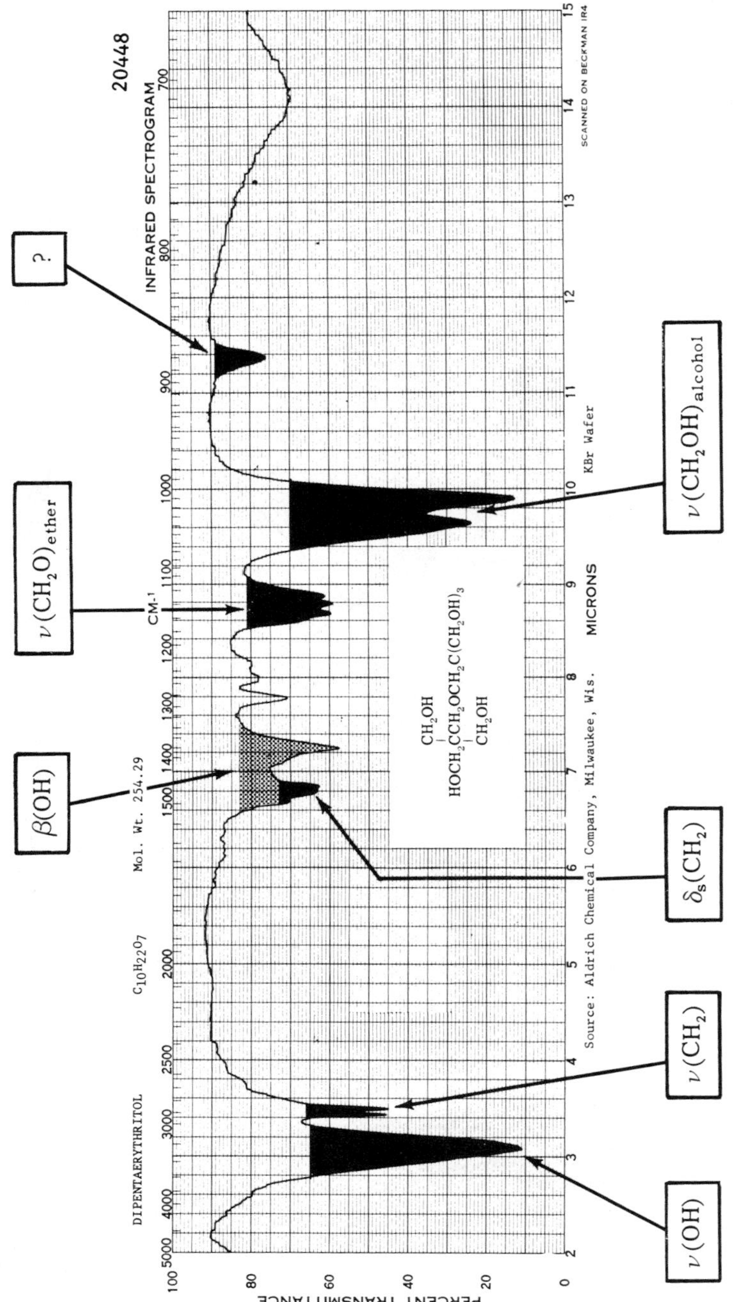

16. The spectrum of dipentaerythritol is an interesting one because of the strong ν(C−O) band near 1020 cm^{-1}. We assign this to the alcoholic part of the molecule and the weaker band near 1110 cm^{-1} to the ether part. The doubling of the alcoholic ν(C−O) is not easily explained, although this does occur for a number of simple alcohols (see Volume 2, this series).

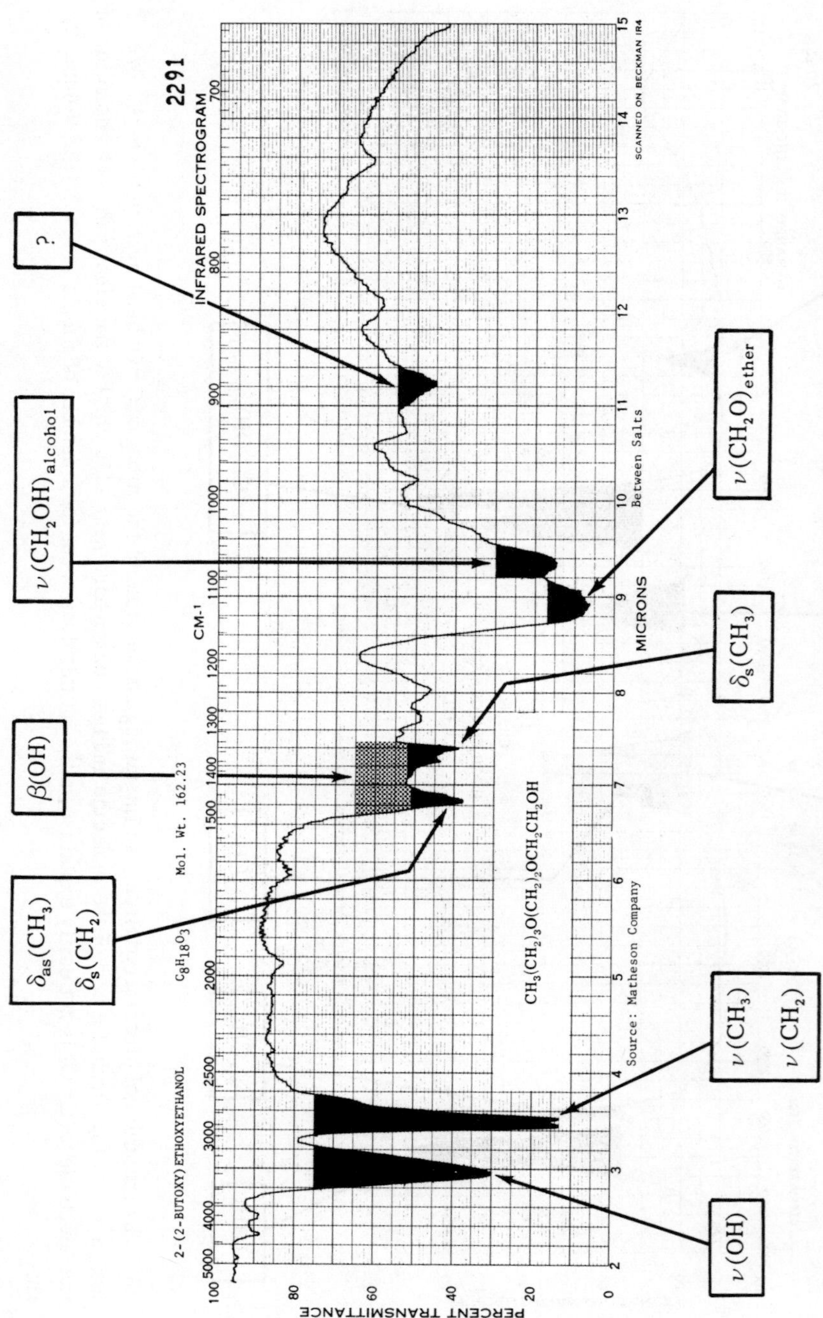

17. The ether and alcohol linkages are easily recognized in this spectrum by the ν(C−O) bands in the 1100-1050 cm^{-1} region. The ether is assigned as the higher of the two bands.

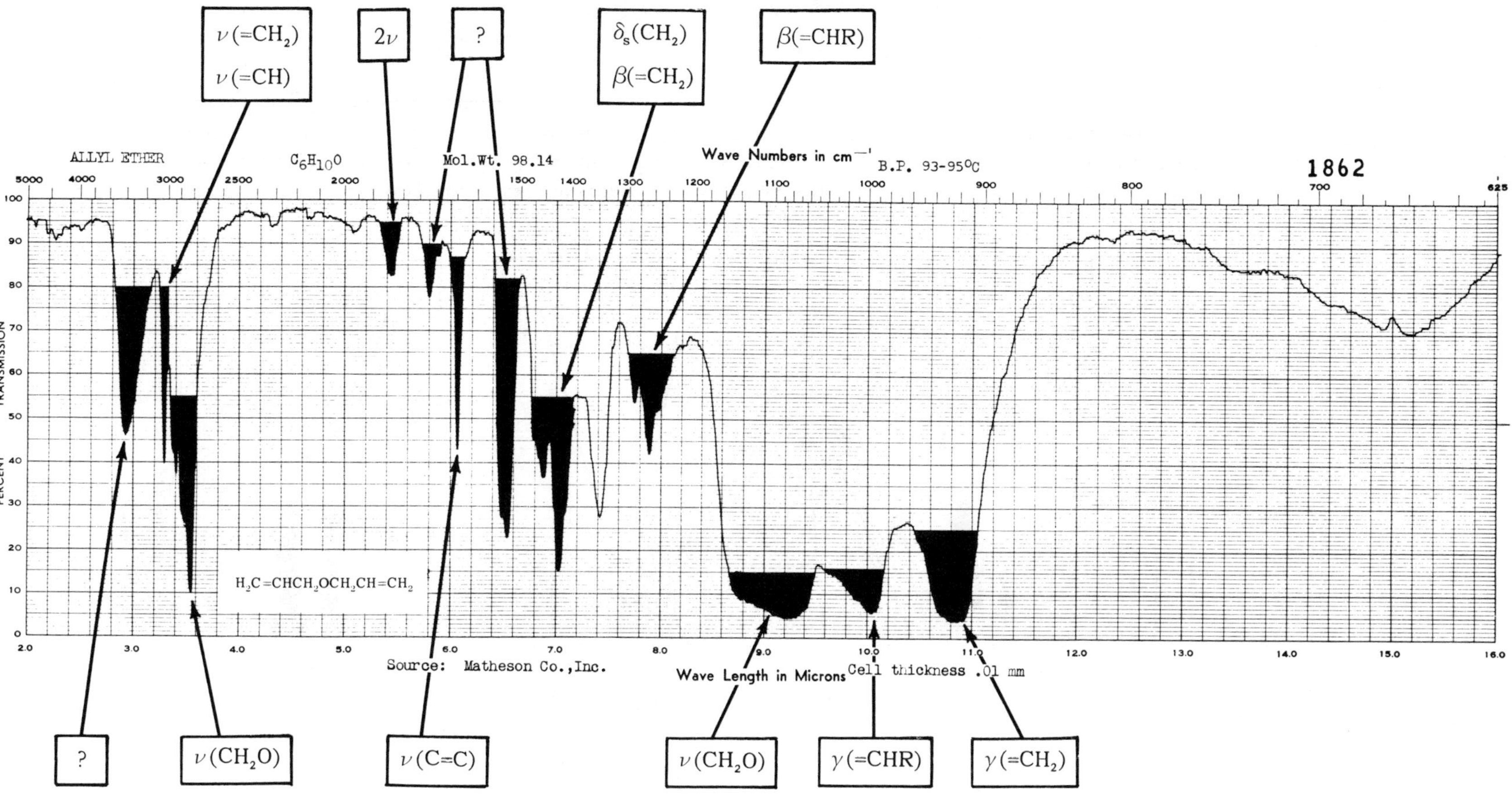

18. Allyl ether is the first ether we will examine which has unsaturation present. Attention should be directed to the fact that the ether grouping is still $-CH_2OCH_2-$ similar to the previous spectra, so that we should expect the ν(C−O) band near 1110 cm^{-1}. A strong band is found here in the spectrum, and is given this assignment. The olefinic group frequencies are found in the positions observed for olefins of this type where the ether grouping is not present. We therefore conclude no shifting of either the olefinic or ether bands occurs for this type of compound.

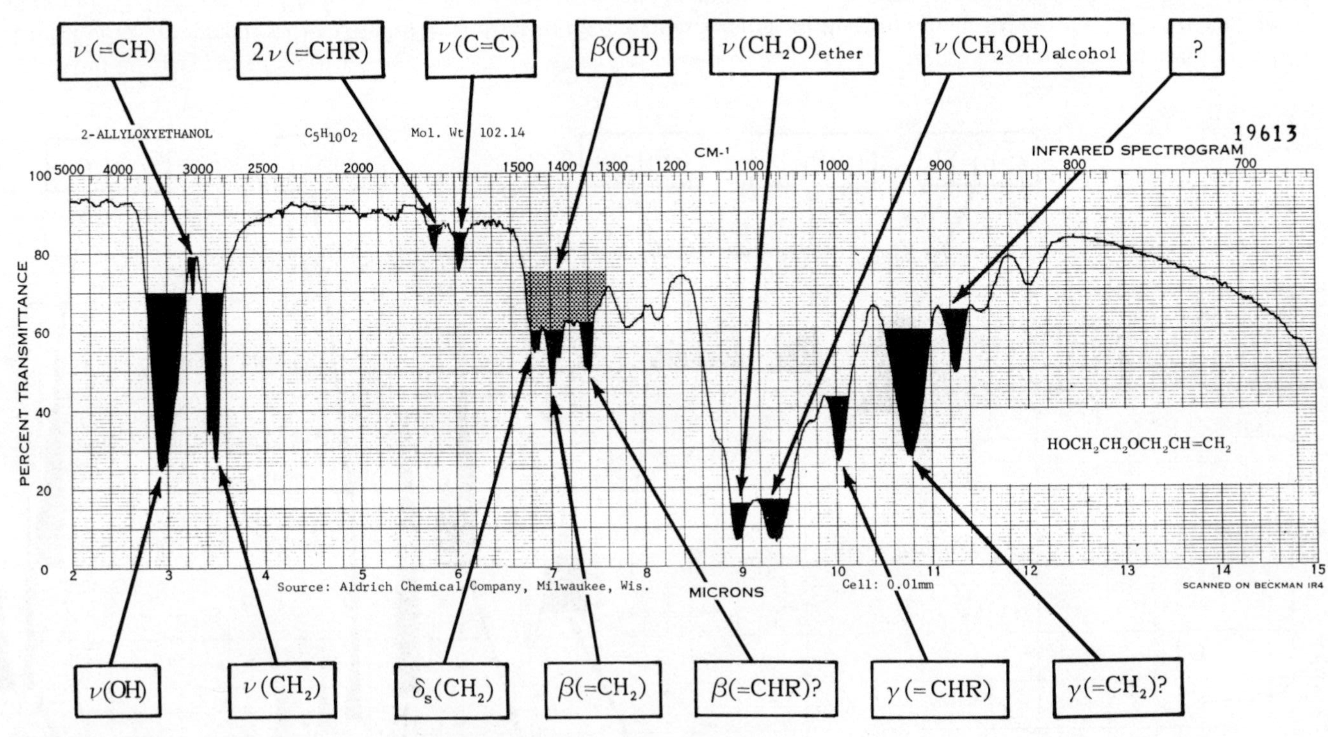

19. The compound 2-allyloxyethanol has the groups $-CH_2OH$, $-CH_2OCH_2-$, and $CH=CH_2$. If the concept of isolated group frequencies is applicable, we should observe group frequencies for each of these units in positions similar to that observed for compounds where only that group is present. This is observed in the spectrum of this compound, and the assignments for each group are noted on the spectrum.

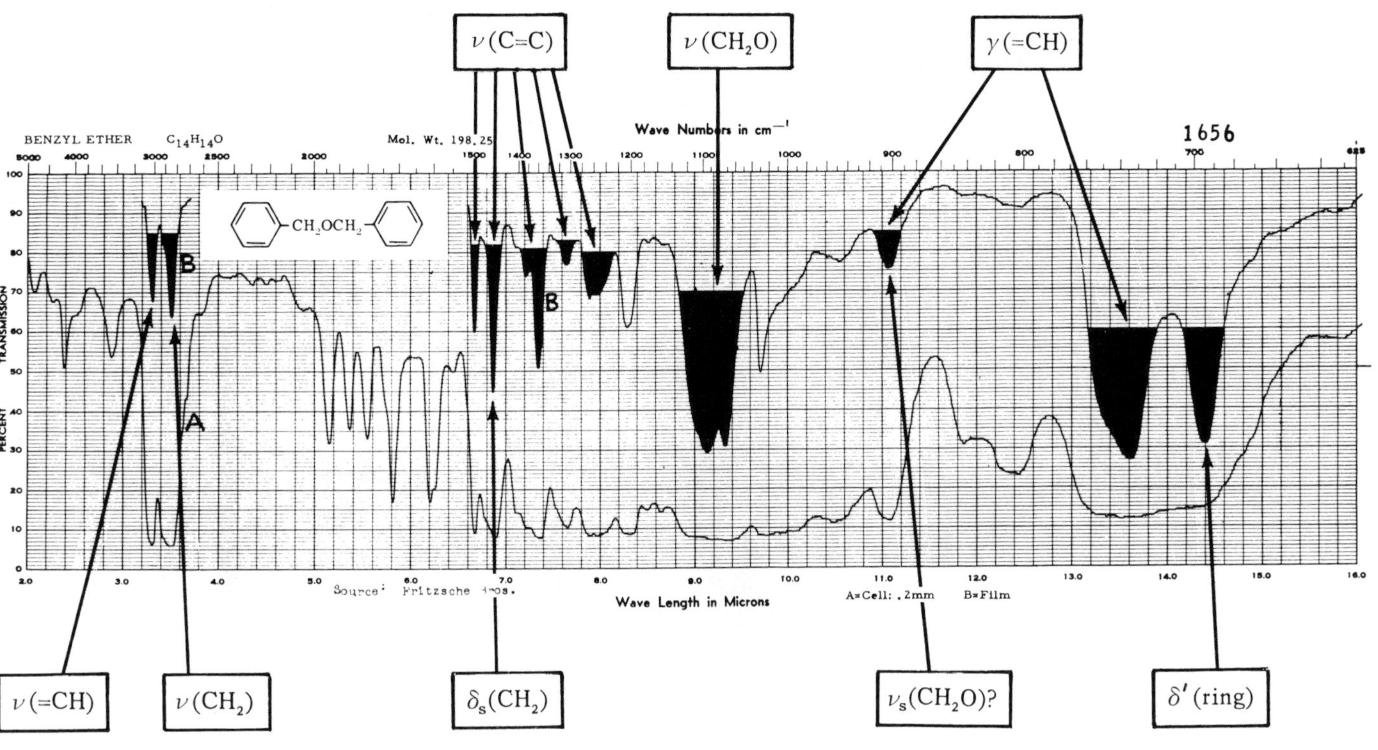

20. Dibenzyl ether has the unit $-CH_2OCH_2-$, in addition to the mono-substituted aromatic rings. We therefore expect the ν(C−O) band to appear near 1110 cm^{-1} as in previous spectra, and the aromatic ring vibrations at normal positions as for the olefinic.

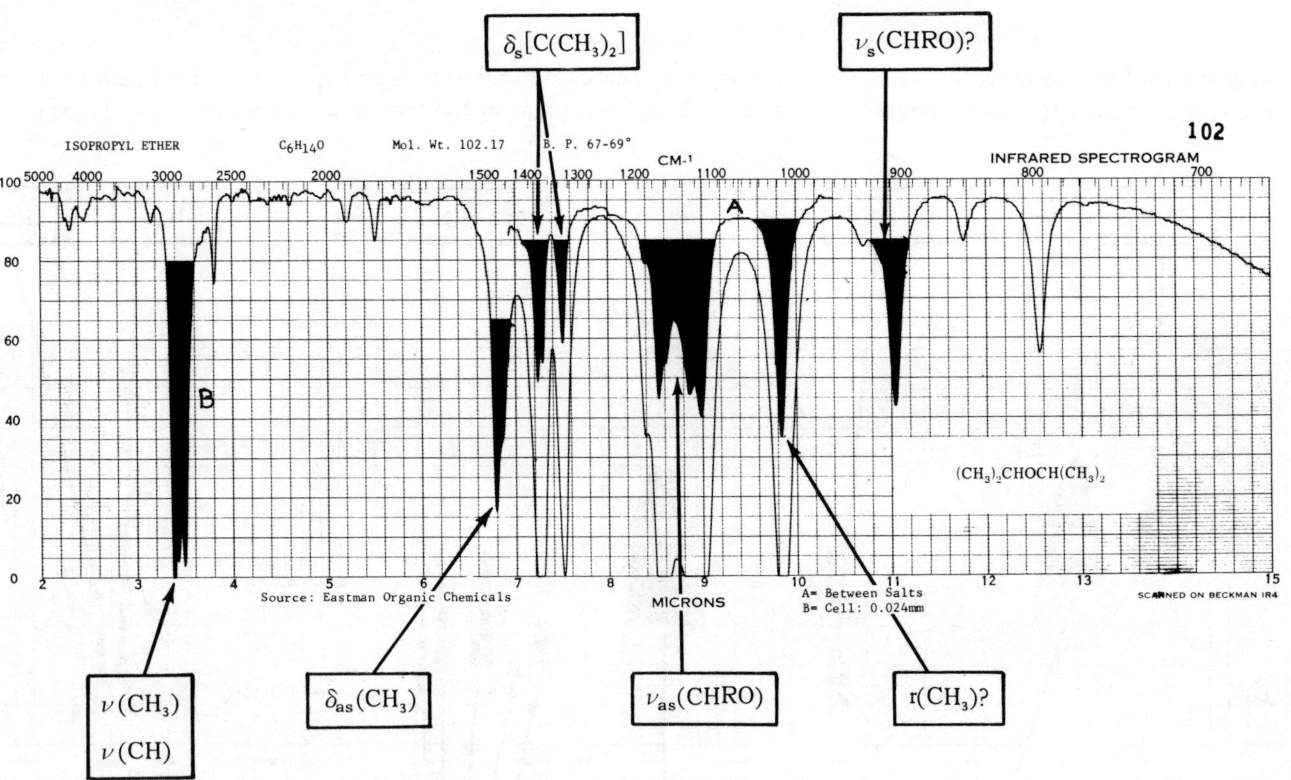

21. The spectrum of isopropyl ether is the first example presented where the ether grouping is not $-CH_2OCH_2-$, the grouping being $>CHOCH<$. The ν(C−O), however, appears near 1110 cm^{-1}, as it did for the other ethers. Apparently the secondary carbon grouping does not shift the position of the ν(C−O) band in these ethers, as it does in secondary alcohols (see Volume 2).

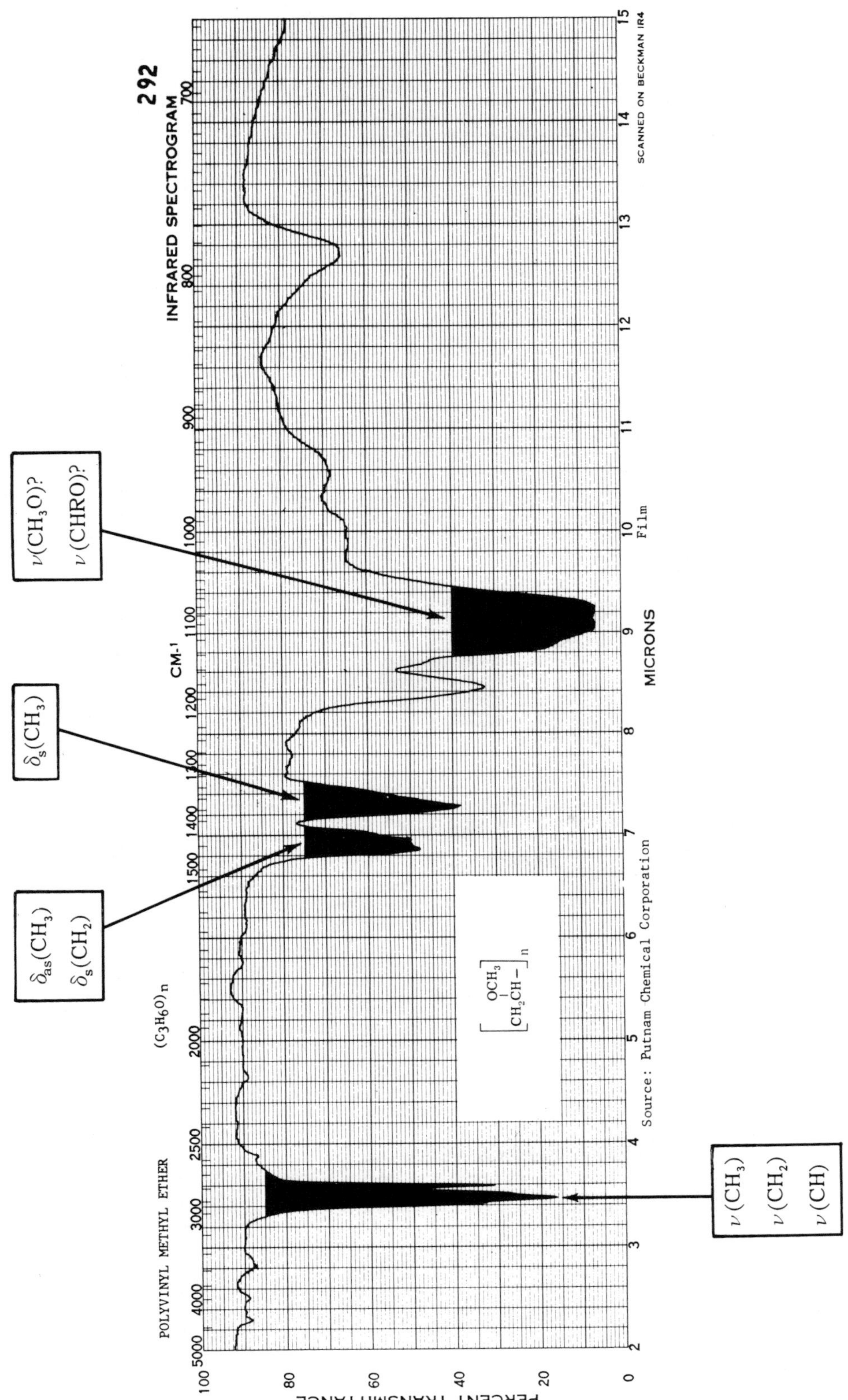

22. Polyvinyl methyl ether has the grouping CH_3OCHR. The ν(C−O) appears near 1095 cm^{-1}, which is lower than for previous ethers. The next spectrum is the ethyl derivative related to this ether, and the ν(C−O) band is also near 1100 cm^{-1}. This lower position for these two polymers may be due to their polymeric state.

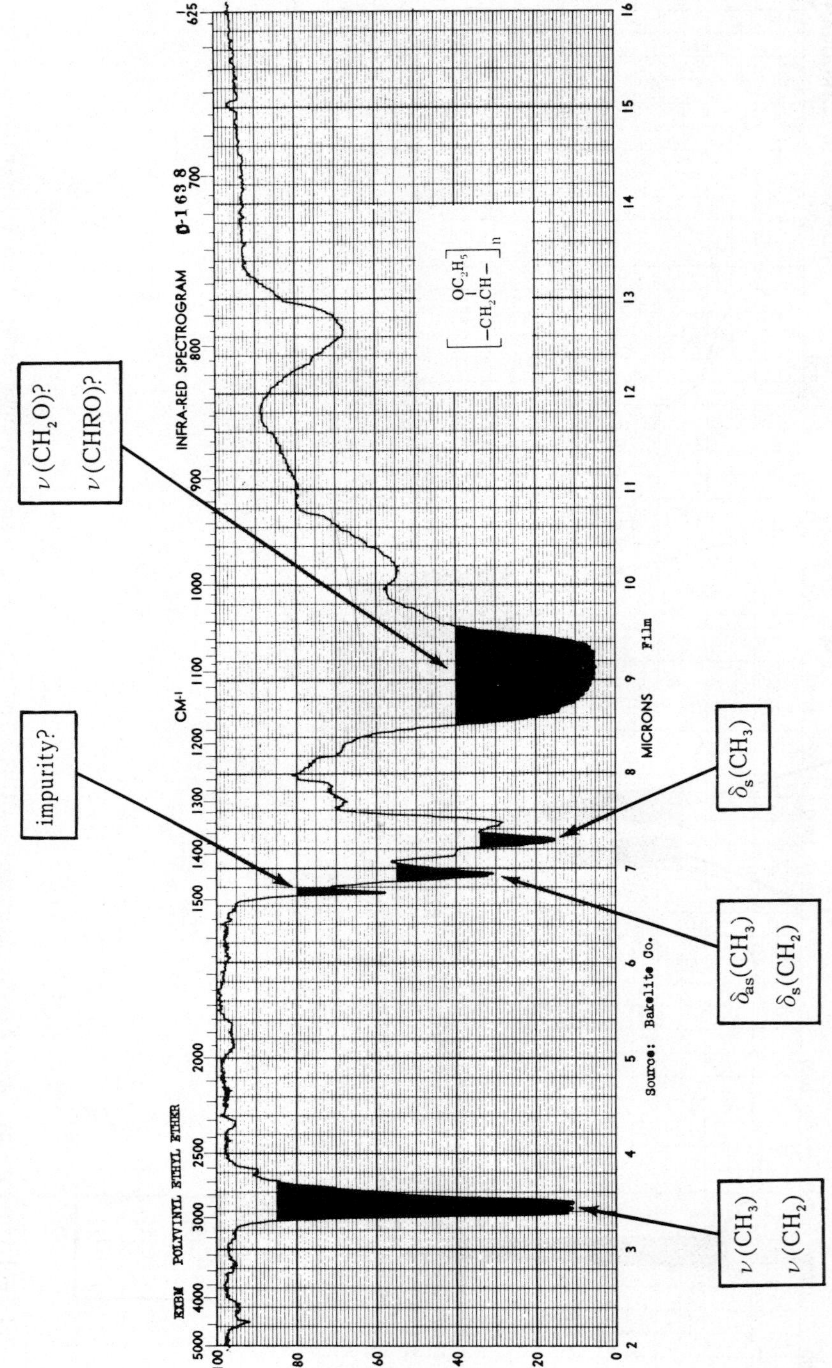

23. We can compare the spectrum of polyvinyl ethyl ether to polyvinyl methyl ether (previous spectrum). There is coincidence of most major bands; however, the ethyl derivative has a more complex band structure in the 1500-1300 cm^{-1} region. The ν(C–O) is near 1100 cm^{-1} and abroad in both spectra.

㉔ NONCYCLIC ETHERS

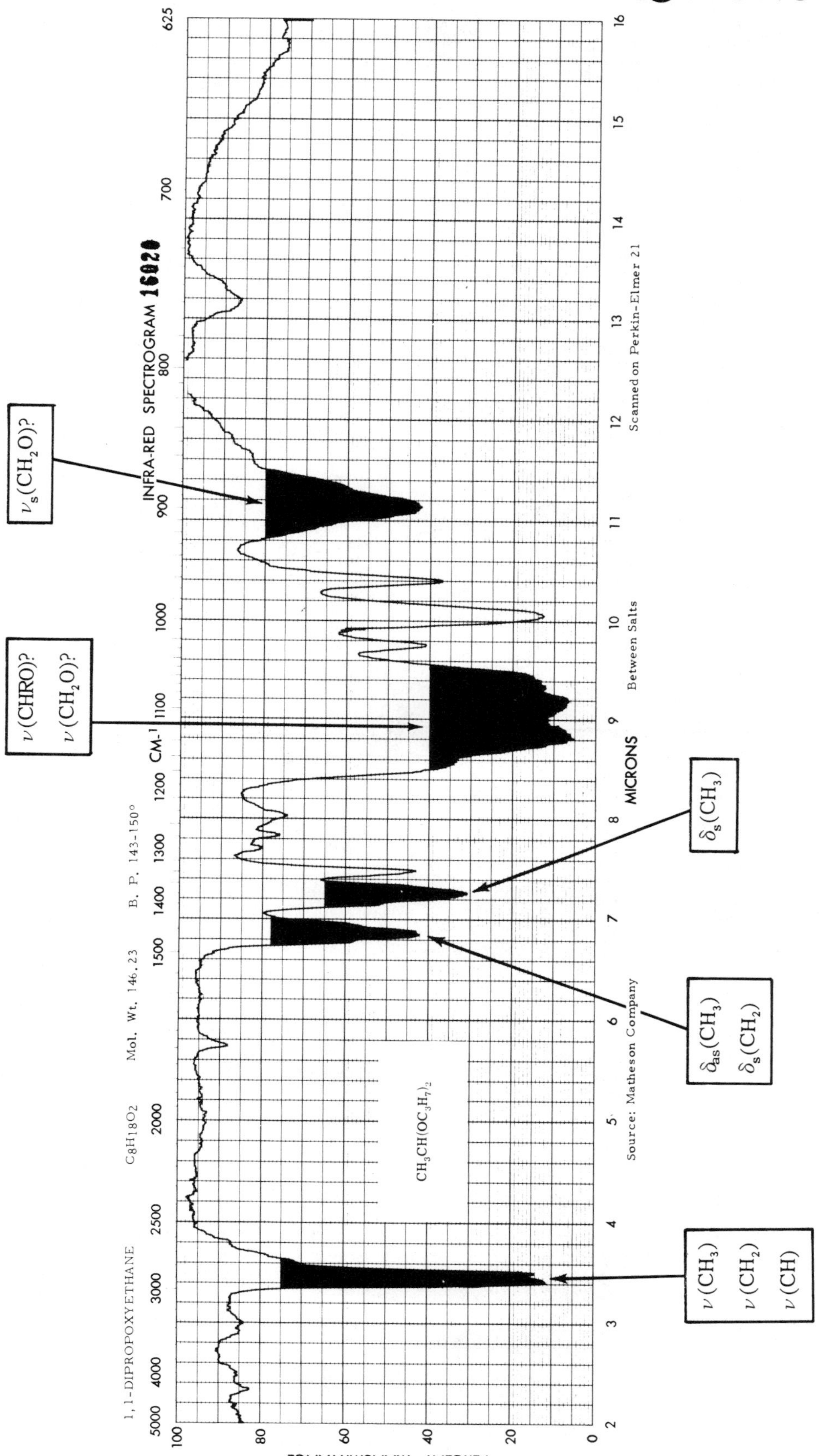

24. The spectrum of 1,1-dipropoxyethane has again the typical spectrum of an aliphatic ether. There is no distinguishing feature of this spectrum to allow the spectroscopist to distinguish the presence of two oxygen atoms or the tertiary CH group present between them. Note the 900 cm^{-1} band which could be $\nu_s(C-O)$.

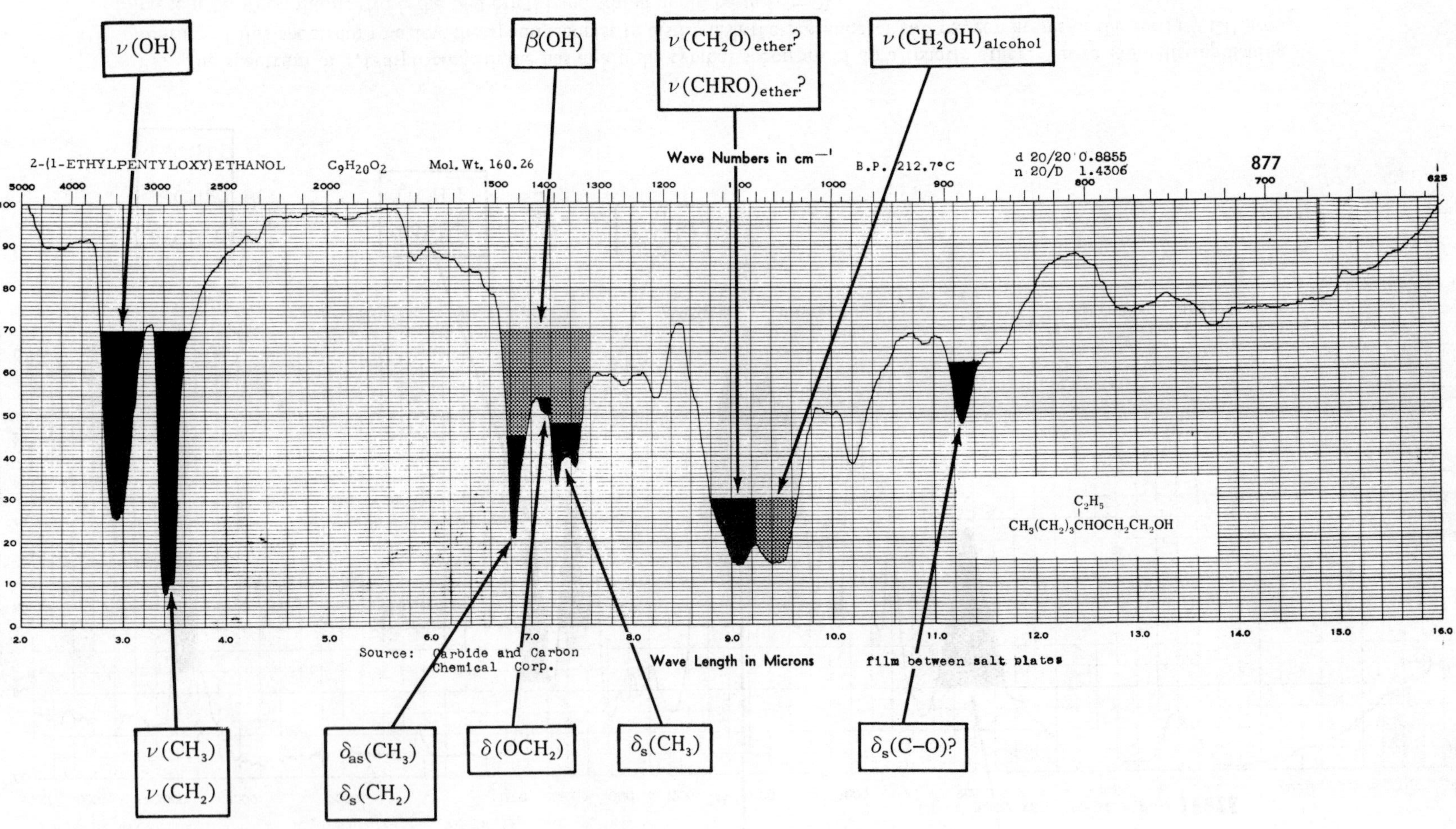

25. The spectrum of 2-(3-heptyloxy)ethanol has the groups $CHOCH_2$ and CH_2OH. The two ν(C−O) groups give distinct vibrations, with the alcohol at the lower frequency. The other assignments are the expected ones. We cannot, however, distinguish between the OCH and OCH_2 groups, since apparently the ν(C−O) band is in the same position.

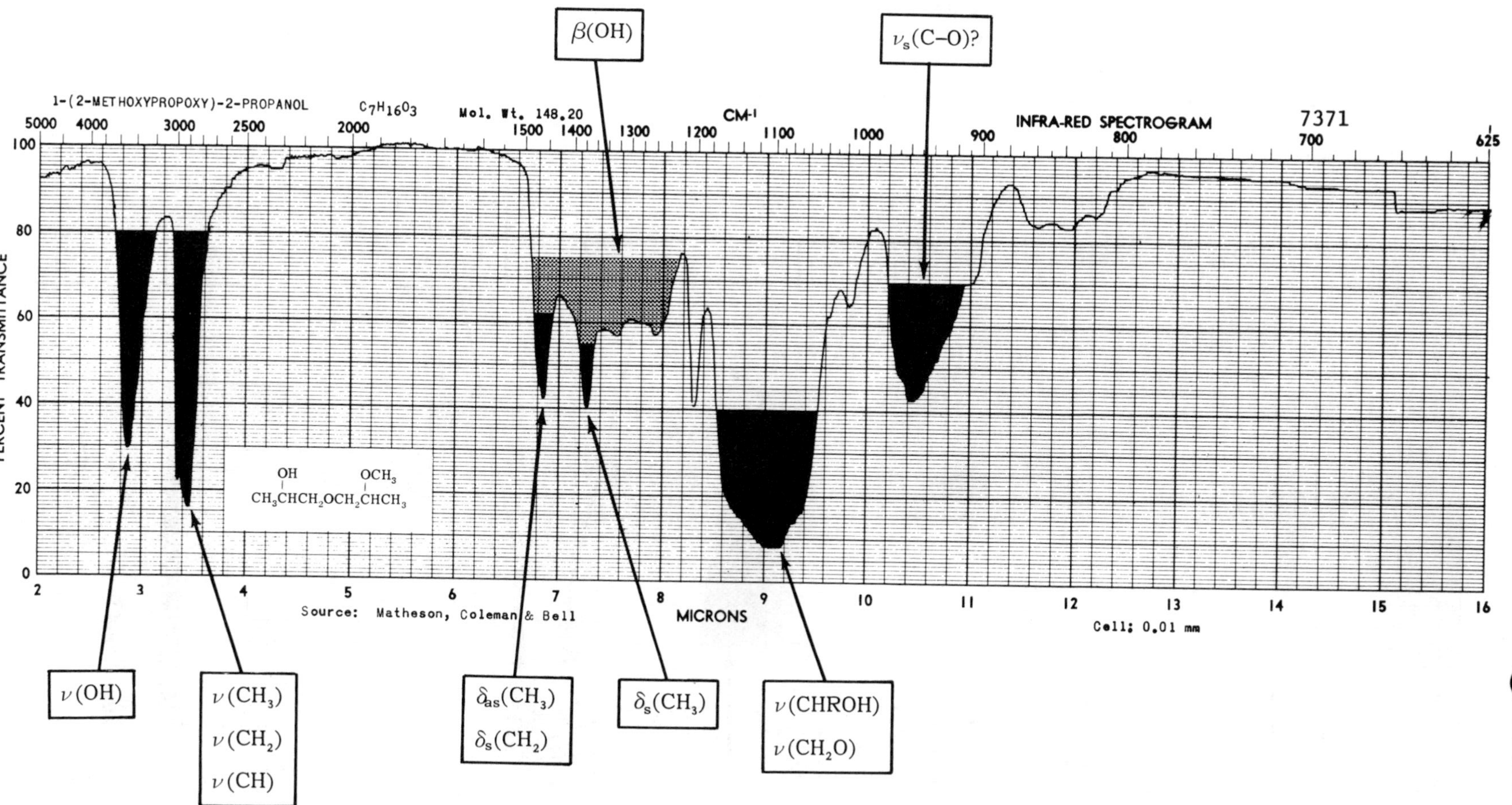

26. This compound has the groups CHOH, CH_2OCH_2, and $CHOCH_3$. We would predict the secondary alcoholic group to have a ν(C–O) near 1100 cm^{-1}. The CH_2O group should also have a band near 1100 cm^{-1}. The OCH_3 group assignment is a puzzling one, since it can be at 1050 or 1100 cm^{-1}, depending on the compound (see explanation in correlation section). This spectrum has a very broad band near 1100 cm^{-1} that represents all three of the oxygen groups.

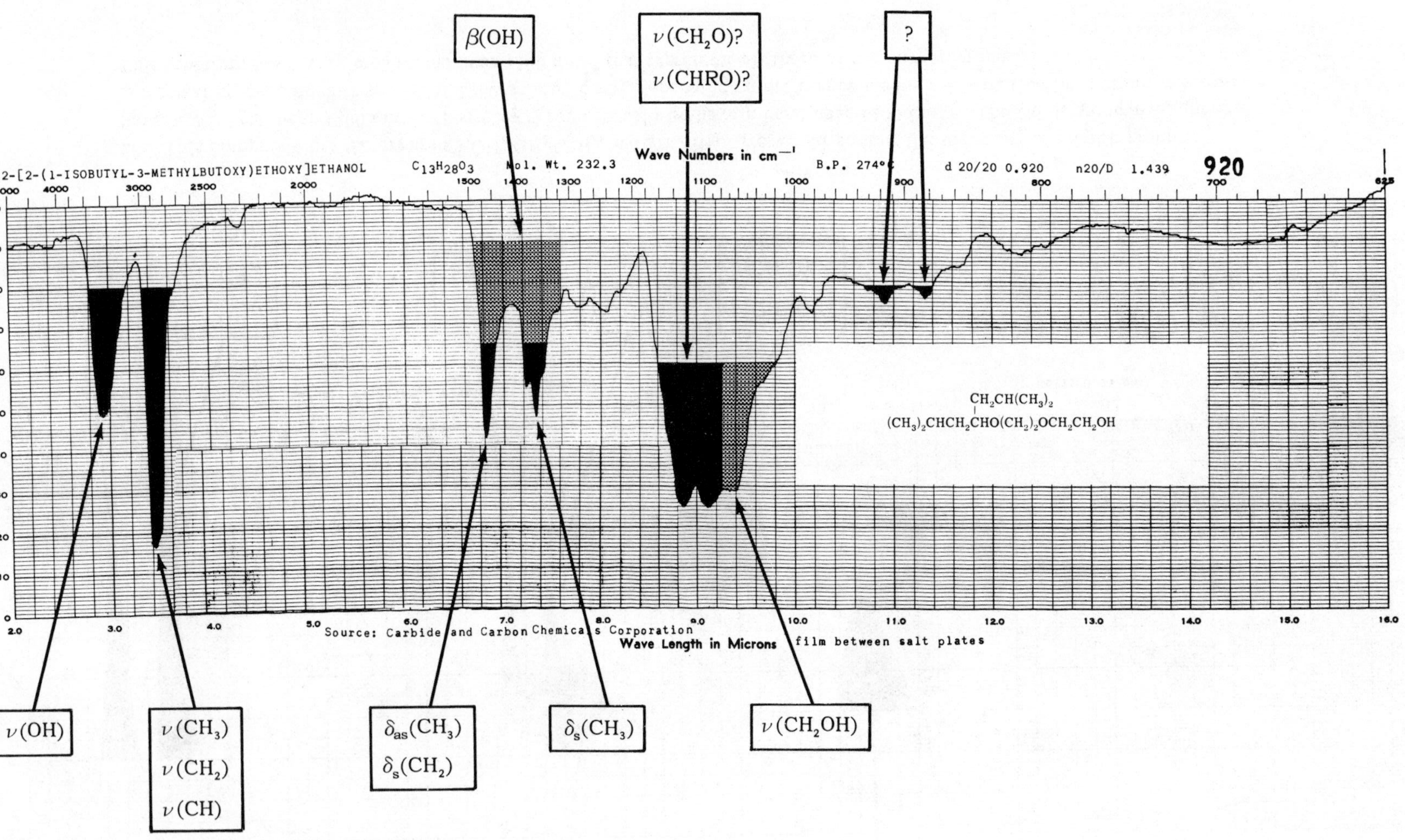

27. This compound has the groups $CH-O-CH_2$, CH_2-O-CH_2, and CH_2OH. As in the previous example, we cannot distinguish each group from the position of the $\nu(C-O)$, except perhaps the alcoholic one, since this $\nu(C-O)$ appears lower than the rest. Actually three maxima are observed in the $\nu(C-O)$ region; however, it is not obvious how the higher two maxima should be assigned. This spectrum has many broad bands, and these would be sharpened if a dilute solution of the compound were examined.

28 NONCYCLIC ETHERS

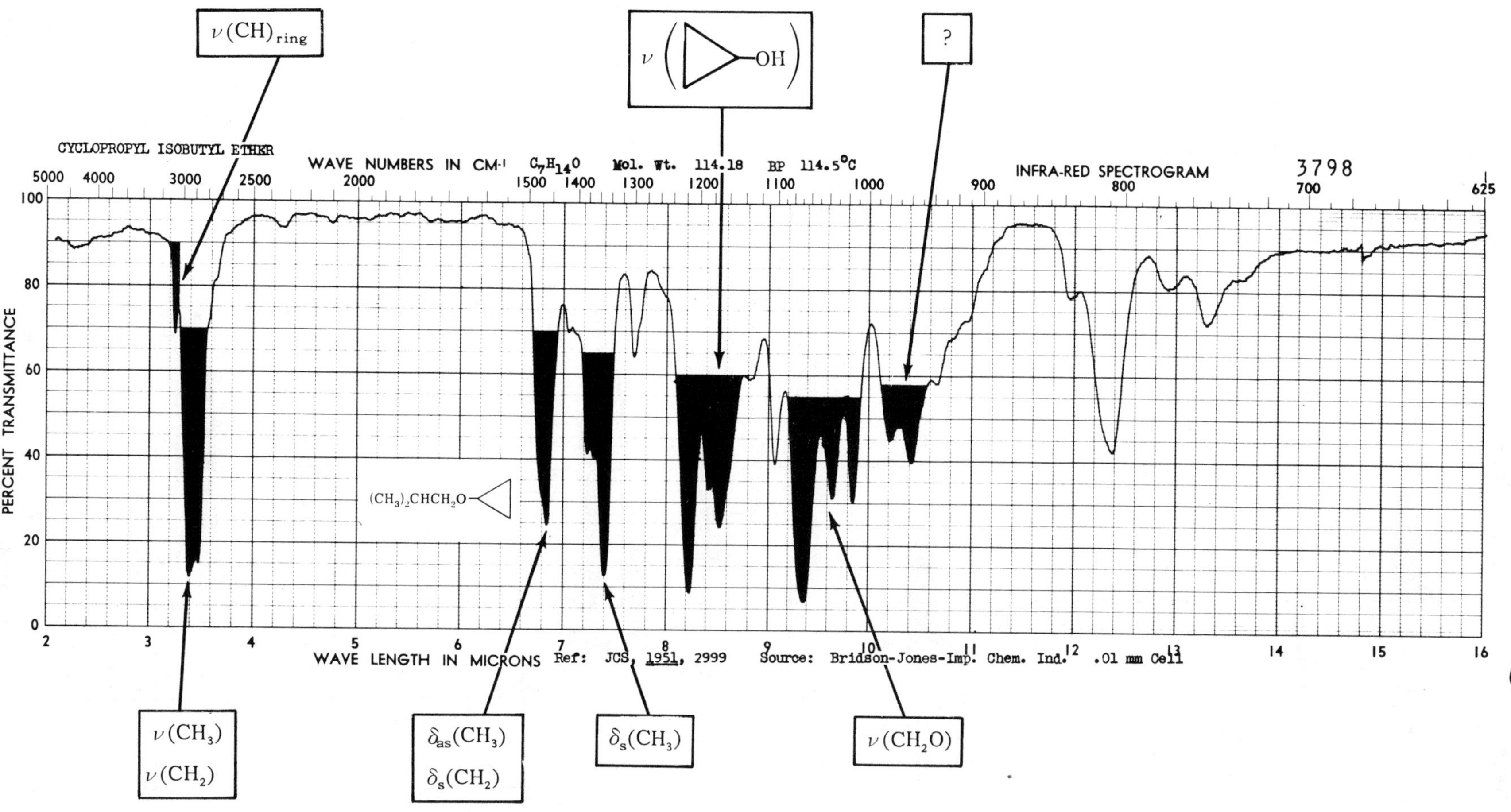

28. Cyclopropyl isobutyl ether appears to have two strong bands assignable as ν(C−O). The higher positioned one, near 1200 cm^{-1}, is assigned as the ν(C−O) of the cyclopropyl part of the ether. The lower frequency one, near 1060 cm^{-1}, is due to the CH_2−O group. These are new assignments and are therefore only tentative.

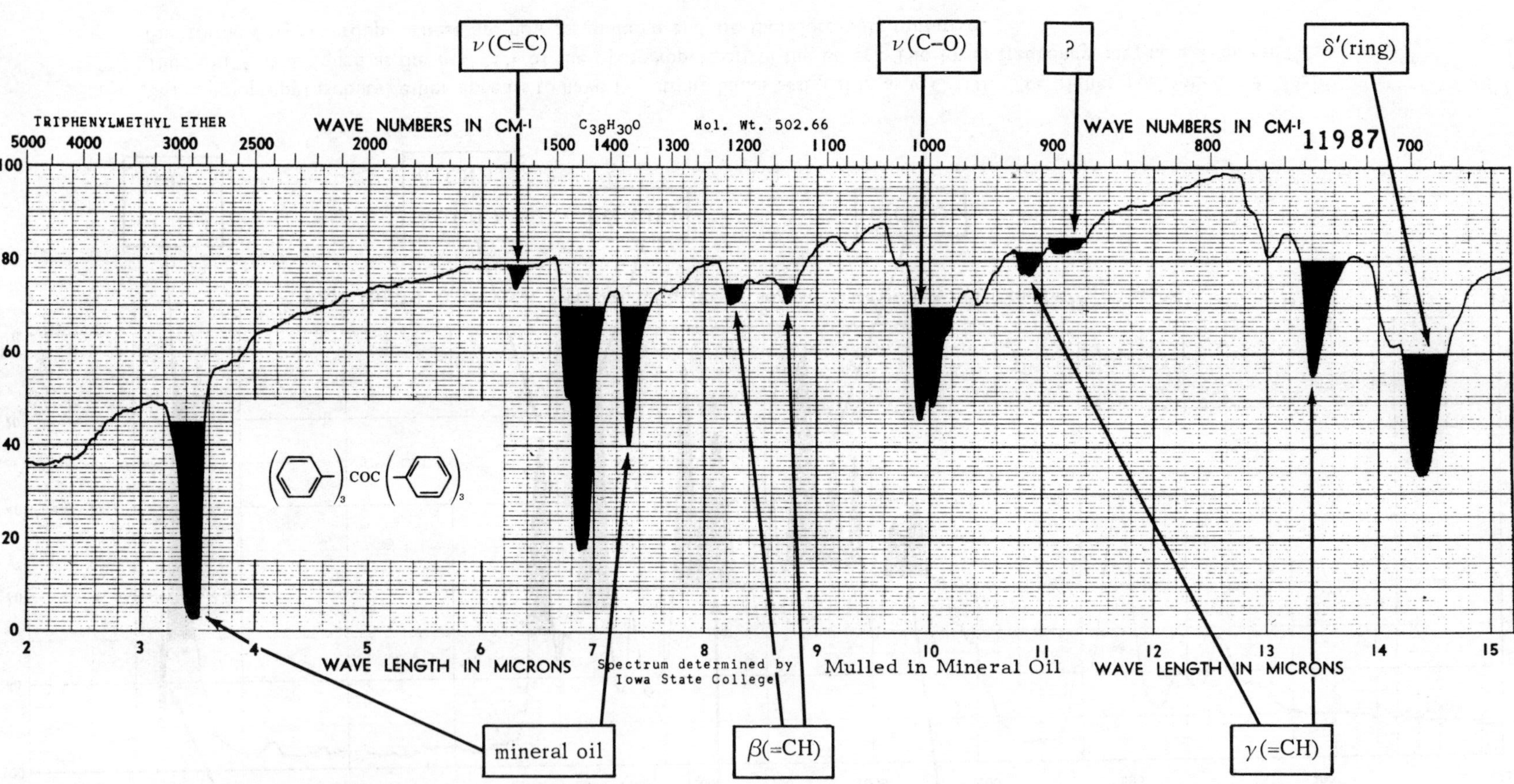

29. The triphenylmethyl ether spectrum illustrates a very important point. The six phenyl groups are strong electron-withdrawing groups. This results in the ν(C−O) appearing near 1000 cm^{-1}. This is the same position as for $(C_6H_5)_3COH$. Since no other strong band appears in this region, the assignment is fairly well established. The other assignments are the expected ones.

30 NONCYCLIC ETHERS

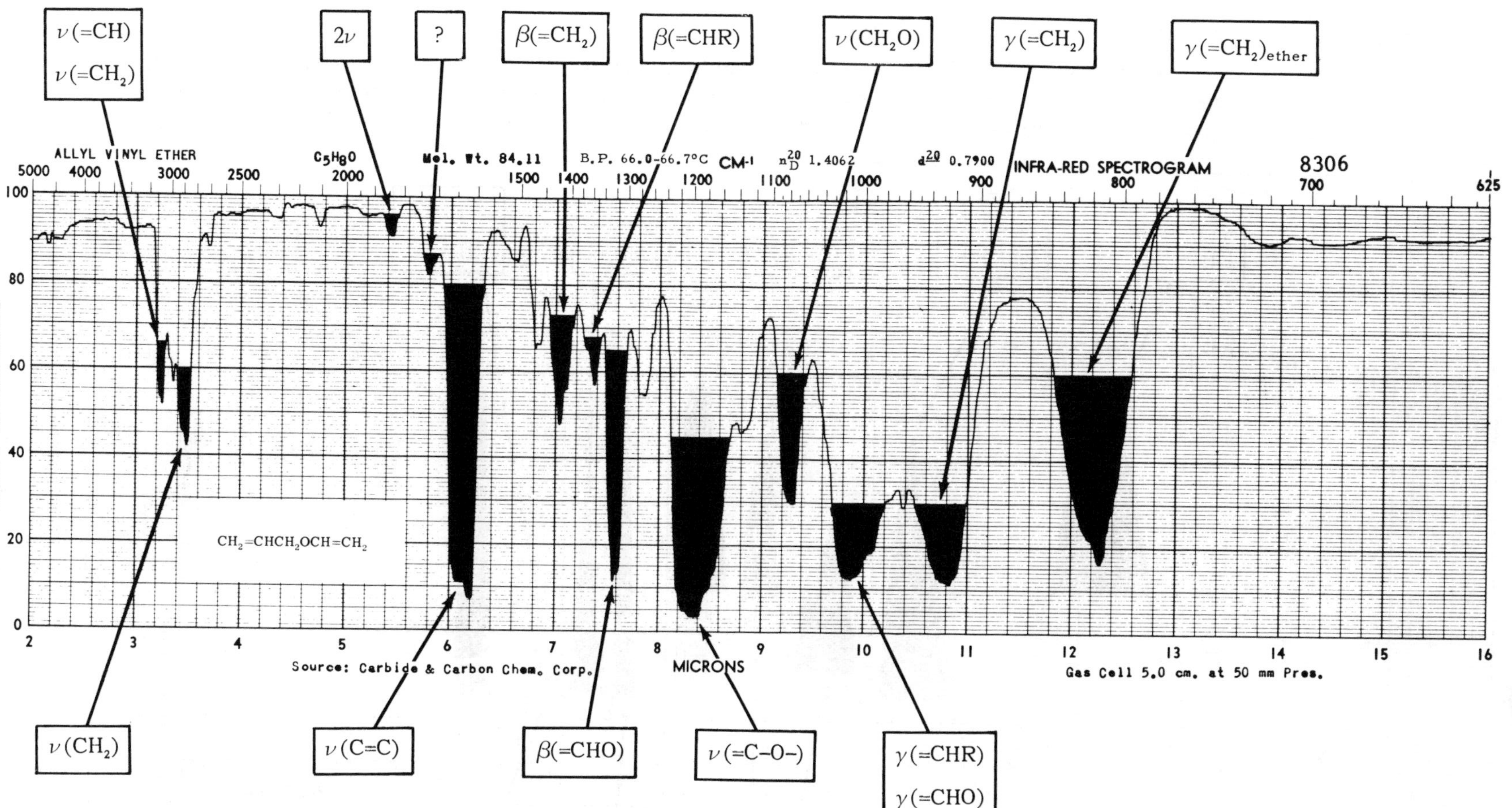

30. Allyl vinyl ether is the first example of a compound where the group $=C-O$ occurs. There is a strong band near 1180 cm^{-1} which is in the correct position for this structure. The grouping CH_2-O should have a band near 1100 cm^{-1}, so we assign the band near 1075 cm^{-1} to this group. The group $=C-O$ has a $\nu(=C-O)$ in the same position as the group $=CHR$, however, the $\gamma(=CH_2)$ of the ether part is shifted to a lower frequency, and appears near 810 cm^{-1}.

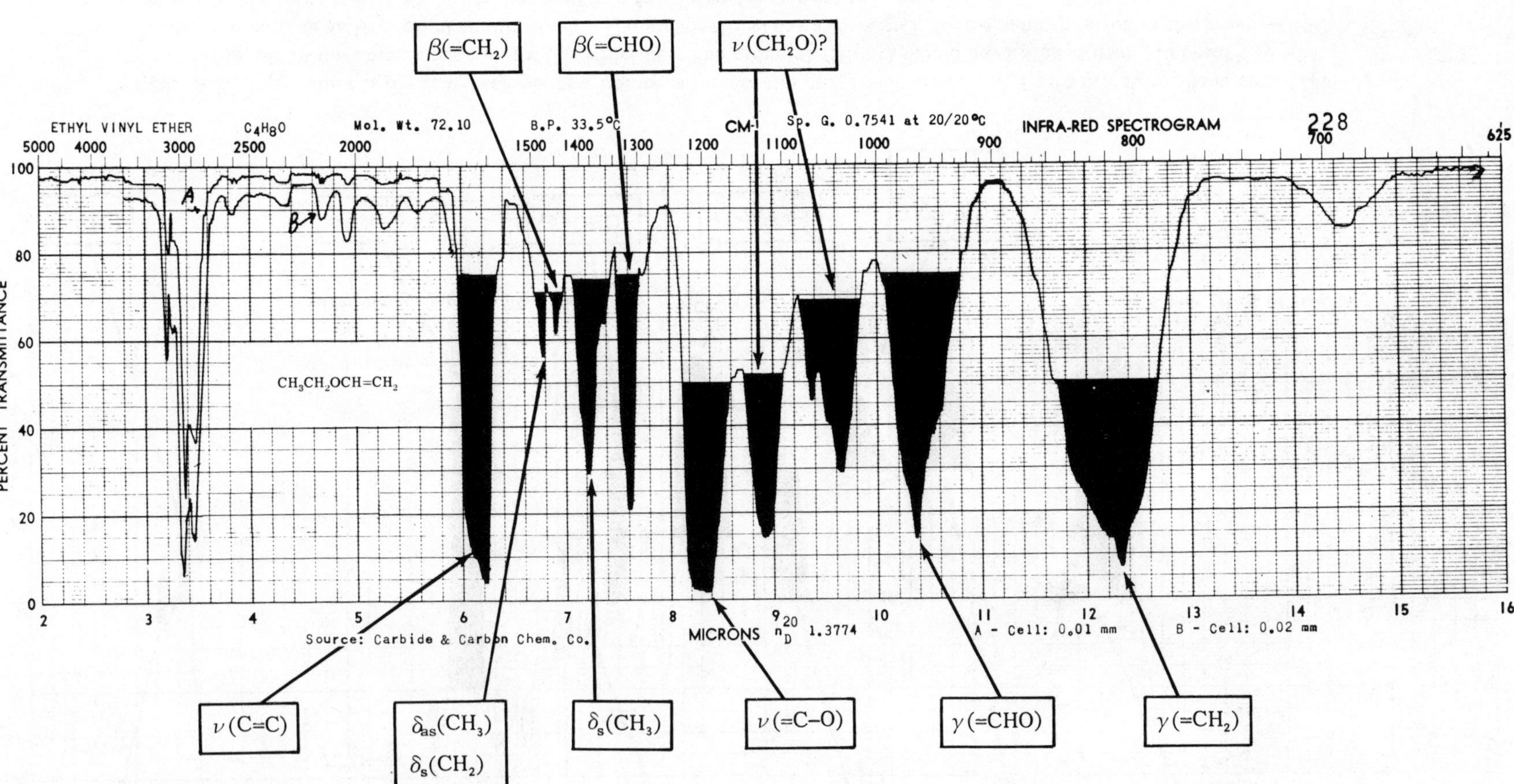

31. Ethyl vinyl ether has a strong band near 1200 cm^{-1} assigned to $\nu(=C-O)$. The group CH_2-O must have the $\nu(C-O)$ either at 1125 or 1050 cm^{-1}. The assignment is not obvious, since for alcohols the CH_2O is near 1060 cm^{-1}, while for ethers it is near 1100 cm^{-1}. The $\gamma(=CH_2)$ band is again shifted from its position for the non-oxygenated olefins.

32 NONCYCLIC ETHERS

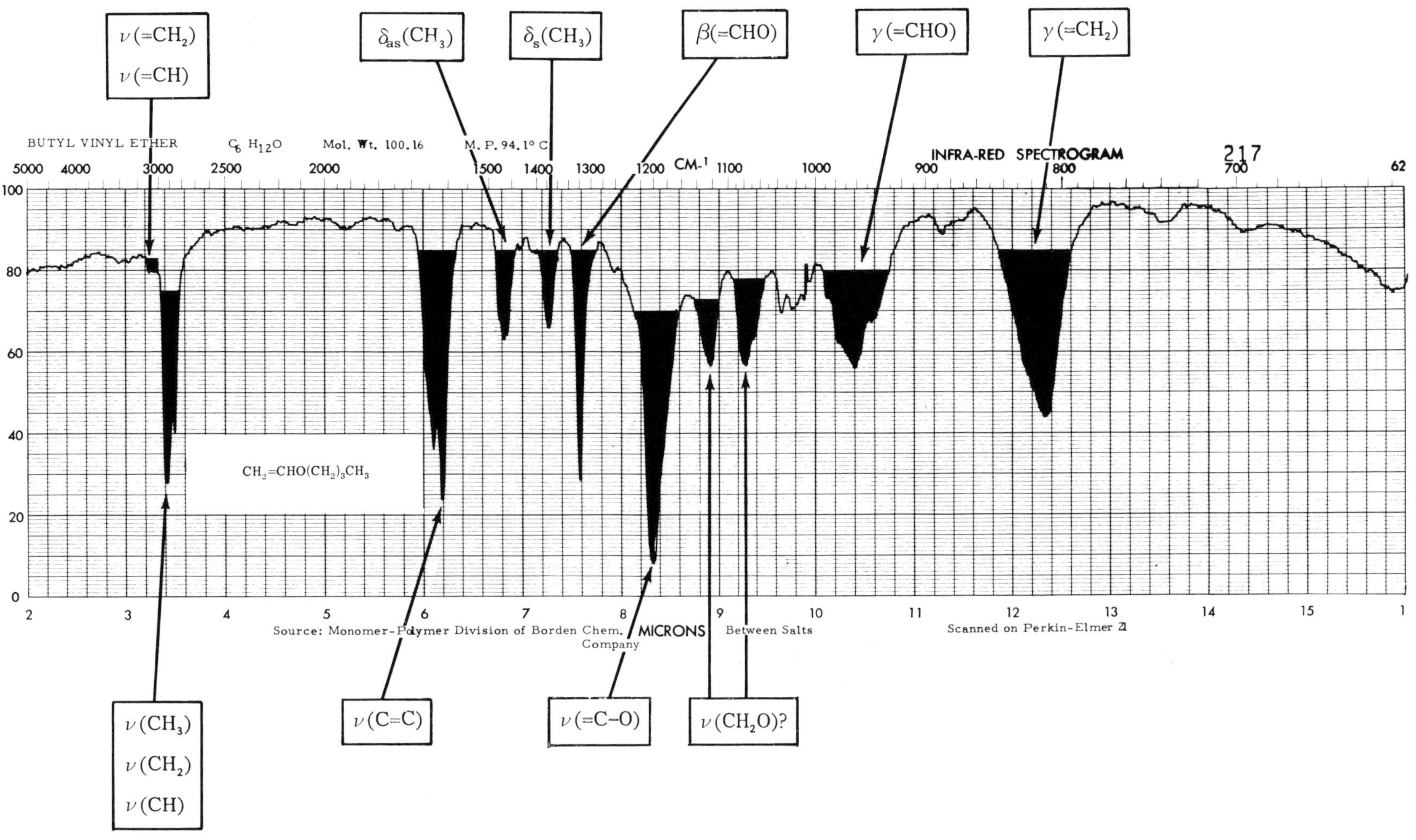

32. The n-butyl vinyl ether spectrum is related to the previous one in that both have the CH_2CHO unit with an alkyl chain attached to the oxygen. Note again the strong $\nu(=C-O)$ band near 1200 cm^{-1}. The weaker bands near 1120 and 1080 cm^{-1} again can be suggested for $\nu(CH_2O)$, but the correct assignment is not obvious. The $\nu(C=C)$ band is doubled, and quite strong as expected. The position of $\gamma(CH_2)$ is near 800 cm^{-1}, lower than for the vinyl group in non-ether systems, but at the position expected for vinyl ethers. The $\gamma(=CHO)$ is also shifted. The strong $\nu(=C-O)$ band near 1190 cm^{-1} is the stretch of the C–O adjacent to unsaturation, while the weaker C–O stretch of the aliphatic group is assigned near 1070 cm^{-1}. Note the strong, sharp $\beta(=CHO)$. This band is usually found quite intense and sharp in vinyl ethers.

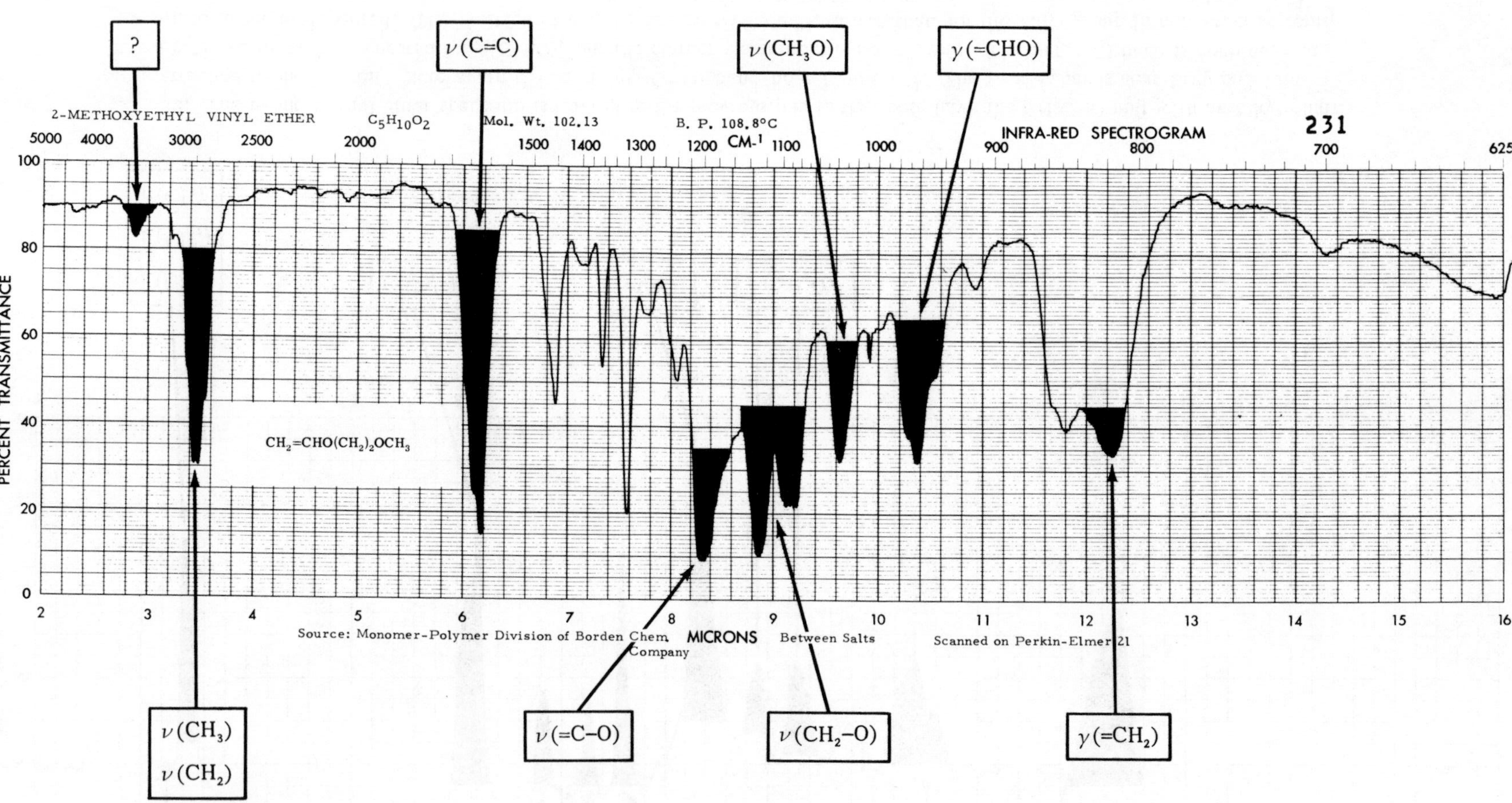

33. The compound 2-methoxy vinyl ether has the groups =CHO, CH_2O, and OCH_3. We predict bands at 1200, 1100, and 1050 cm^{-1} for these groups respectively. Bands are found here, and these assignments are made; however, we call attention to the discussion in the correlation section, and the uncertainty of position of the $\nu(CH_3O)$. The $\gamma(=CH_2)$ band of vinyl ethers appears at the low position of 820 cm^{-1} compared to its position in alkyl olefins. The $\nu(C=C)$ is also doubled.

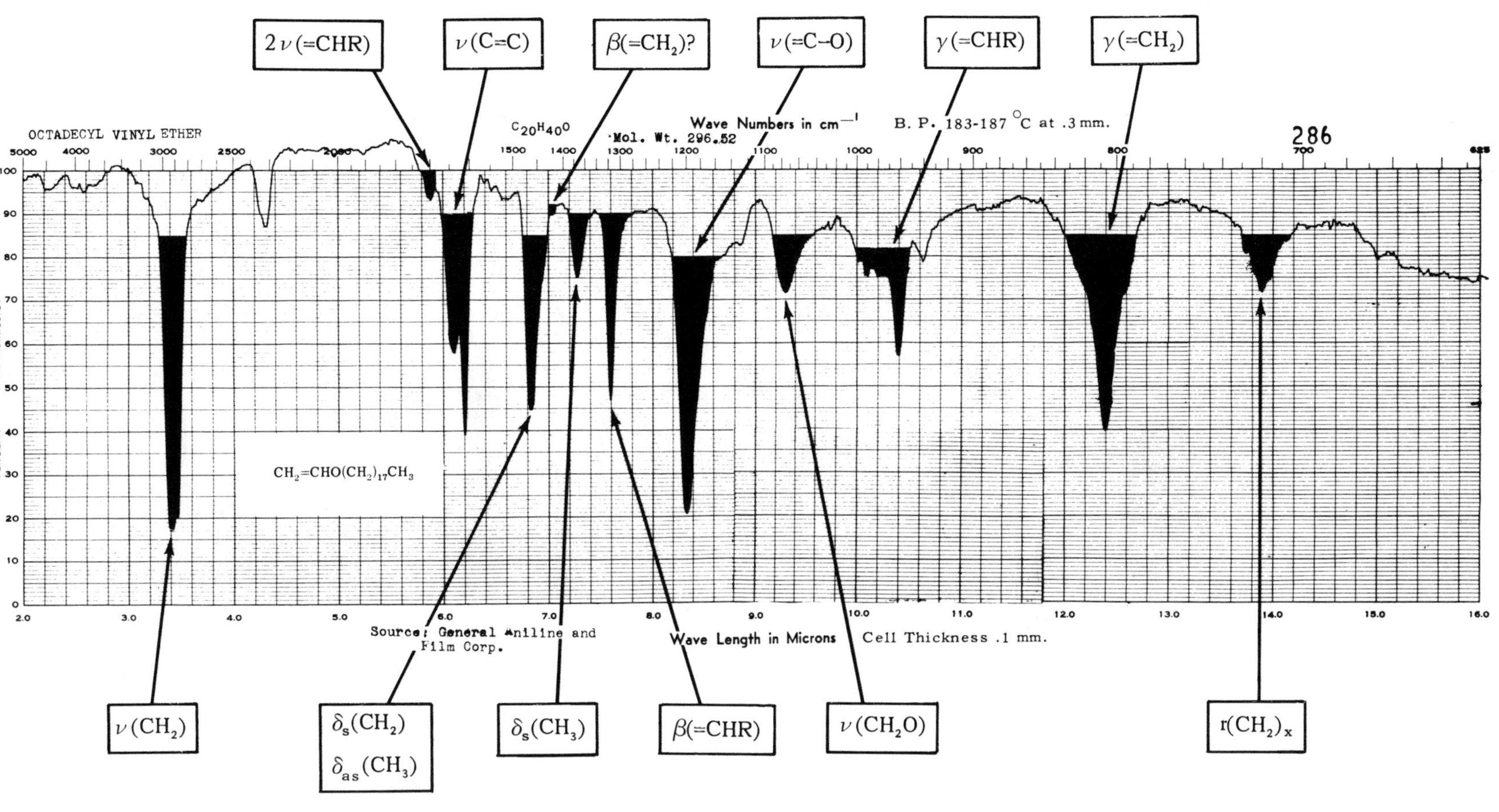

34. This compound is also related to the previous four spectra having similar groupings. The strong ν(=C−O) is observed near 1200 cm^{-1}, while a weaker band near 1080 cm^{-1} is assigned as $\nu(CH_2{-}O)$.

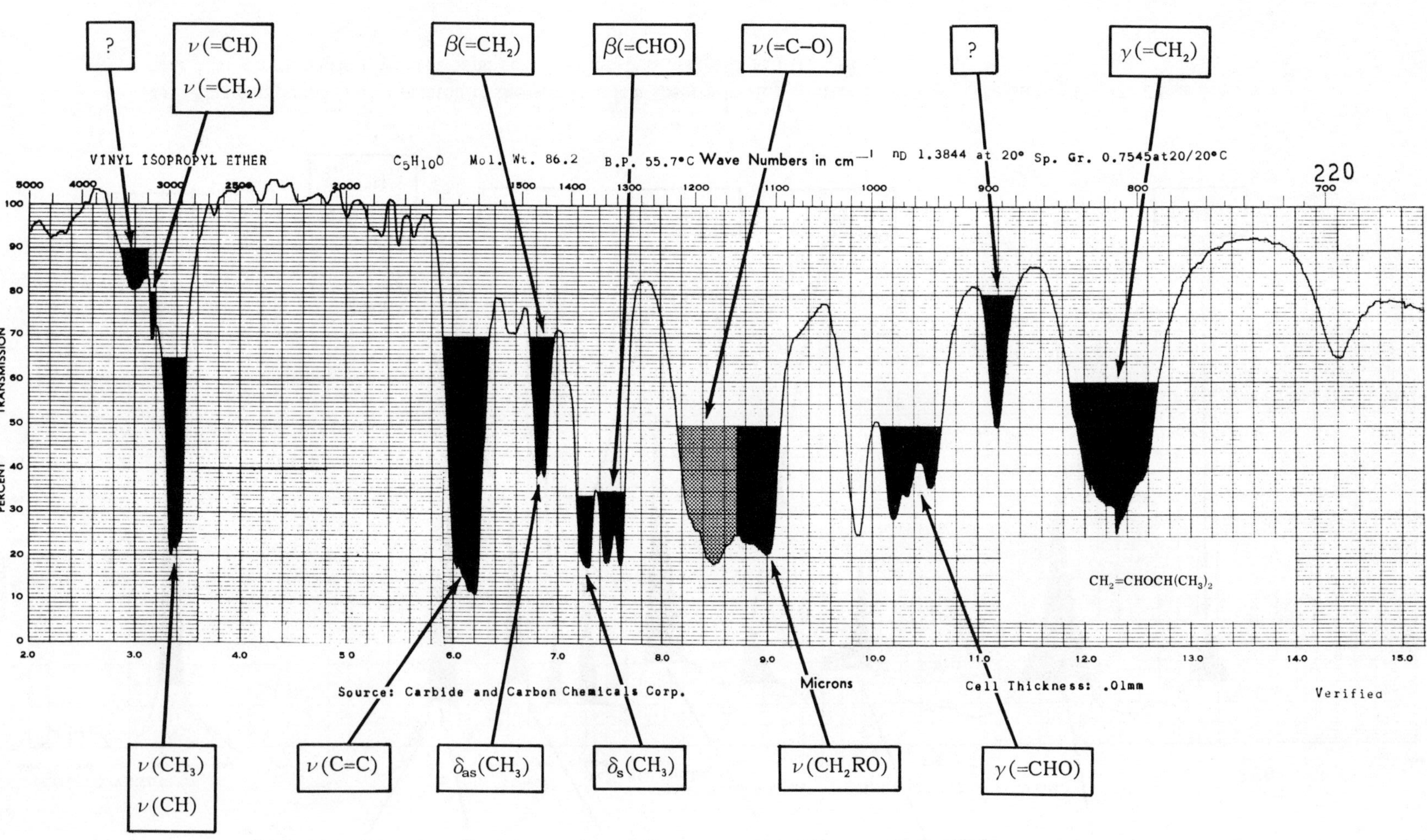

35. This compound has the groups =CHO and $CH(CH_3)_2O$. These groups results in a ν(C−O) band for each group almost coinciding near 1100 cm^{-1}. The other assignments are as on previous spectra.

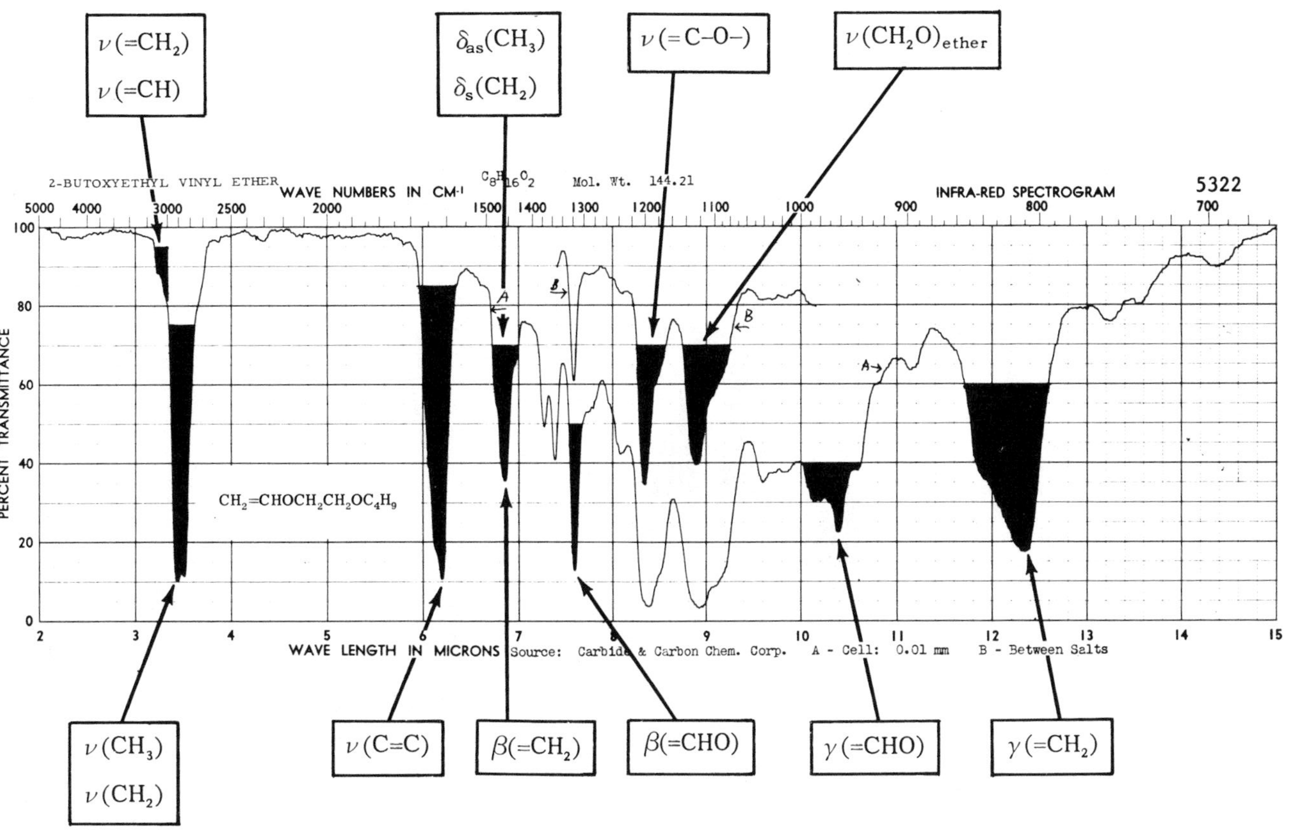

36. This compound has the groups $=CHO$ and CH_2O. This results in two ν(C–O) bands assigned at 1200 and 1120 cm^{-1}. Note how difficult it is to assign the CH_2O, as it has appeared either at 1120 or 1080 cm^{-1}. Note the very strong $\nu(C=C)$. The $\gamma(=CH_2)$ appears at the position for vinyl ethers.

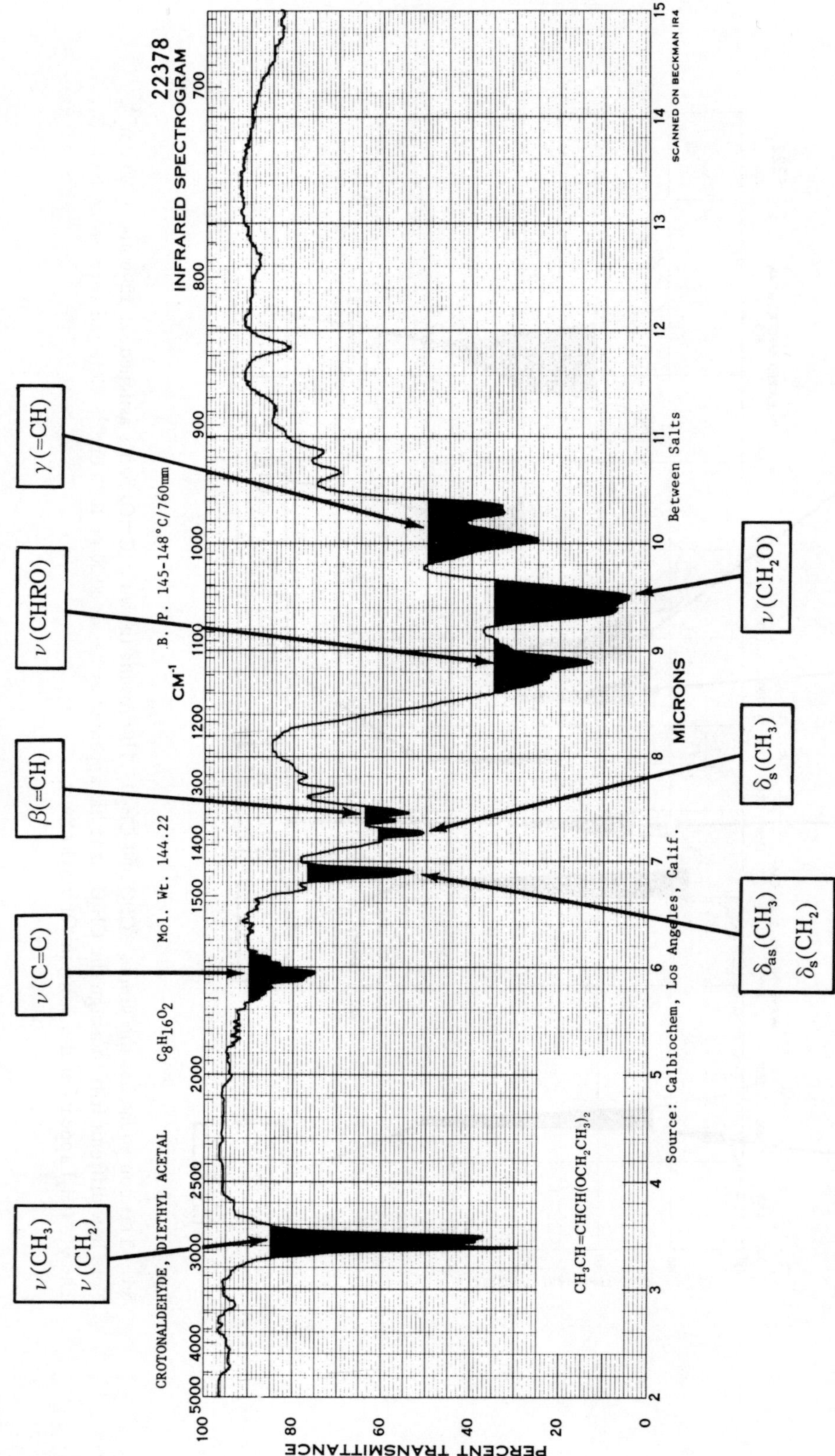

37. The groups CHO and CH_2O occur here, and the assignments are made as ν(CHO) near 1130 cm^{-1} and $\nu(CH_2O)$ near 1080 cm^{-1}. Again we face the problem of making the $\nu(CH_2O)$ assignment, since it has appeared at both 1120 and 1080 cm^{-1}.

38 NONCYCLIC ETHERS

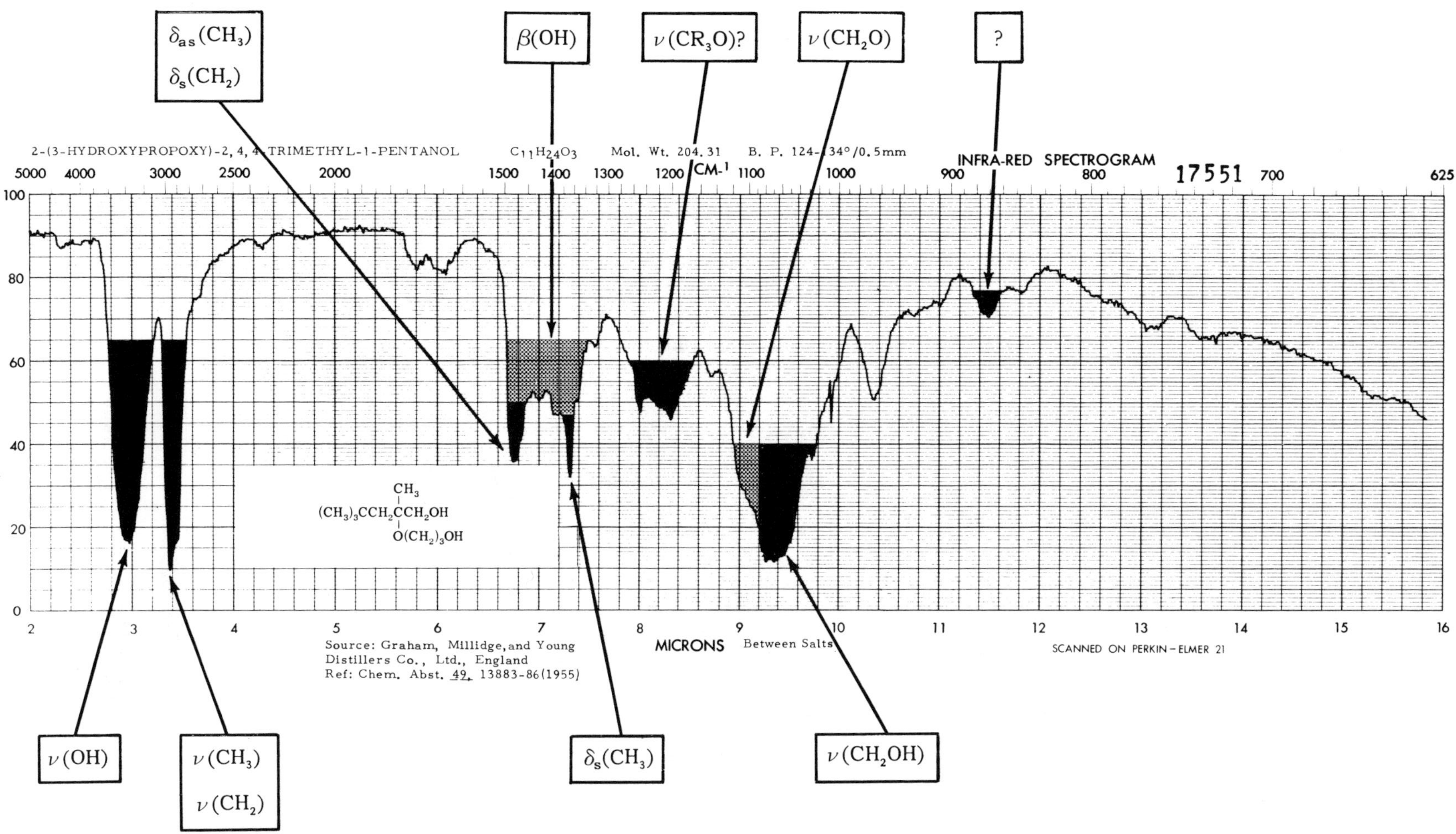

38. The groups CR_3O, CH_2O, and CH_2OH appear in this molecule. If we are to follow the concept of isolated group frequencies, we predict 1200, 1120 (or 1080), and 1060 cm^{-1} respectively for the $\nu(C-O)$ of these groups. There are bands at these positions, and we can make these assignments if it is remembered that many of the previous spectra did not always have bands in agreement with these isolated group frequencies.

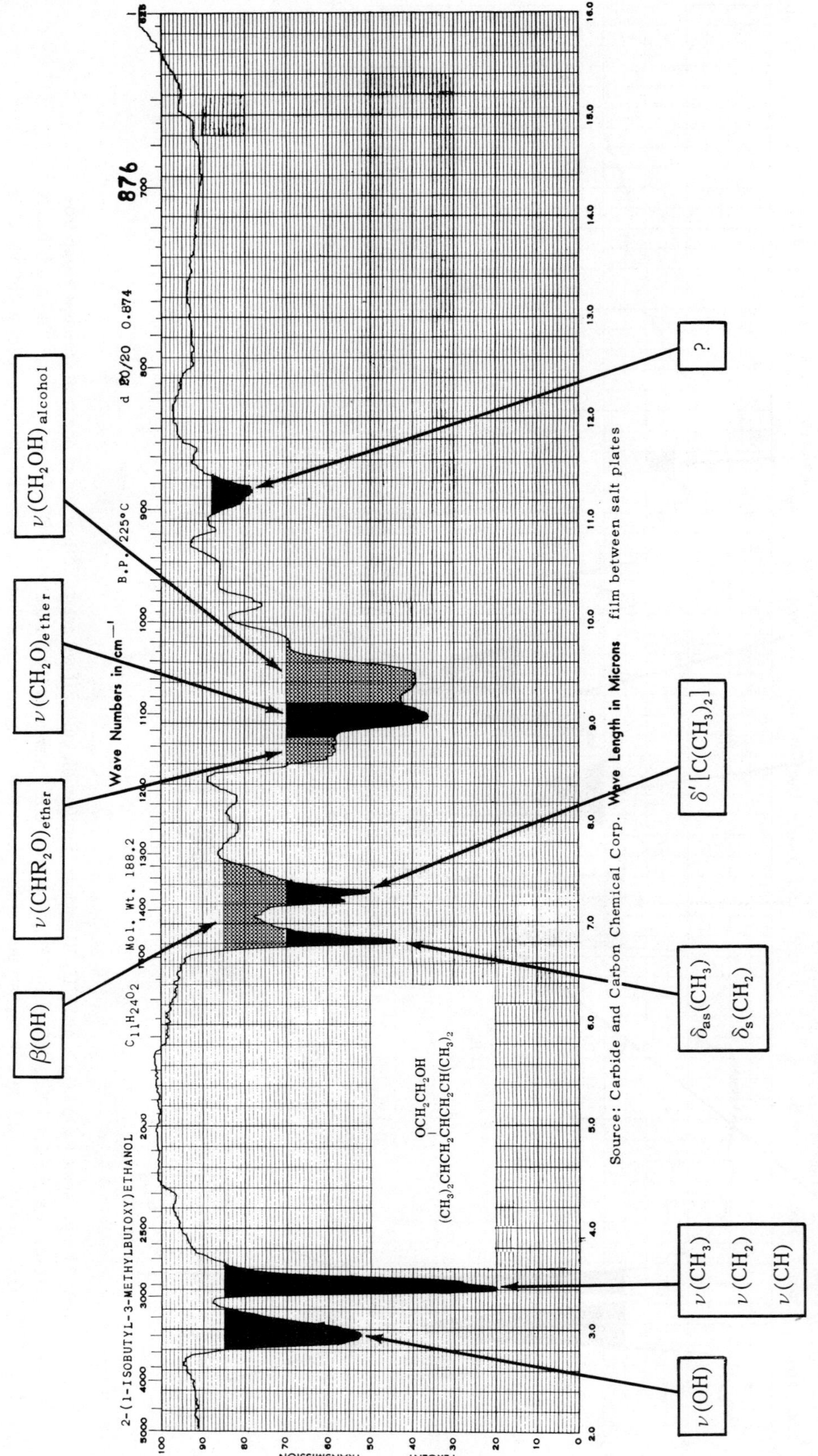

39. This compound has the groups CH_2O, CHR_2O, and CH_2OH. The alcoholic $\nu(C-O)$ is assigned as the band near 1050 cm^{-1}. The $\nu(C-O)$ of the CH_2O group is assigned near 1100 cm^{-1}, leaving the shoulder near 1120 cm^{-1} as the $\nu(C-O)$ of the CHR_2O group. Other assignments are as on previous spectra.

40 NONCYCLIC ETHERS

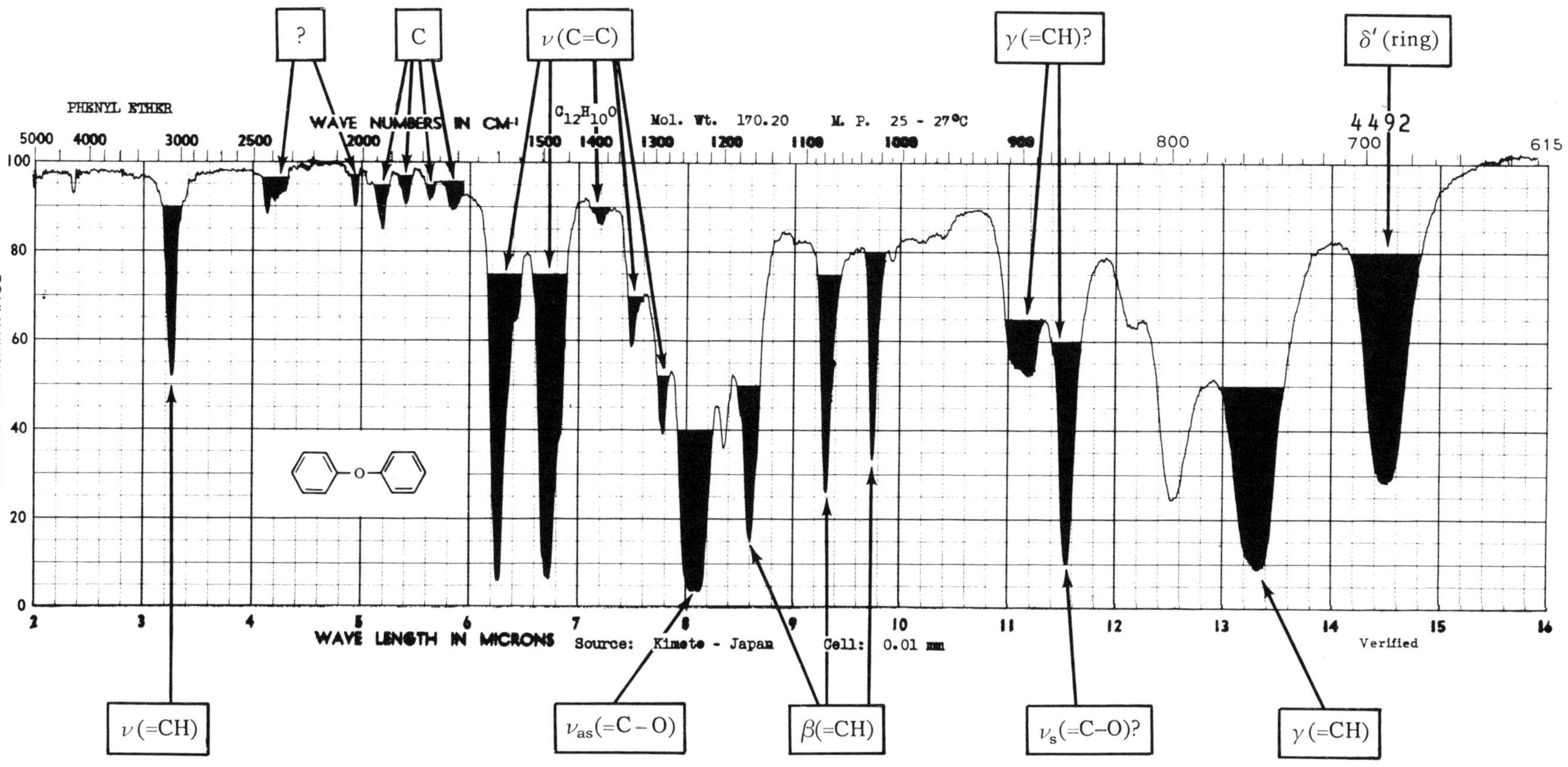

40. Our first example of an aromatic ether is the phenyl ether whose spectrum is presented here. The phenyl group can give partial double-bond character to the C–O group, so that the ν(C–O) appears at a higher frequency than for aliphatic ethers. It is assigned as the band near 1220 cm^{-1}, and given the notation ν_{as}(=C–O). We should also expect the symmetric ν(C–O), but since no authors report the position of this band we must guess at its position. It is logical to assign it to the 900-800 cm^{-1} region, and we have chosen the stronger of the two bands in this region as the correct assignment. This is by no means certain, as it is possible the weaker band is correct. As we have seen, the ν_s(C–O) is often a weak band. Recall also the band near 900 cm^{-1}, which has been referred to in a number of previous spectra. The γ(=CH) bands, so indicative of the monosubstituted ring, are in the expected position. However, a strong band nearby, at 800 cm^{-1} confuses the spectrum in this region. It is doubtful that this compound could be identified by group frequencies alone if it were given as an unknown.

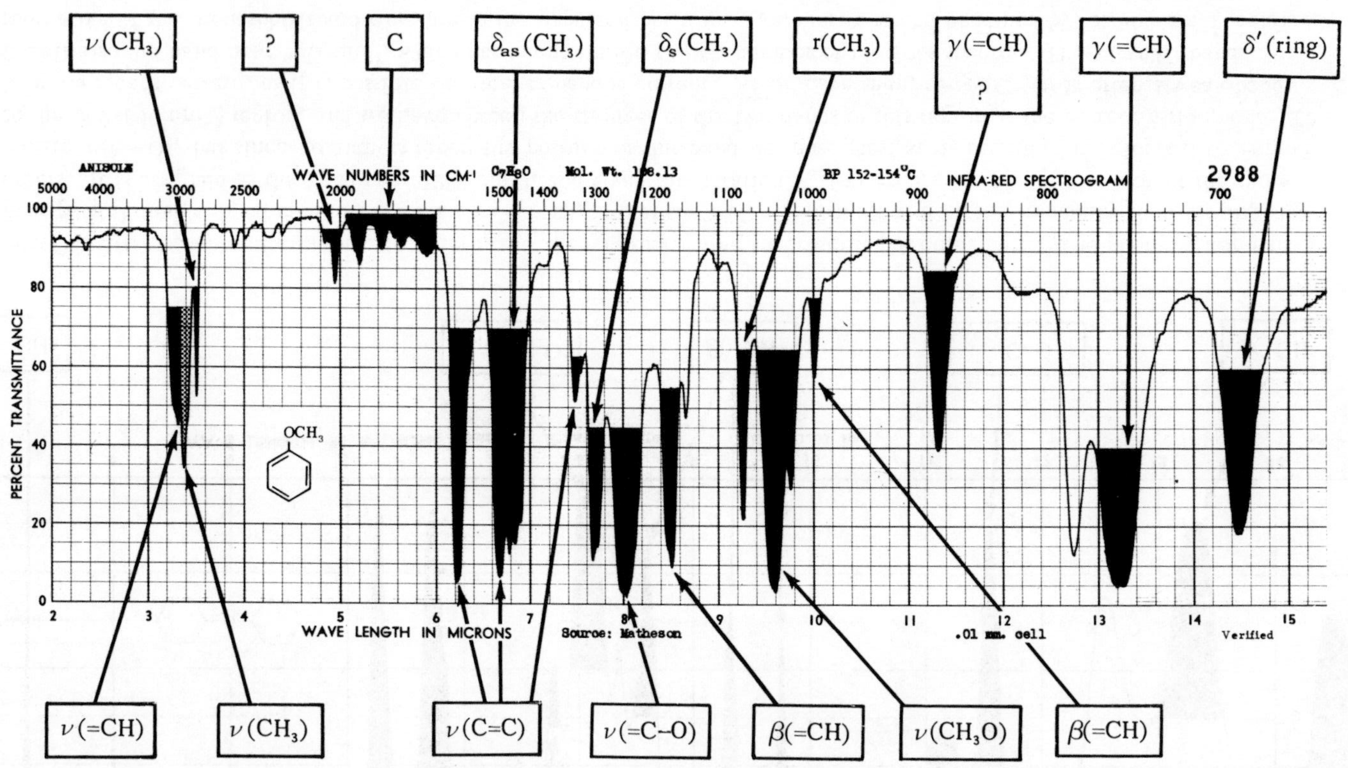

41. Anisole has the groups $=C-O$ and $O-CH_3$, and in the correlation section we extensively discussed group frequencies for these groups. We expect the former to have a $\nu(=C-O)$ near 1200 cm^{-1}, and the latter a $\nu(CH_3O)$ band either at 1050 or 1100 cm^{-1}. For anisole most spectroscopists assign the 1050 cm^{-1} band as the correct position for $\nu(CH_3O)$. We should recall, however, the discussion on hindered anisoles in the correlation section, showing the band appearing at either position. The $\gamma(=CH)$ band of monosubstituted rings appears near 760 cm^{-1}, and a strong band here is so assigned. However, a second band at 790 cm^{-1} also appears. This band persists in other ethers of this type, and can be of value. For anisole it is assigned as an X-sensitive vibration, meaning its position is determined by the substituents on the ring.

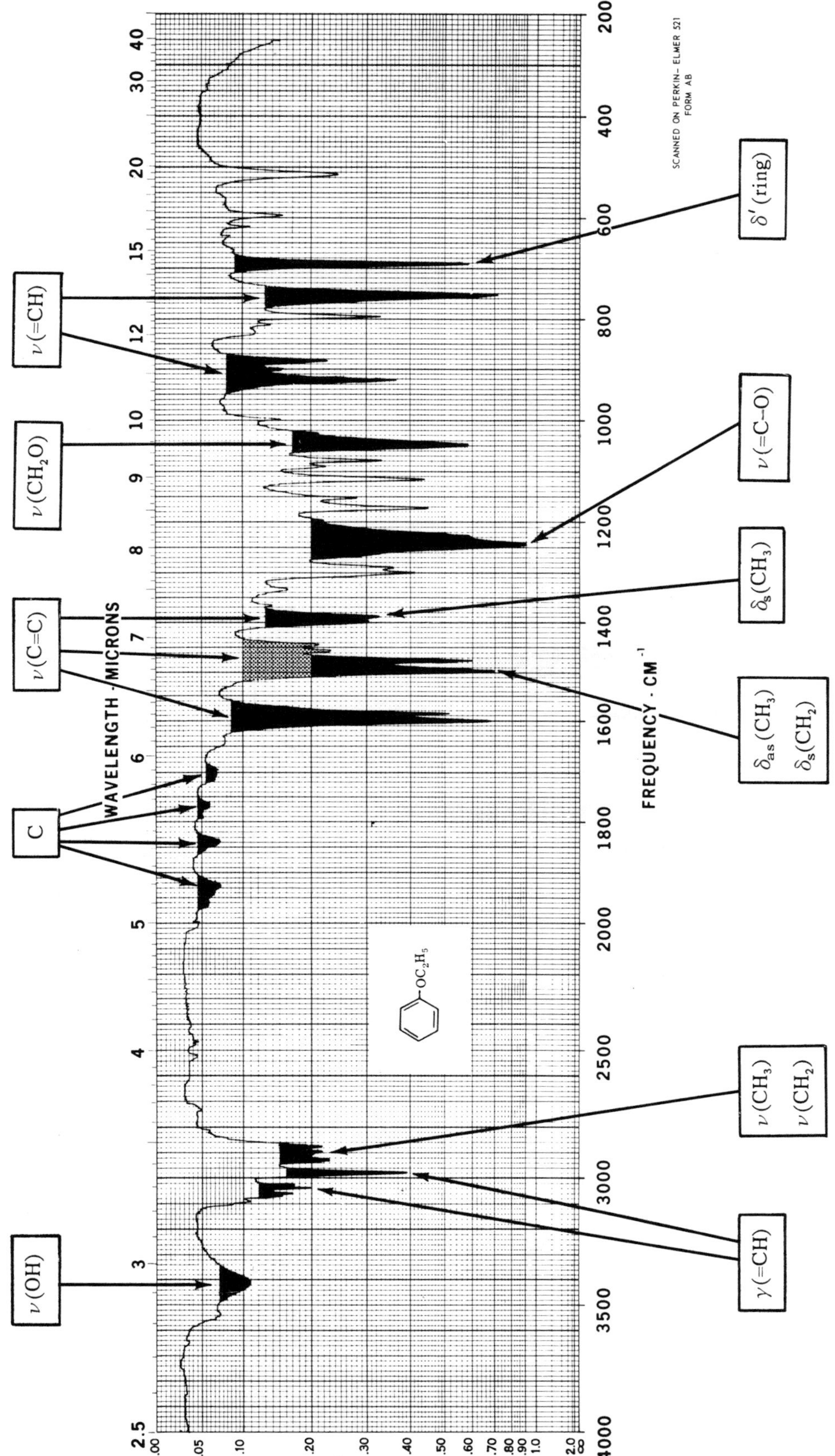

42. Phenetole has the groups =C−O and CH$_2$O, and strong bands at 1200 and 1050 cm^{-1} are assigned as the ν(C−O) of these groups. The 1040 cm^{-1} assignment, however, is not in agreement with the CH$_2$O assignments in previous spectra. We are assigning the 1050 cm^{-1} band as the CH$_2$O, since we have seen that coupling can shift this band to near 1100 cm^{-1}, while uncoupled, the band is near 1050 cm^{-1} (see introductory section for the explanation of coupling).

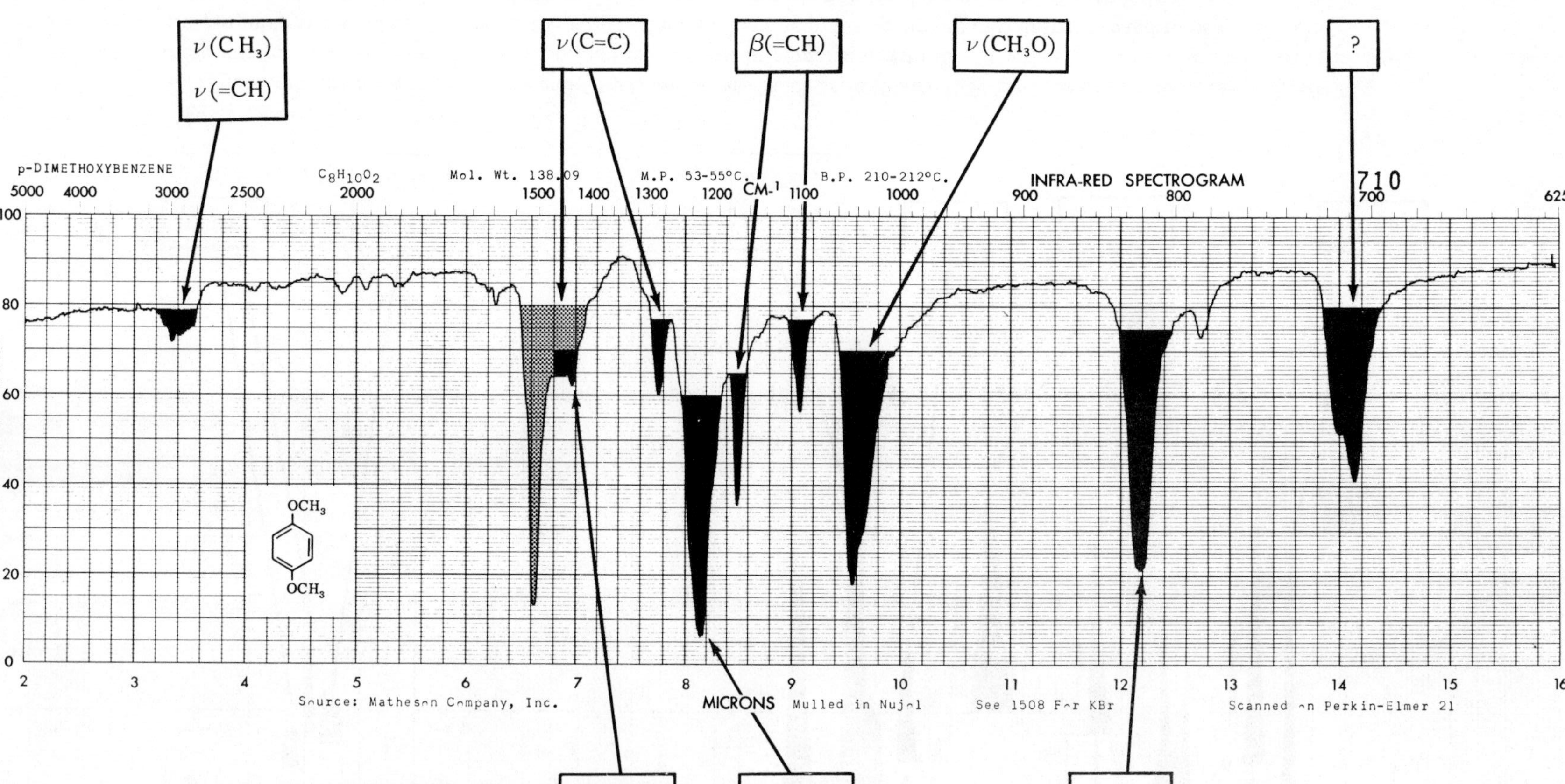

43. This compound is related to anisole, and it should be possible to compare the $\nu(=C-O)$ and $\nu(CH_3O)$ vibration for both compounds. We can note that bands near 1200 and 1030 cm^{-1} occur in both compounds, and support our assignment of these bands as $\nu(=C-O)$ and $\nu(CH_3O)$. The 1100 cm^{-1} band in this spectrum is shifted in the spectrum of anisole. There is a band near 710 cm^{-1} which occurs in these parasubstituted anisoles, and is not easily assigned, although its presence may be of diagnostic value.

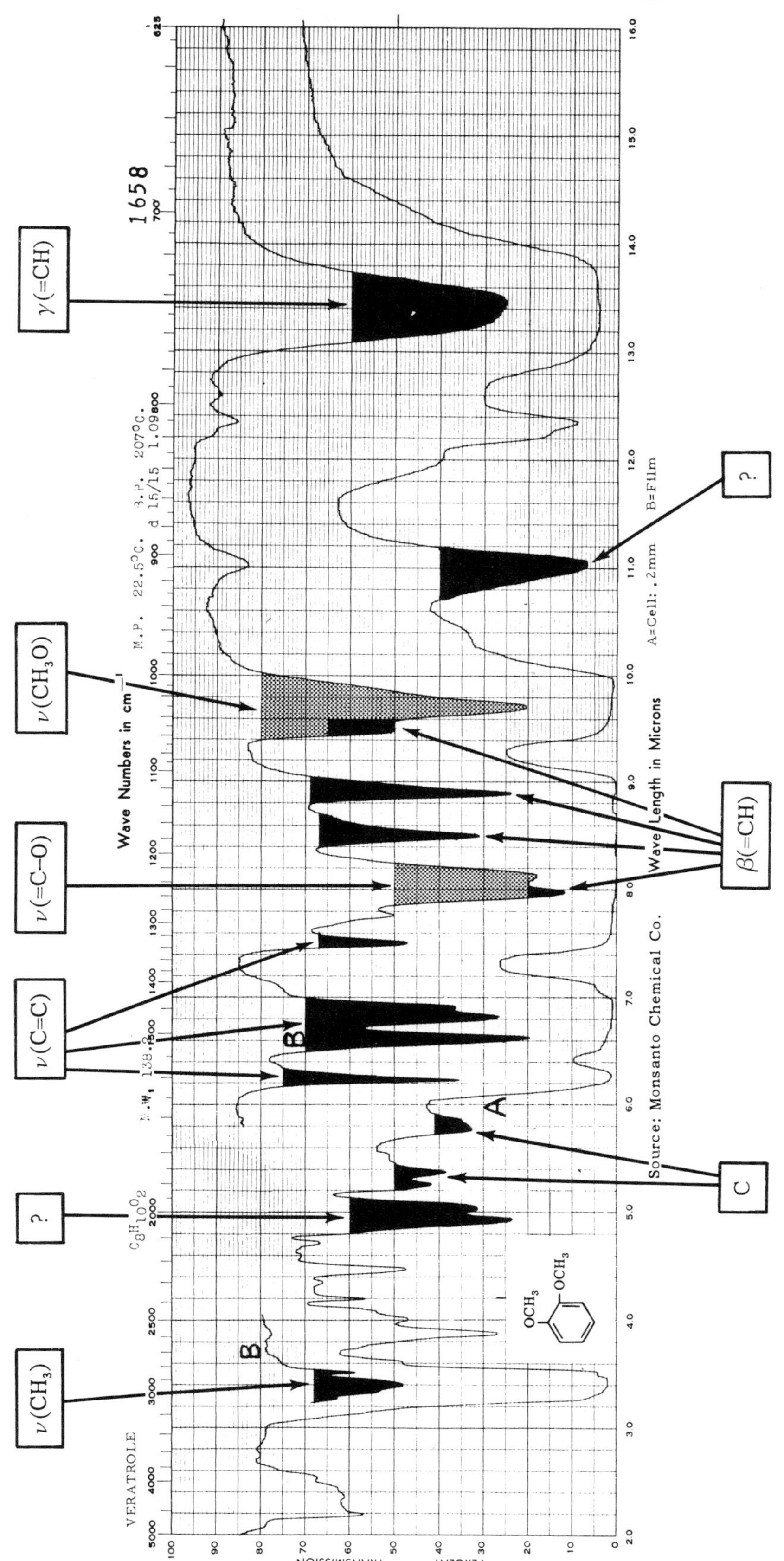

44. This compound is also related to anisole, and we can note the strong 1200 and 1030 cm^{-1} bands so indicative of the groupings = C–O and CH_2O respectively. The γ(=CH) band is in the expected position for this aromatic ring substitution.

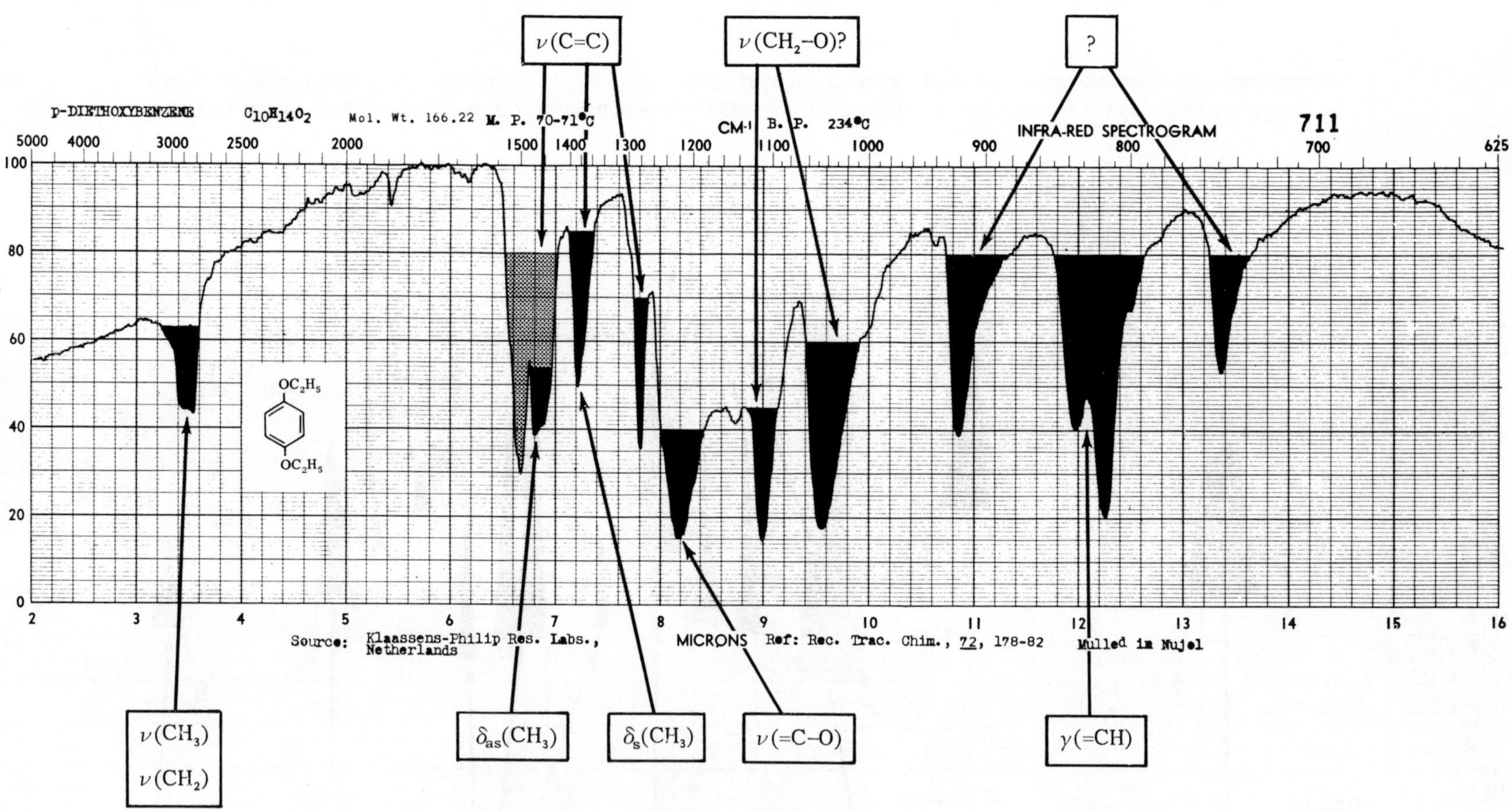

45. This compound is related to phenetole as the previous compound was related to anisole, and we can compare the phenetole spectrum accordingly. Again we note the two strong bands near 1200 and 1030 cm^{-1} which are so persistent for these "ole" compounds. These are assigned as before as $\nu(=C-O)$ and $\nu(CH_3O)$ respectively. The band near 710 cm^{-1}, which we could not assign in the previous para compound, appears near 750 cm^{-1} in this spectrum.

46 NONCYCLIC ETHERS

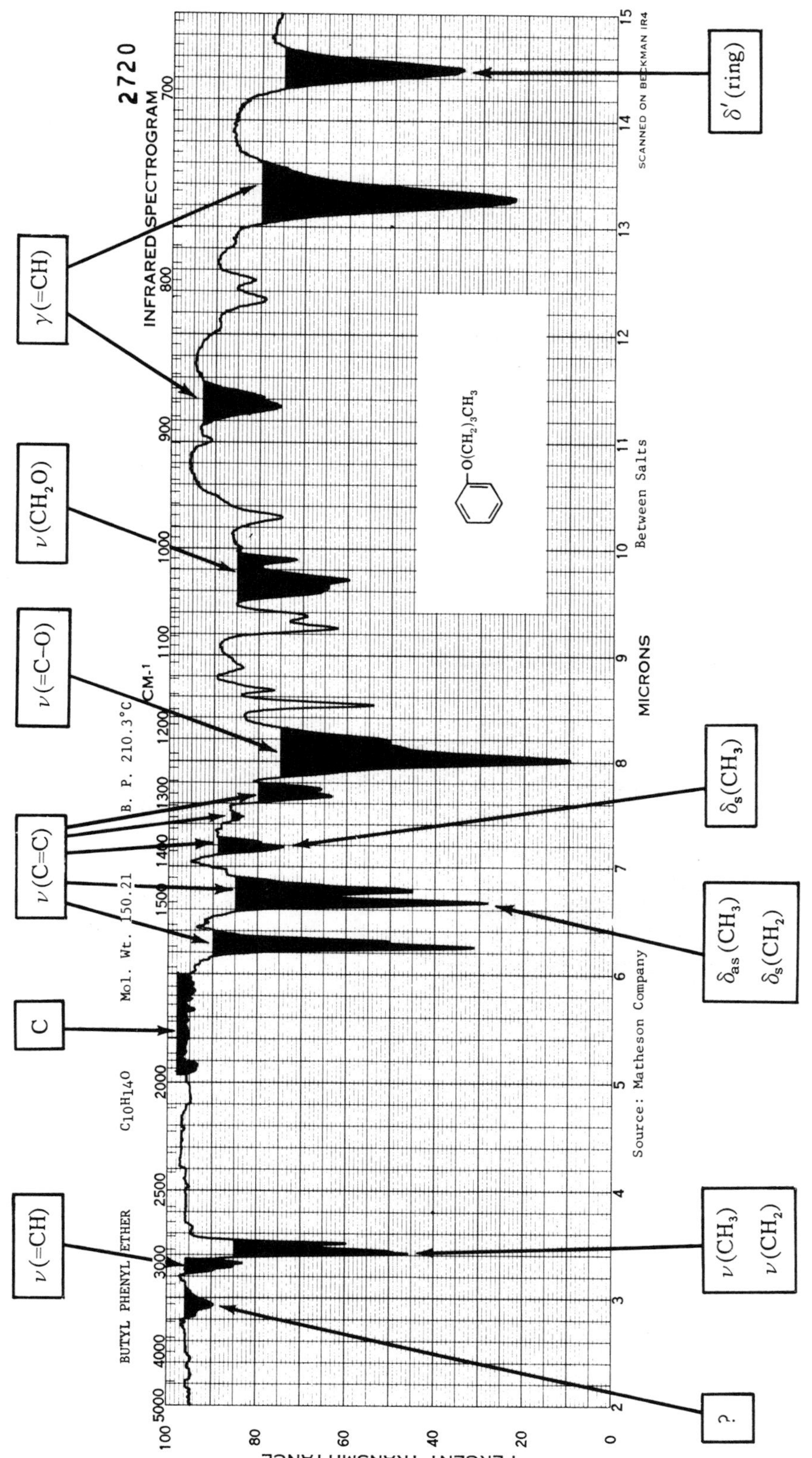

46. The compound n-butyl phenyl ether has the groups = C−O and CH_2O, and again strong bands are found near 1200 and 1030 cm^{-1} which are assigned to these groups. Note the monosubstituted ring vibrations are in the expected positions near 770 and 690 cm^{-1}, and the band near 800 cm^{-1} is now weak.

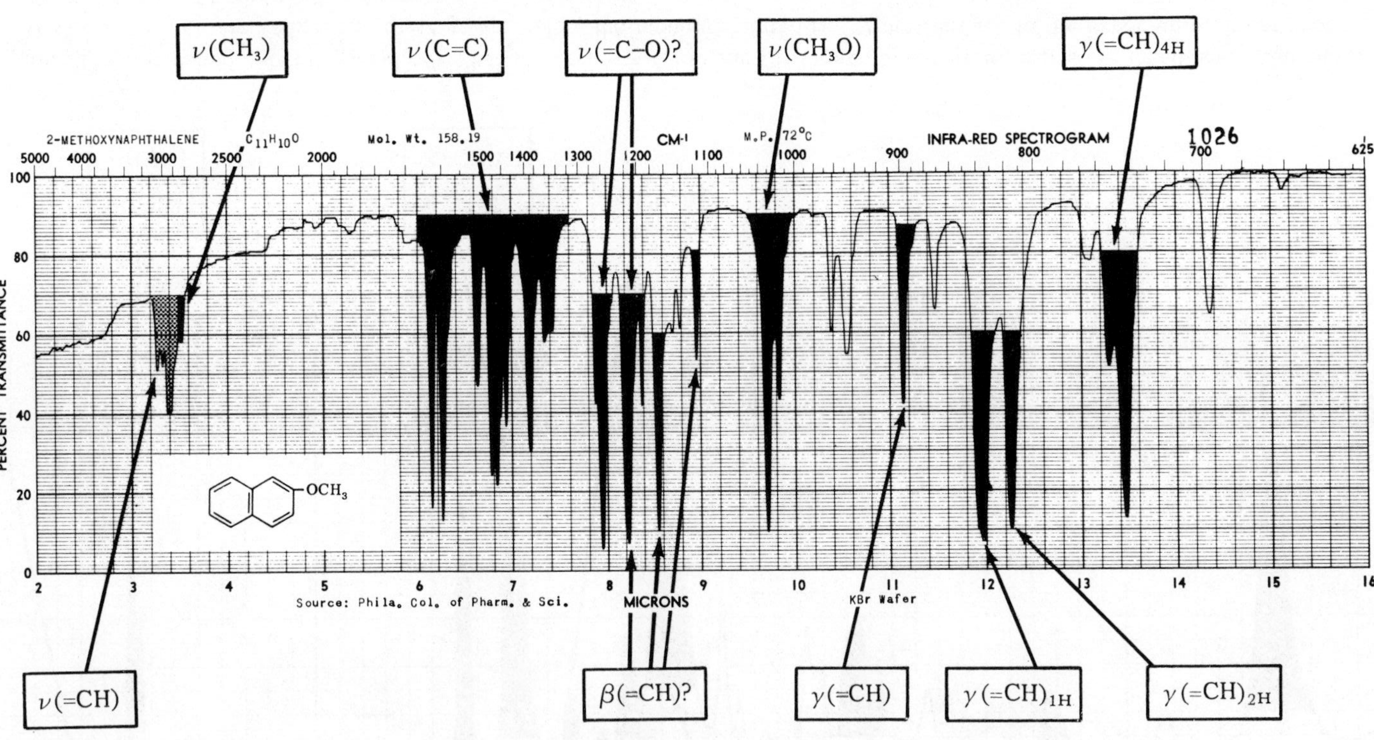

47. The compound 2-methoxynaphthalene has the groups =C−O and CH_3O, and again we find a strong band near 1200 and 1030 cm^{-1}. Note however, two strong bands appear near 1200 cm^{-1}, and it is not obvious which one is the $\nu(=C-O)$. The other assignments are based on previous spectra.

Reproduced with permission from the Ph. D. Thesis of R. E. Erickson

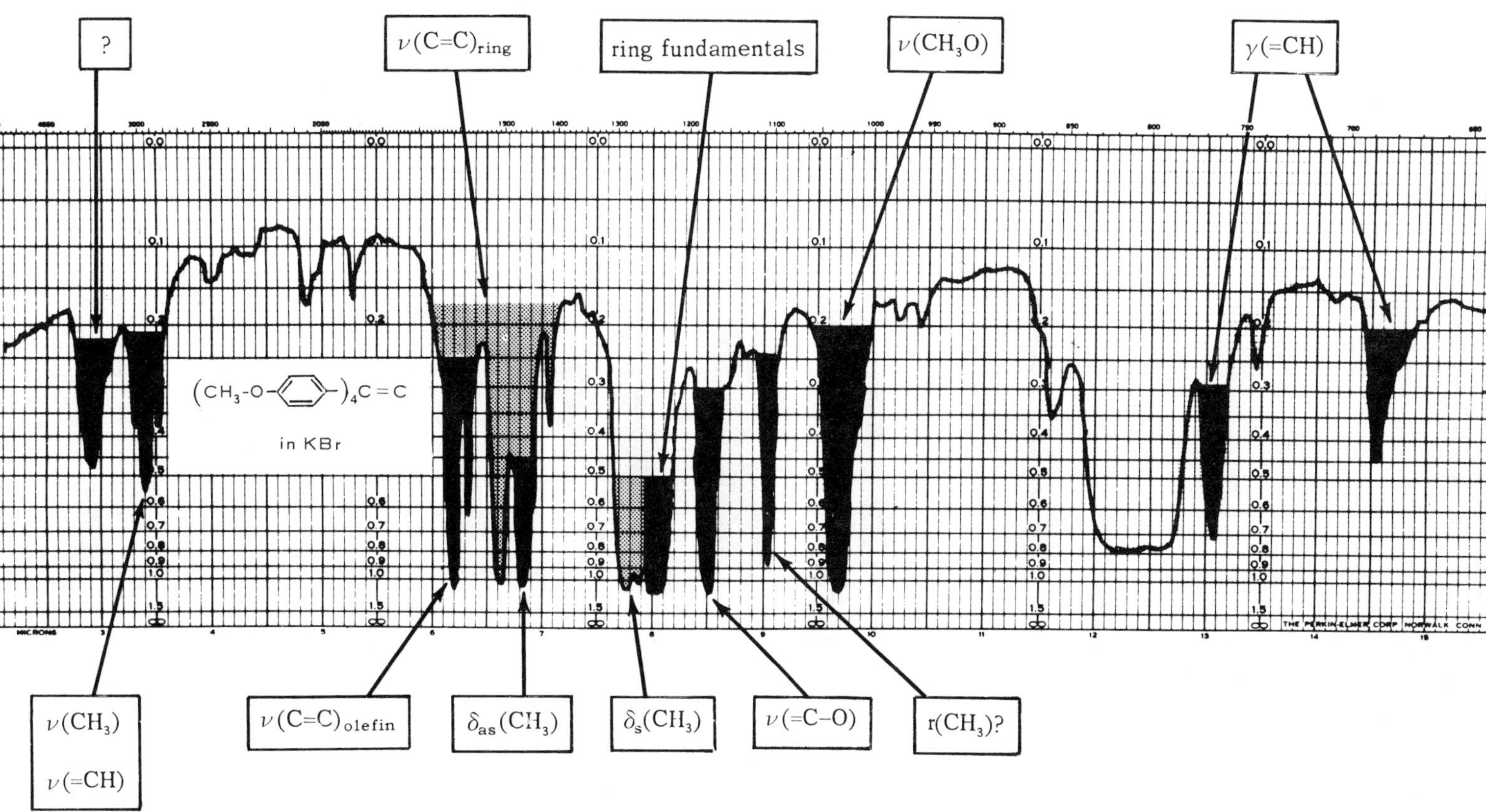

48. This spectrum is of tetranisole ethylene, the compound discussed in the introductory section of this text. The anisole group gives the expected $\nu(=C-O)$ and $\nu(CH_3O)$ bands near 1200 and 1030 cm^{-1}. The next spectrum is of a charge transfer complex of this compound, and it will be these two bands which will shift, since the electron density change occurs in the C−O group. The $\gamma(=CH)$ of the ring is in the expected position.

Reproduced with permission from the Ph. D. Thesis of R. E. Erickson

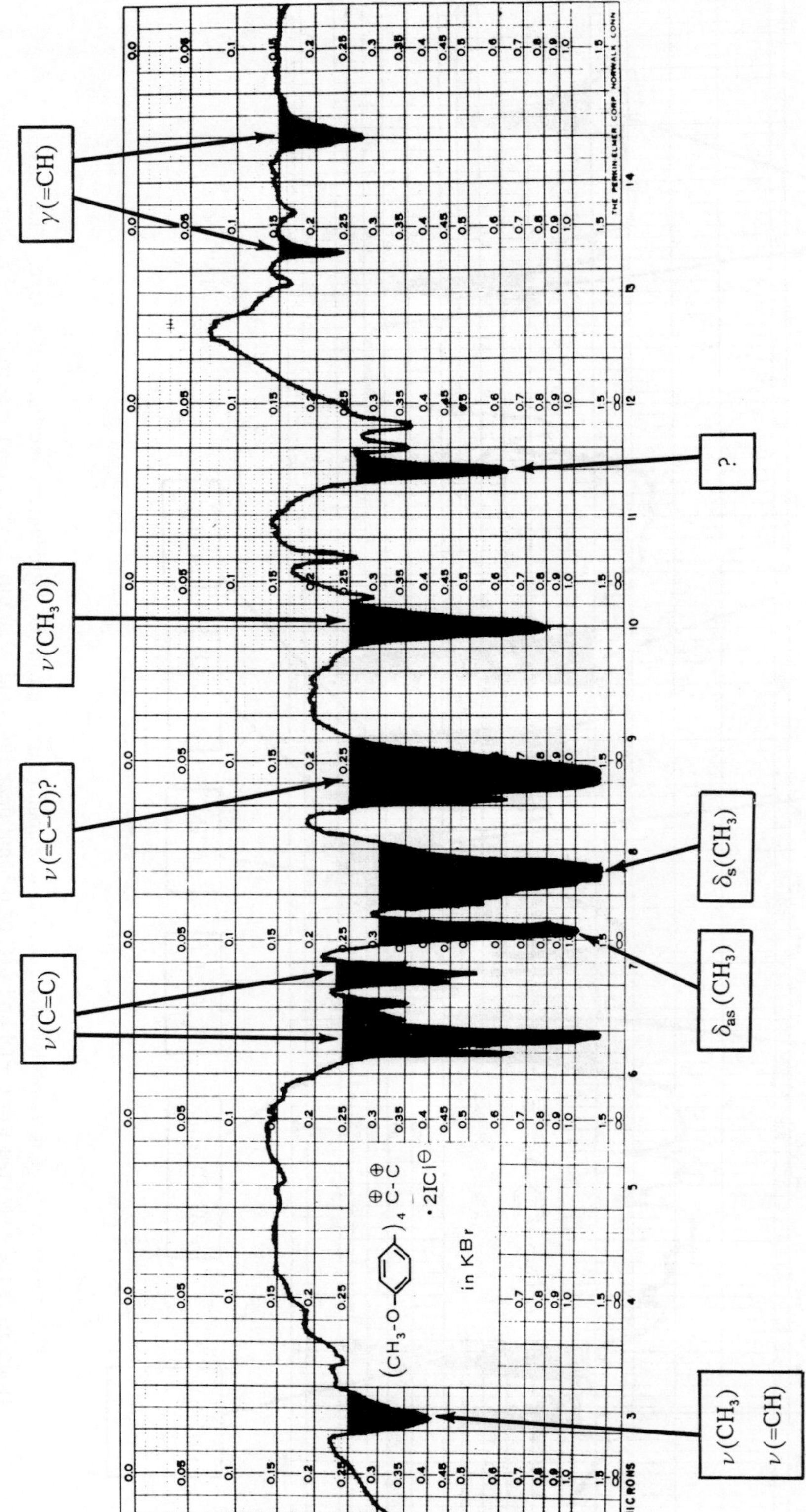

49. Reacting tetranisole ethylene with ICl produces a charge transfer complex and a number of bands shift from the previous spectrum. The 1030 cm^{-1} band shifts to 1000 cm^{-1}. The 1180 cm^{-1} band shifts to 1100 cm^{-1}. There is a sharpening up of a band near 1250 cm^{-1} which is not easily explainable.

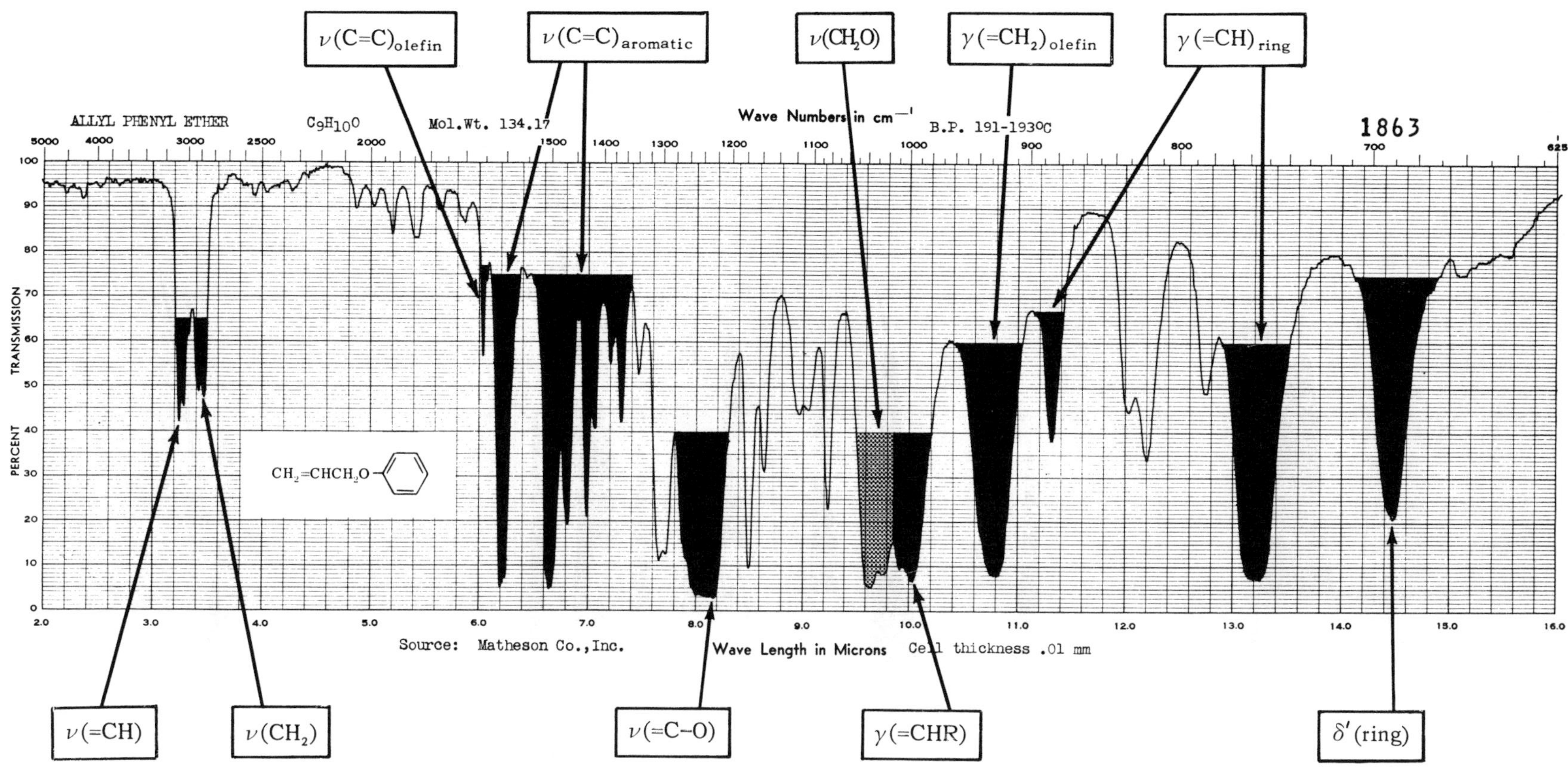

50. This compound has the groups $CH_2{=}CH$, CH_2O, and $=C-O$, the unsaturation coming from both the vinylic and aromatic rings. The $\nu(=C-O)$ is assigned as the 1210 cm^{-1} band, and $\nu(CH_2O)$ as the 1020 cm^{-1}. The other group frequencies are distinct enough to all be identified.

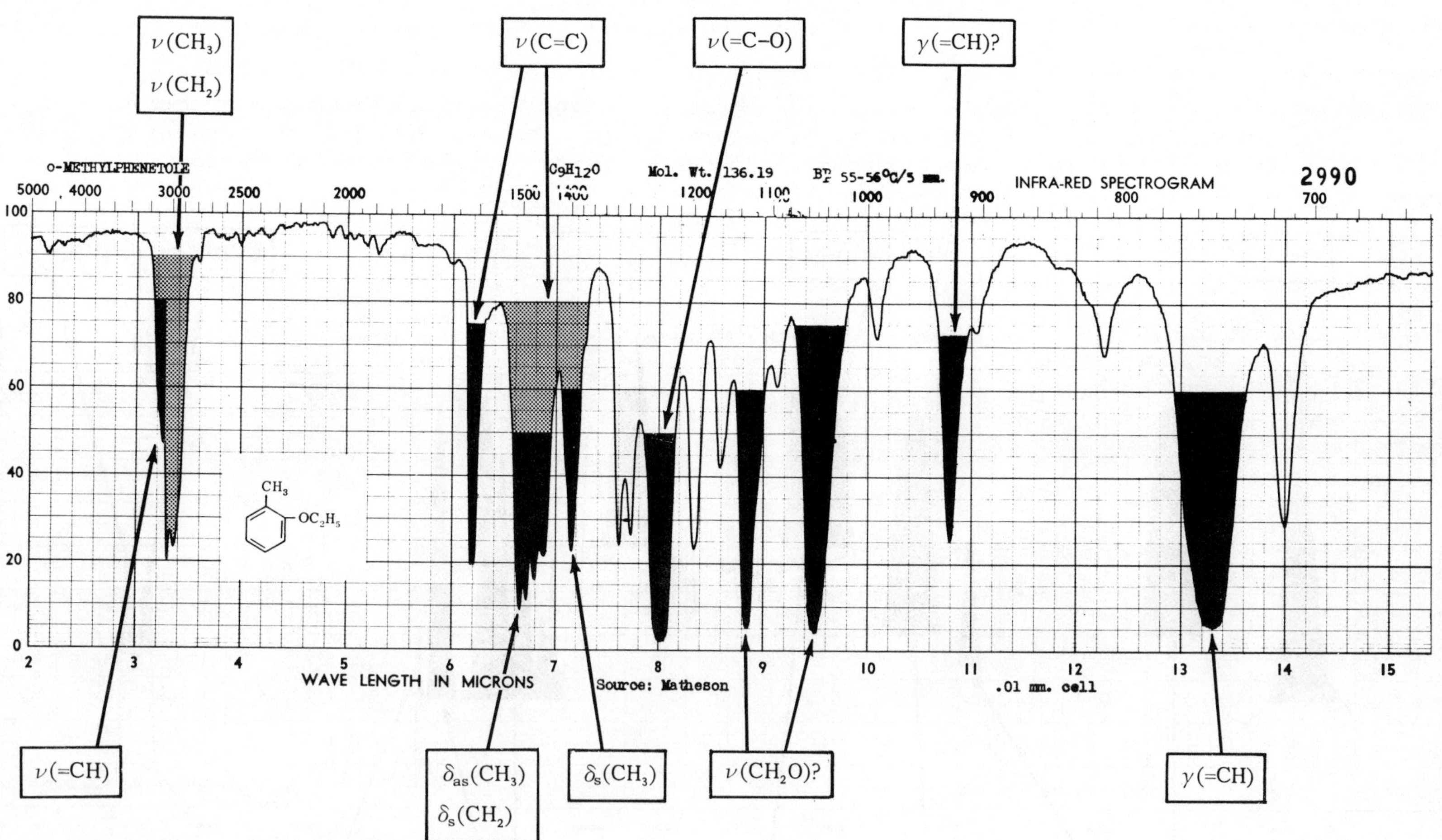

51. This 1, 2-substituted ring has the γ(=CH) in the expected position (770-735 cm^{-1} region), but a second sharp band occurs at 715 cm^{-1}. In Volume 1 of this series, several examples of 1, 2-substituted rings are presented, and none had a sharp, strong band near 715 cm^{-1}. A strong band near 910 cm^{-1} is also not explainable, unless it is also a γ(= CH). We have assigned it in previous spectra to possibly ν_S(C–O). In this example we have both a 1120 and 1050 cm^{-1} band, and as discussed in the correlation section, one or both can occur for various anisoles.

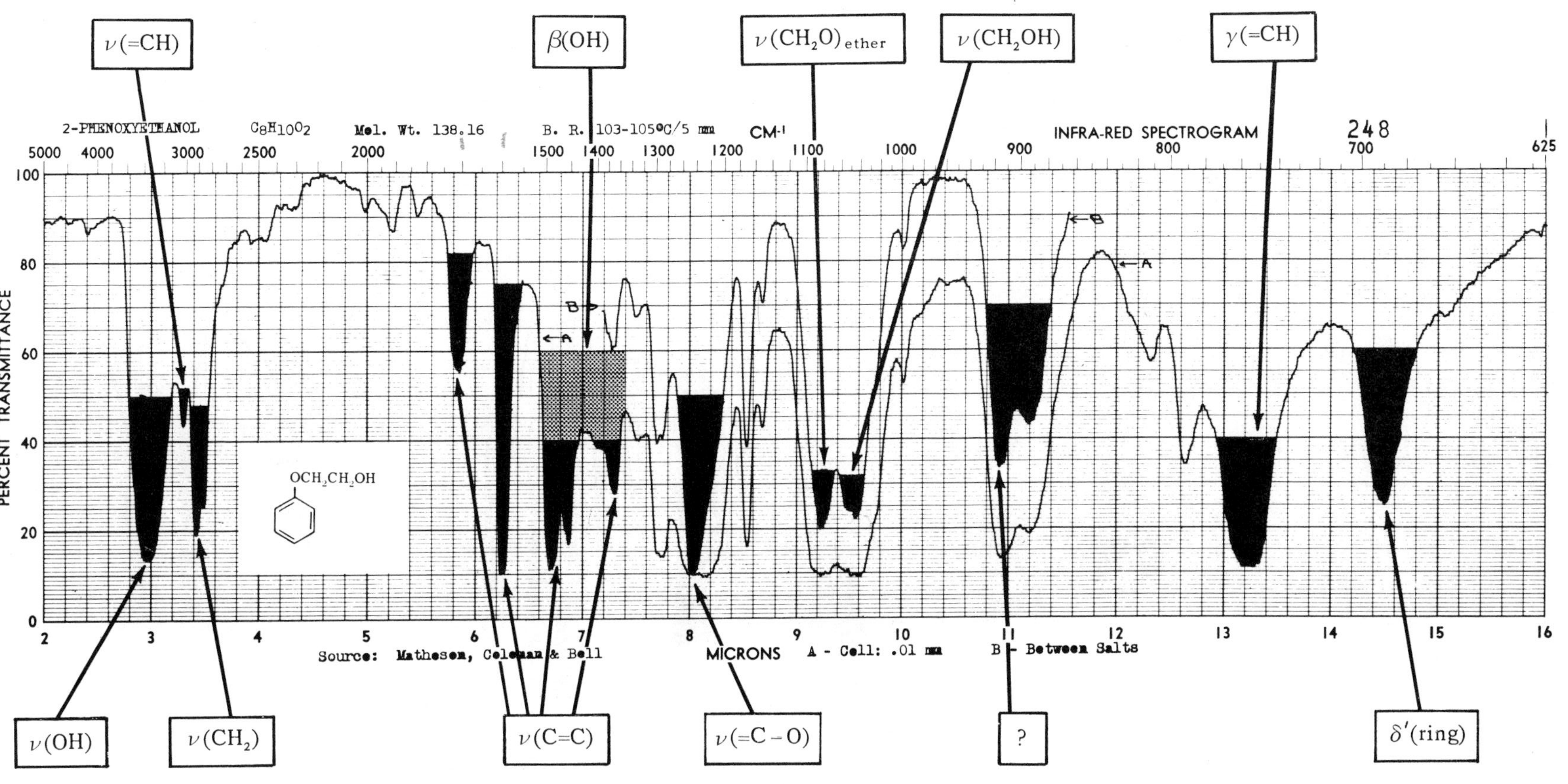

52. The combination of $=C-O$, CH_2O, and CH_2OH results in $\nu(C-O)$ vibrations near 1220, 1080, and 1060 cm^{-1}. The 1220 cm^{-1} band is assigned as $\nu(=C-O)$, but the assignment of the 1080 and 1040 cm^{-1} must be made on the judgment that the alcoholic C–O will be at lower frequencies than the ether CH_2O. The other assignments are based on the group frequencies presented before. A band near 910 cm^{-1} is very strong and puzzling, since we expect no strong band here unless it is $\nu_s(C-O)$. We shall examine a number of these alcoholic ethers.

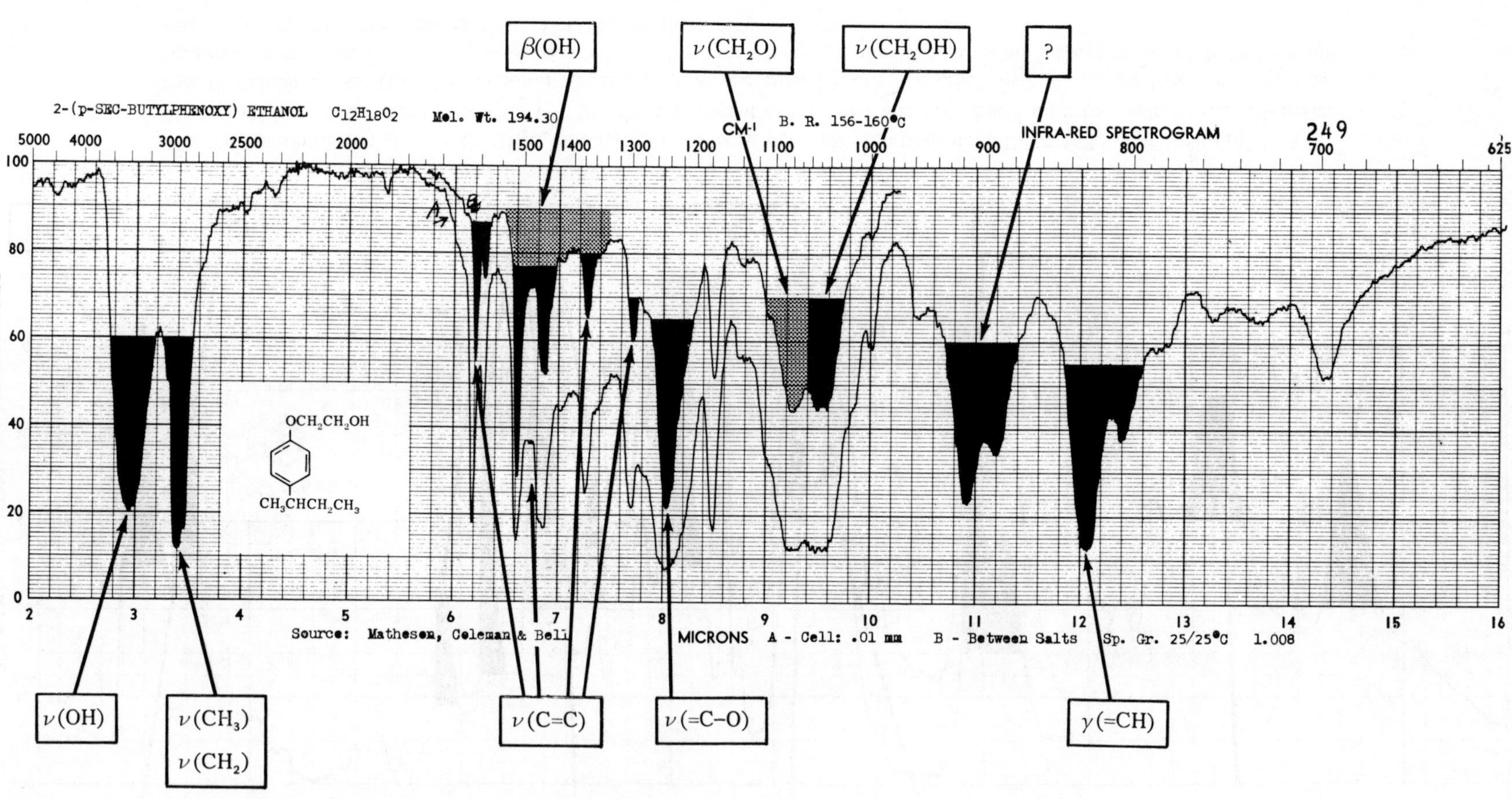

53. This compound also has the $=C-O$, CH_2O, and CH_2OH, as in the previous compound, and the same bands at 1220, 1080, and 1040 cm^{-1} are observed. These are assigned to these groups respectively. The $\gamma(=CH)$ band is found in the position expected for para-substituted rings. The 900 cm^{-1} band is not assignable, unless it can be associated with the alcoholic groups, since it appears in their spectra.

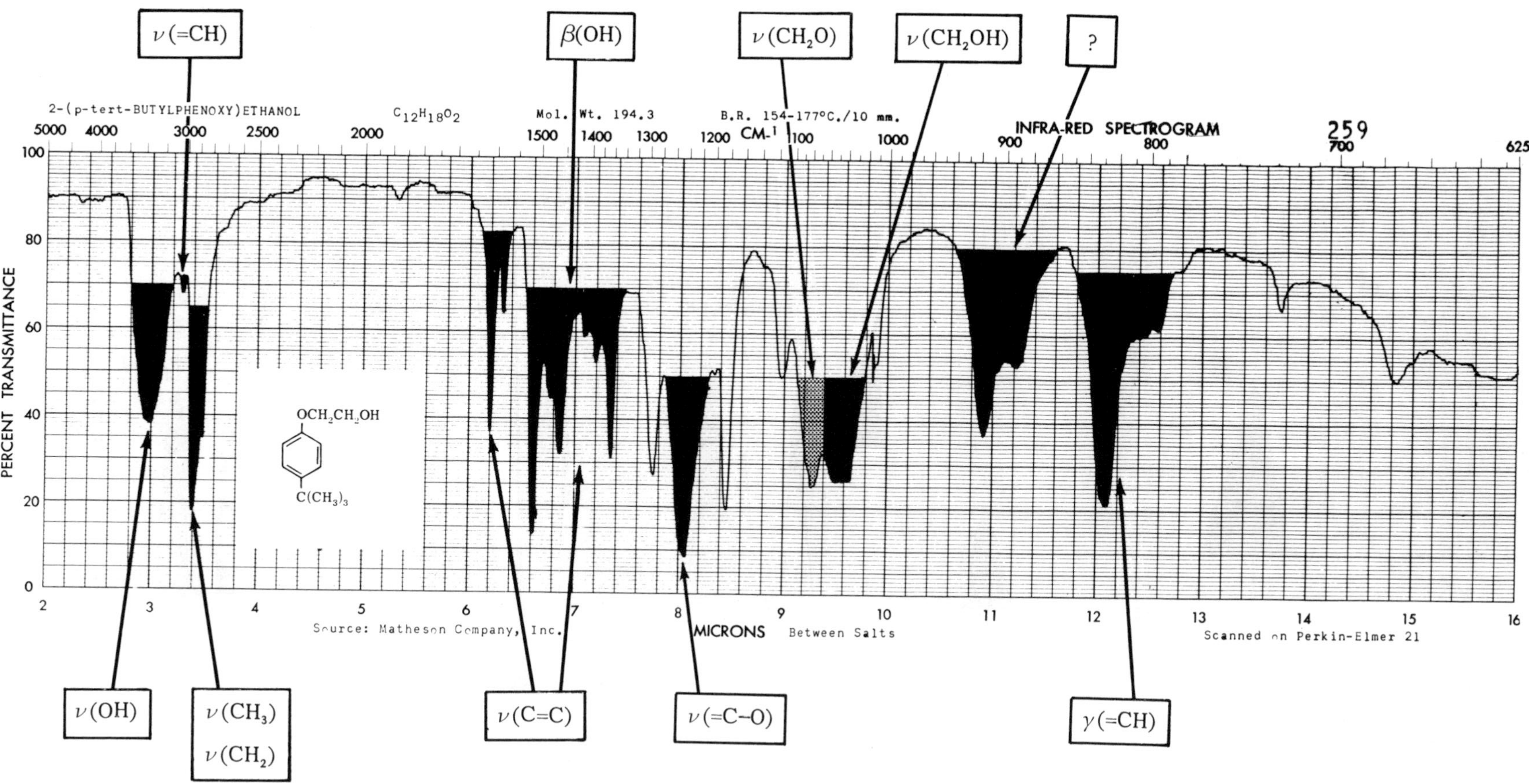

54. This compound is quite similar to the previous one, differing only in the R group in the para position. It will be of value, therefore, to make a close comparison of these two. Note from 1100-800 cm^{-1} exactly the same bands are observed, including the strong 900 cm^{-1} which is not easily explained.

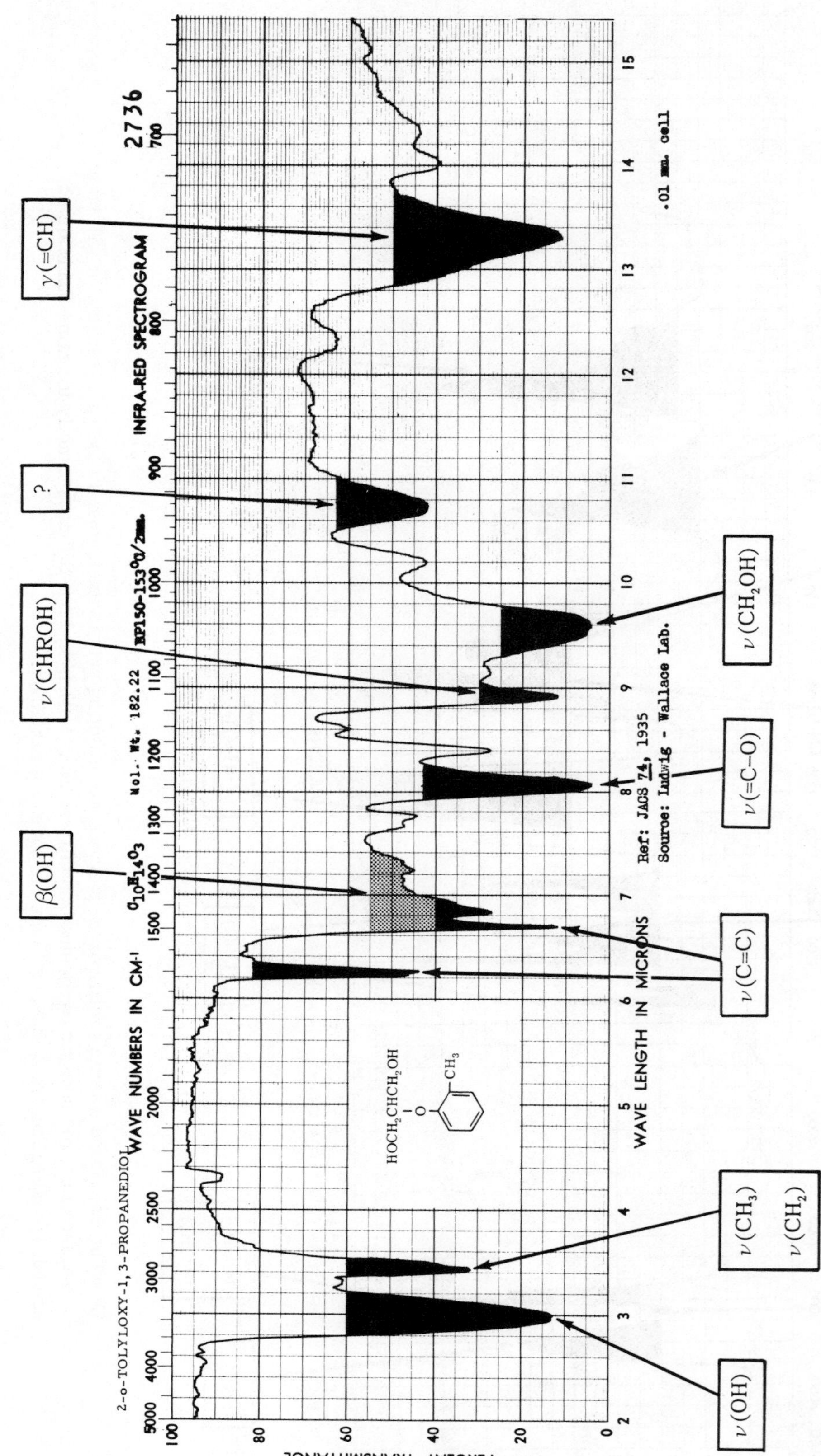

55. This compound is related to the previous two, except the ether group is now CHR_2O. This results in the ether band shifting from the alcohol, and the $\nu(CHR_2O)$ appears at 1110 cm^{-1}, while $\nu(CH_2OH)$ is at 1040 cm^{-1}, where it appeared in the previous two spectra. The γ(=CH) band is in the expected region. Note again a band near 900 cm^{-1} appears.

56 NONCYCLIC ETHERS

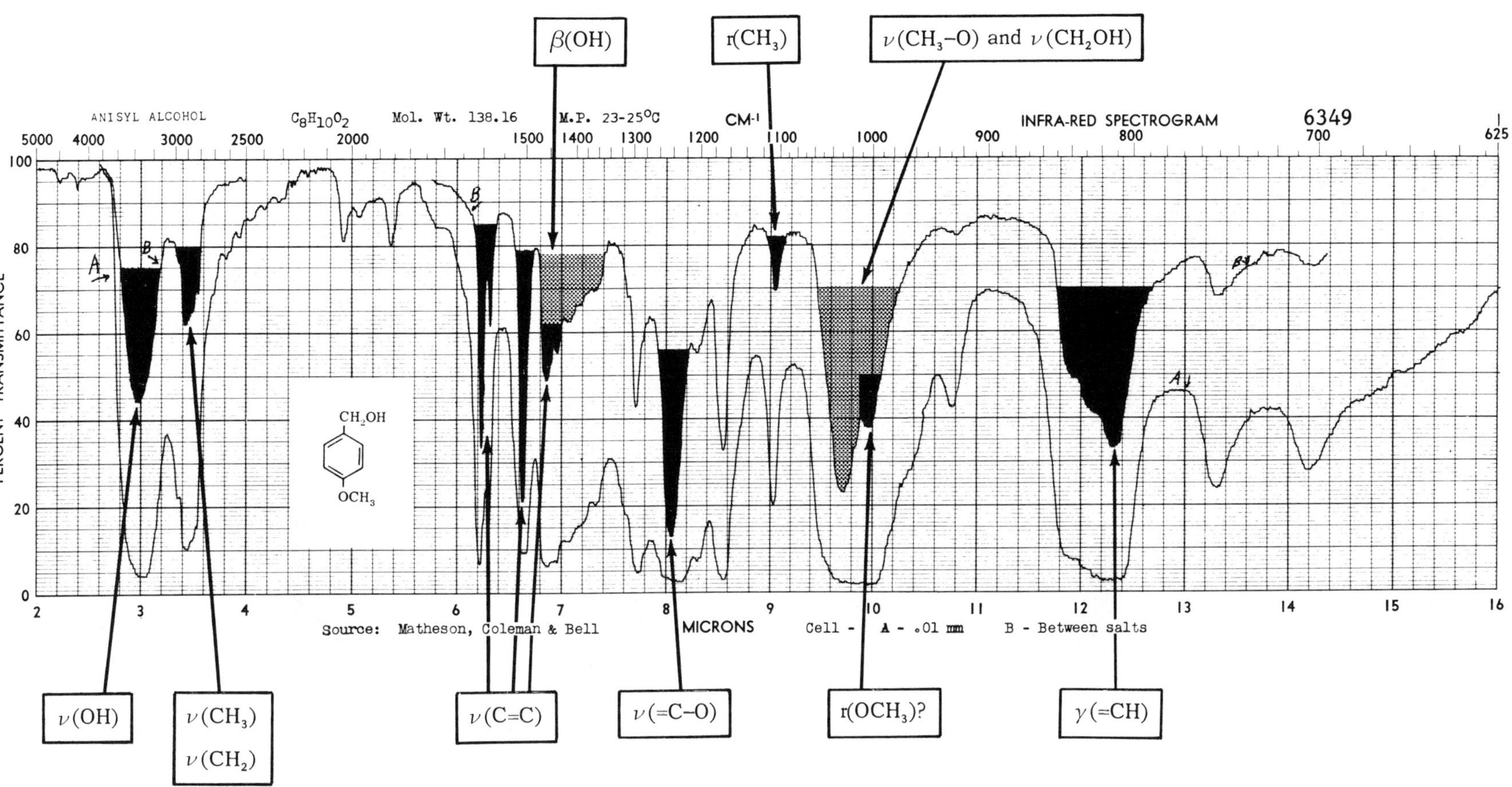

56. We shall examine next a series of anisoles with alcoholic substituents. The first is anisyl alcohol. We observe for this spectrum the alcoholic and OCH_3 group frequencies overlap at 1020 cm^{-1}. The ν(=C–O) appears as a strong band at 1235 cm^{-1}. The γ(=CH) is in the expected position. Note the 900 cm^{-1} band is absent, as expected if it is ν_s(C–O) for aliphatic ethers.

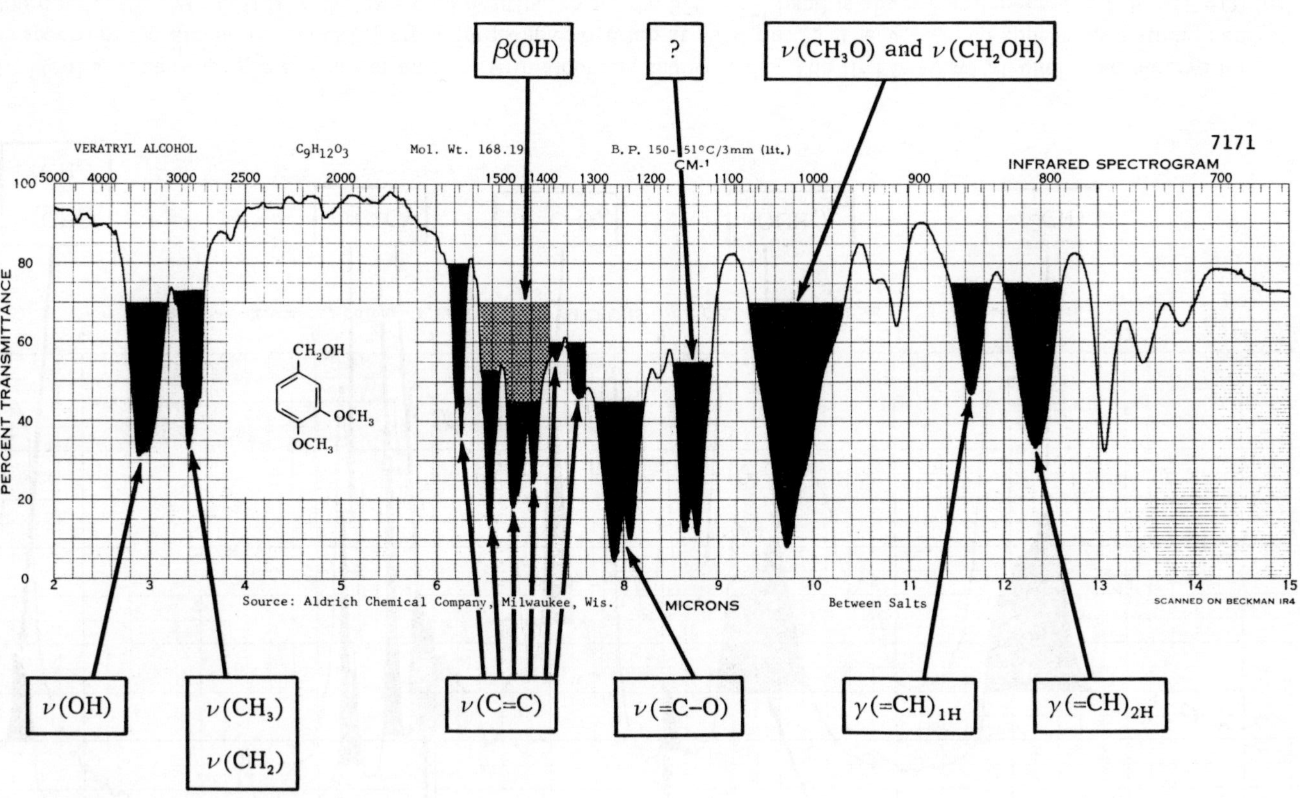

57. This compound can be compared to the previous one. The same considerations concerning $\nu(CH_3O)$, $\nu(CH_2OH)$, and $\nu(=C-O)$ apply as for the previous spectrum. Note the strong 1140 cm^{-1} band. It is not a known group frequency, unless it is the $\nu(CH_3O)$.

58 NONCYCLIC ETHERS

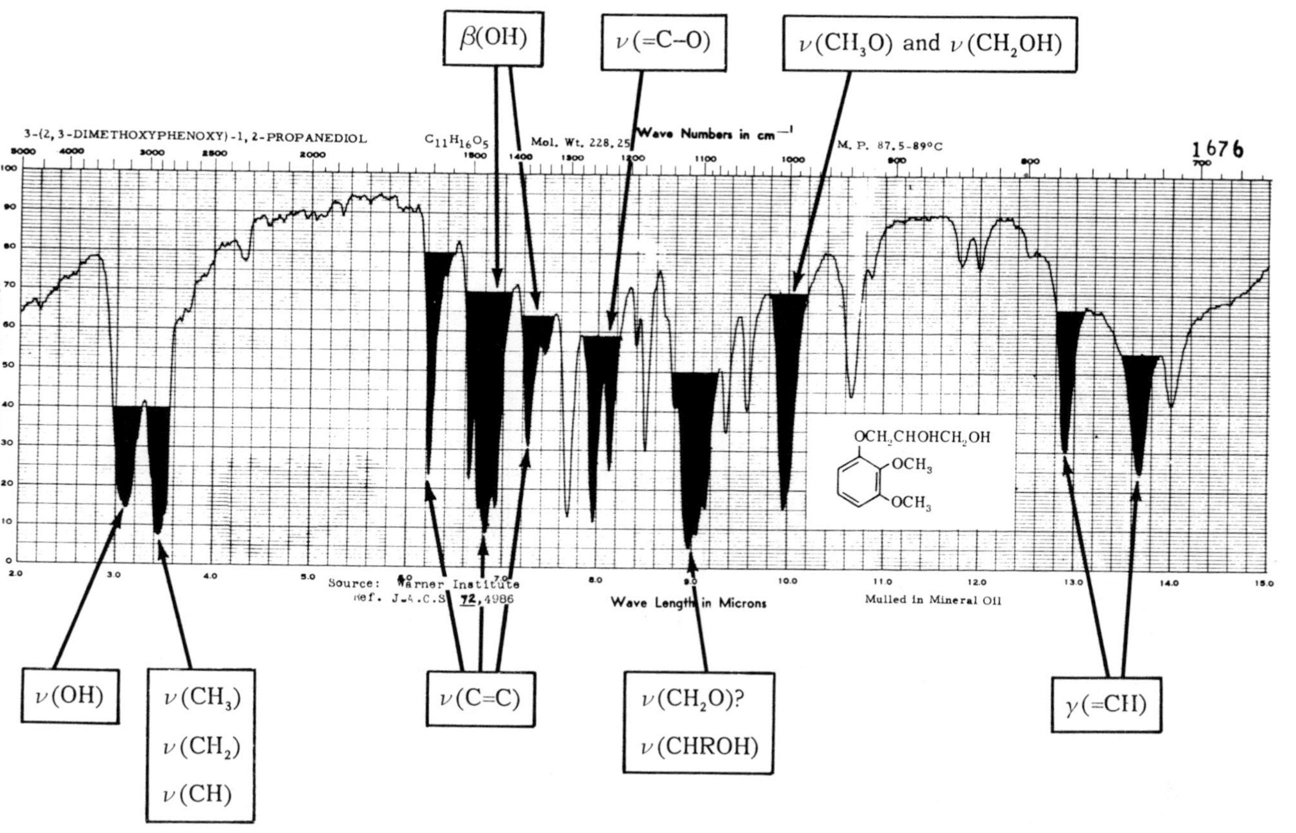

58. The compound is related to the previous two compounds. Again the CH_2OH and OCH_3 bands interfere with each other, and result in a strong band near 1000 cm^{-1}. This is lower than in the previous spectra. Note the secondary alcohol (CHOH) and ether (CH_2O) linkages also interfere, and give a band near 1100 cm^{-1}. The other assignments are based on previous spectra.

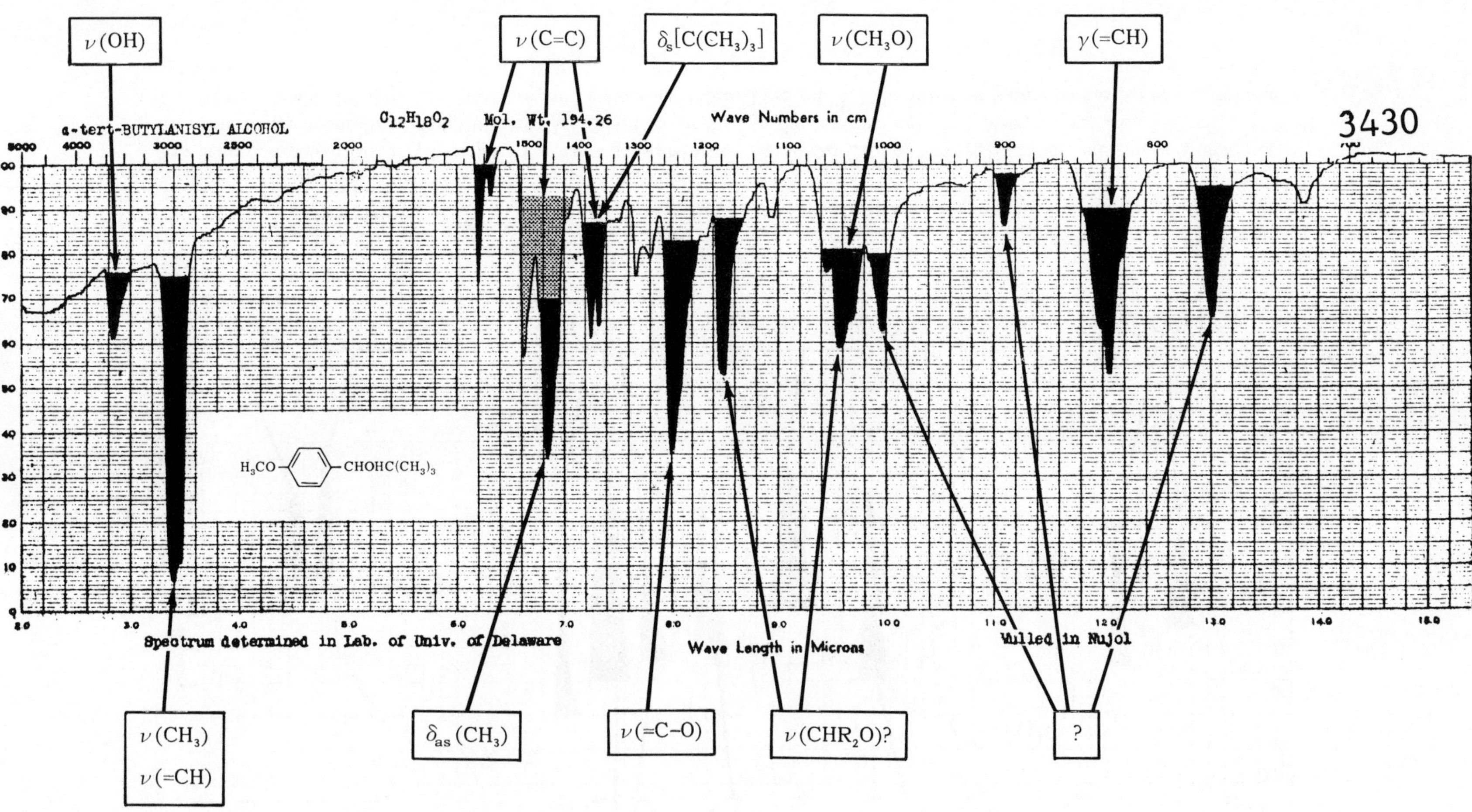

59. This compound has the groups =C–O, CH_3O, and CHOH. We can locate the bands for the first two groups at 1250 and 1050 cm^{-1}, but for the CHOH we must make a choice of the bands near 1050 or 1180 cm^{-1}. If the reader examines Volume 2 of this series he will recall that the alcohols C_6H_5CHOHR had the ν(C–O) near 1030 cm^{-1} due to the electron withdrawing of the ring. We therefore chose the 1050 cm^{-1} band as the correct assignment.

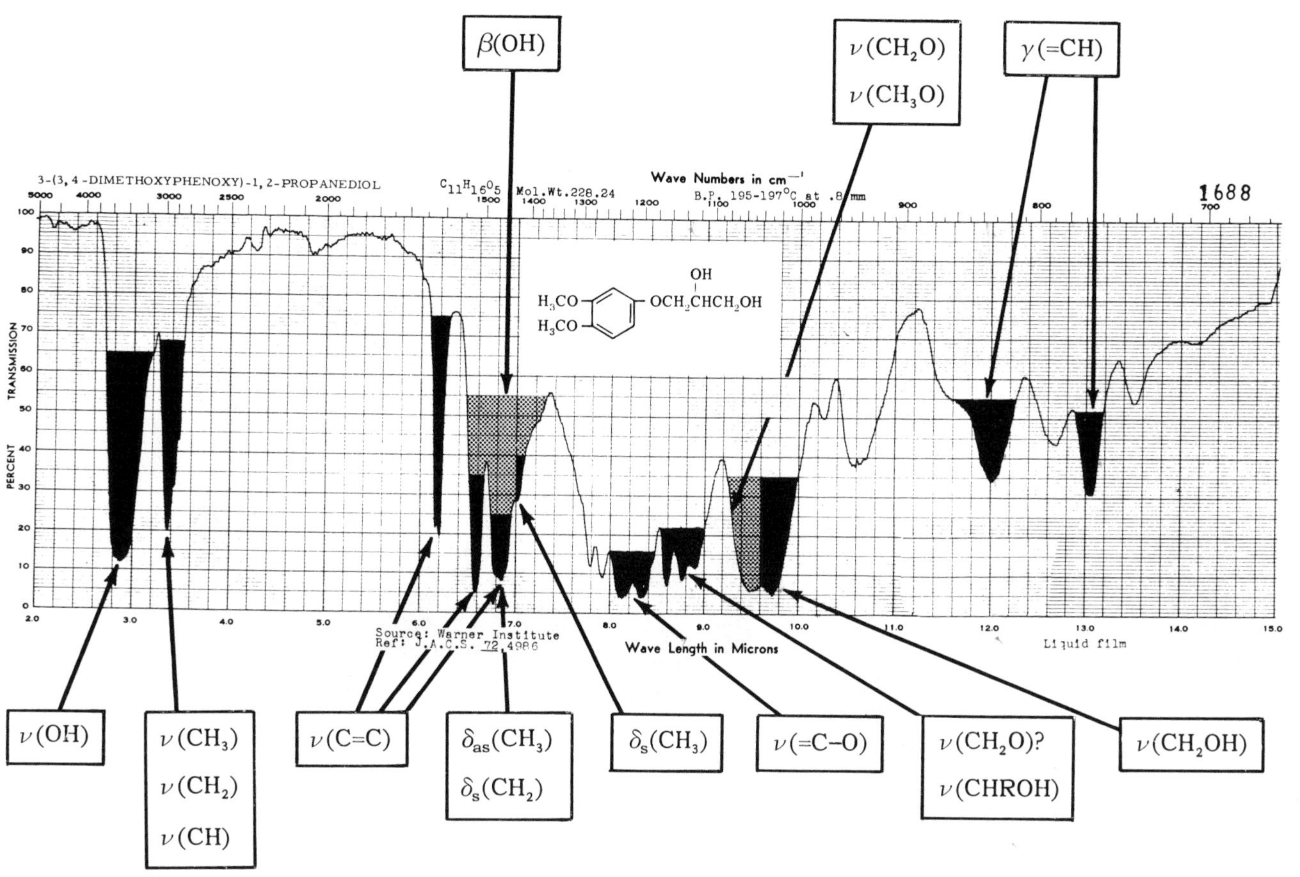

60. This compound has the groups =C–O, CH_3O, CH_2O, CH_2OH, and CHROH. The spectrum is of a liquid film, and the bands are fairly broad. It is therefore only possible to identify a broad region near 1200 cm^{-1} as the ν(=C–O), and a double band near 1040 cm^{-1} due to the $\nu(CH_3O)$ and $\nu(CH_2OH)$. The $\nu(CH_2O)$ could be near 1040 or 1110 cm^{-1} as well as the ν(CHROH).

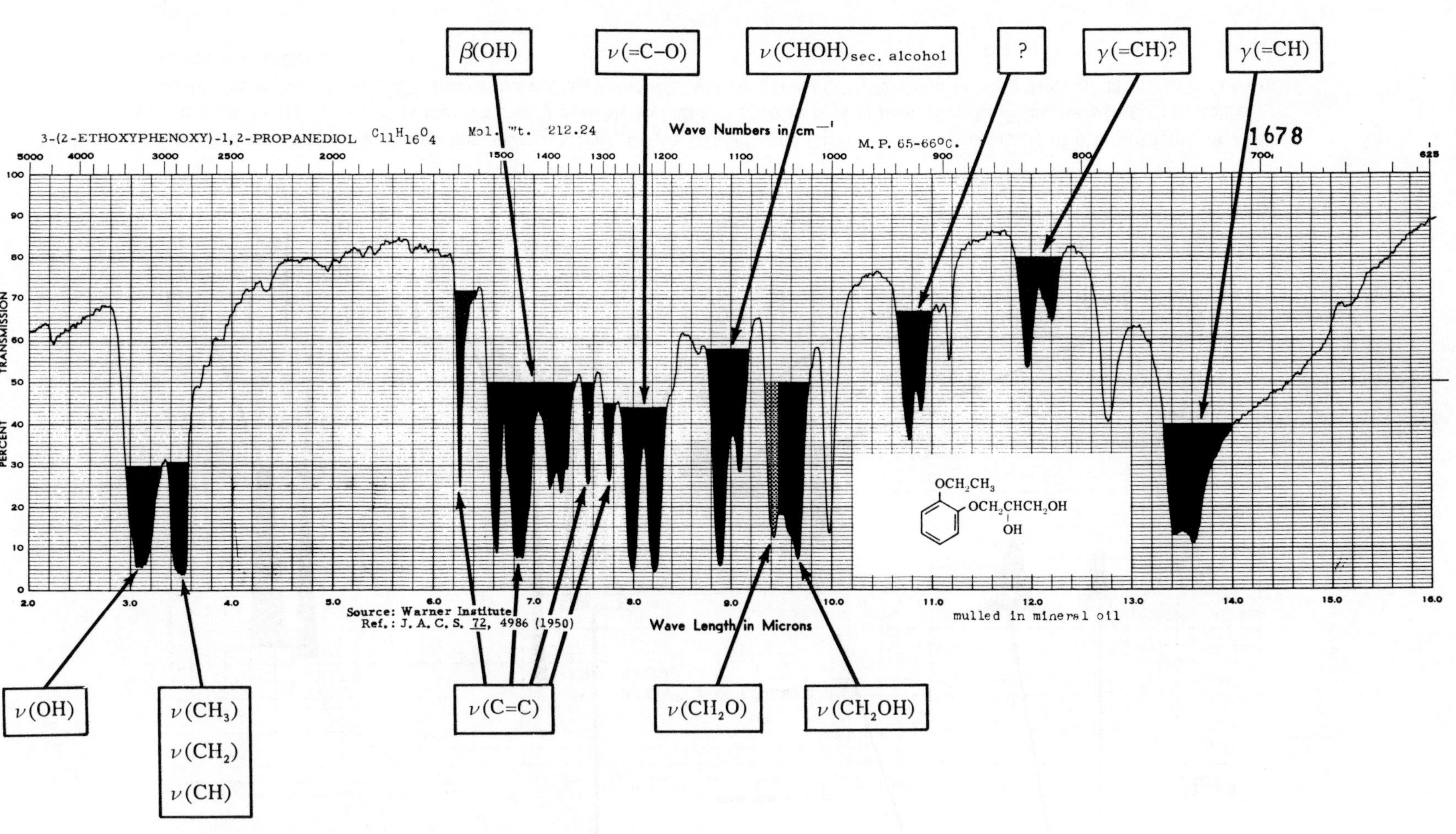

61. The groups present here are =C–O, CH_2O, CH_2OH, and CHOH. We assign these groups respectively as the 1220, 1060, 1110, and 1020 cm^{-1}. There are other bands not assignable, but in such a complex molecule this is not unexpected.

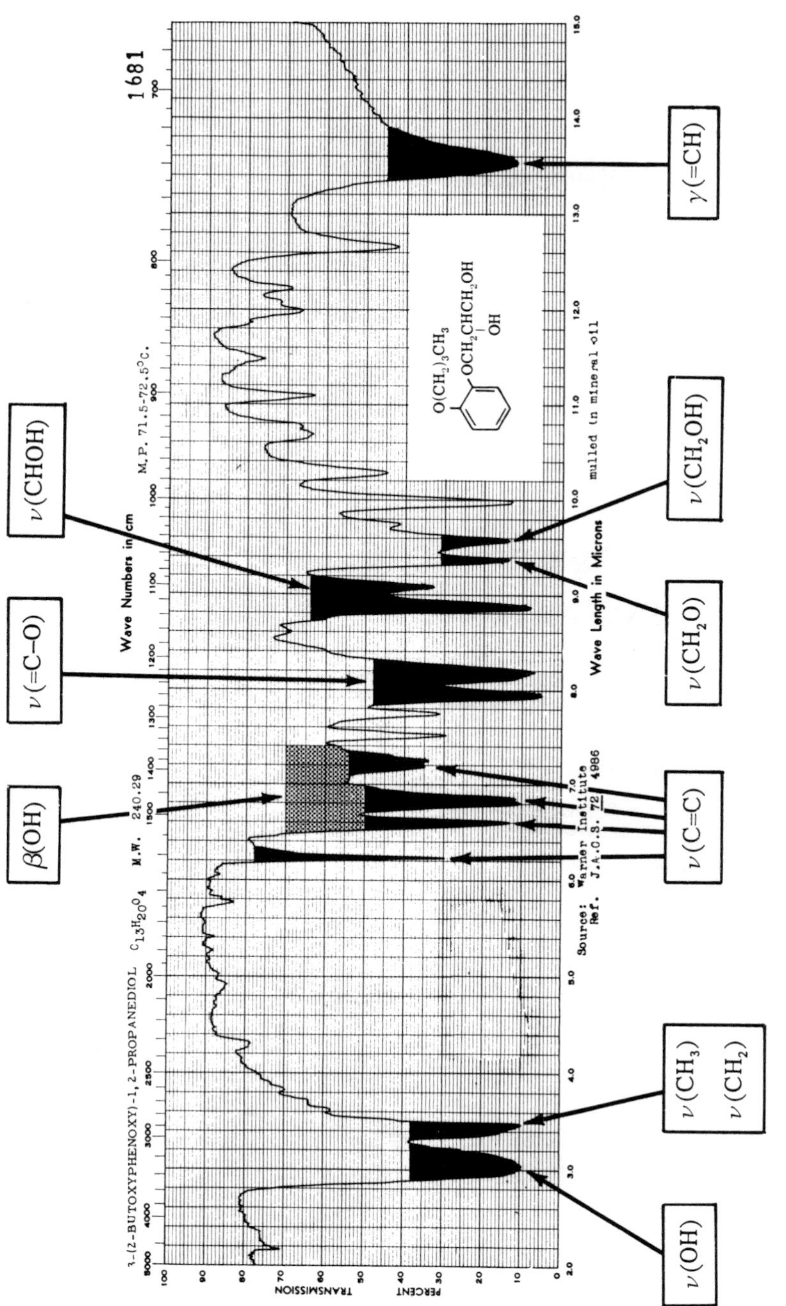

62. This compound has the groups =C–O, CH_2O, CHOH, and CH_2OH. Again we assign these respectively at 1220, 1060, 1110, and 1040 cm^{-1}.

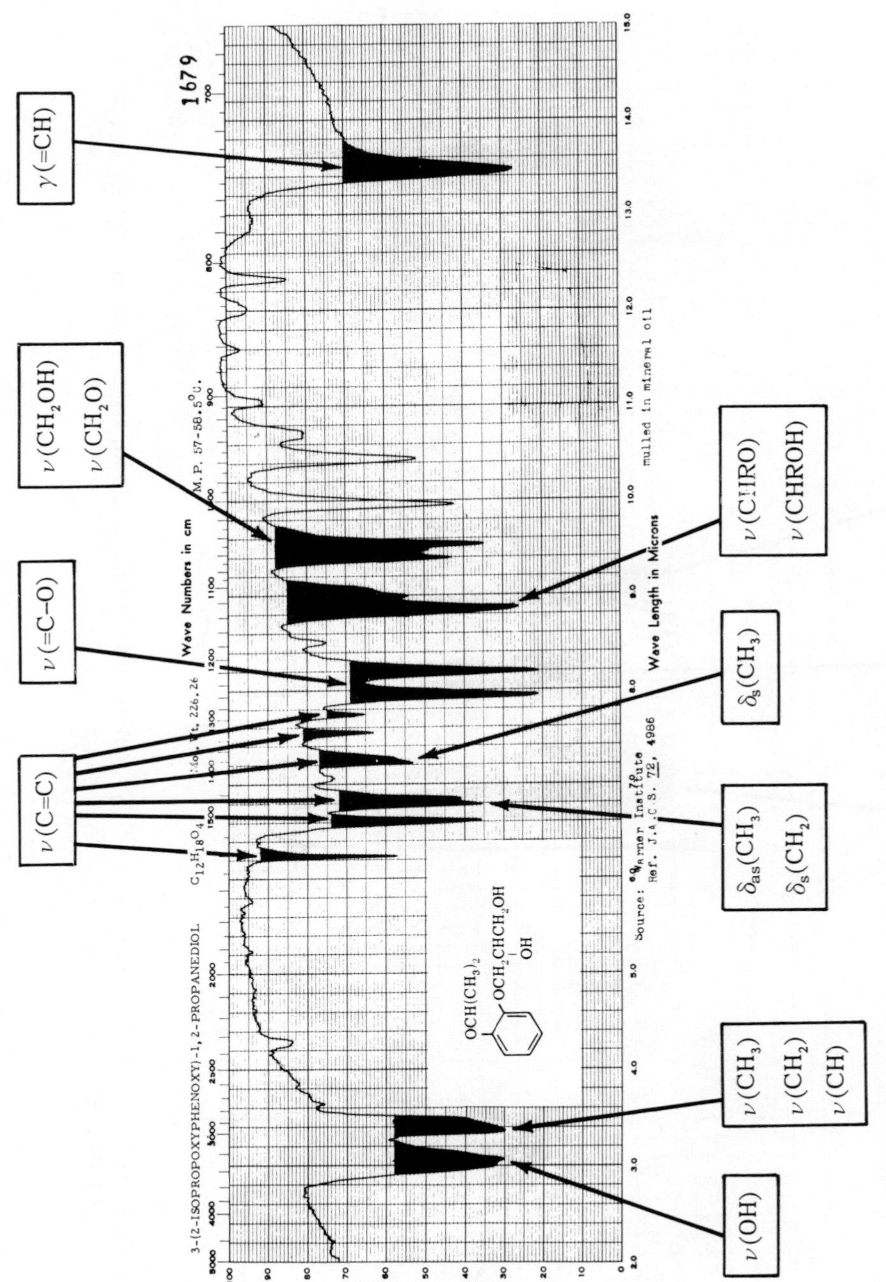

63. The groups present here are $=C-O$, CHRO, CHROH, CH_2O, CH_2OH. These are respectively assigned at 1220, 1110, 1110, 1050 and 1050 cm^{-1}. The other bands are in their expected positions.

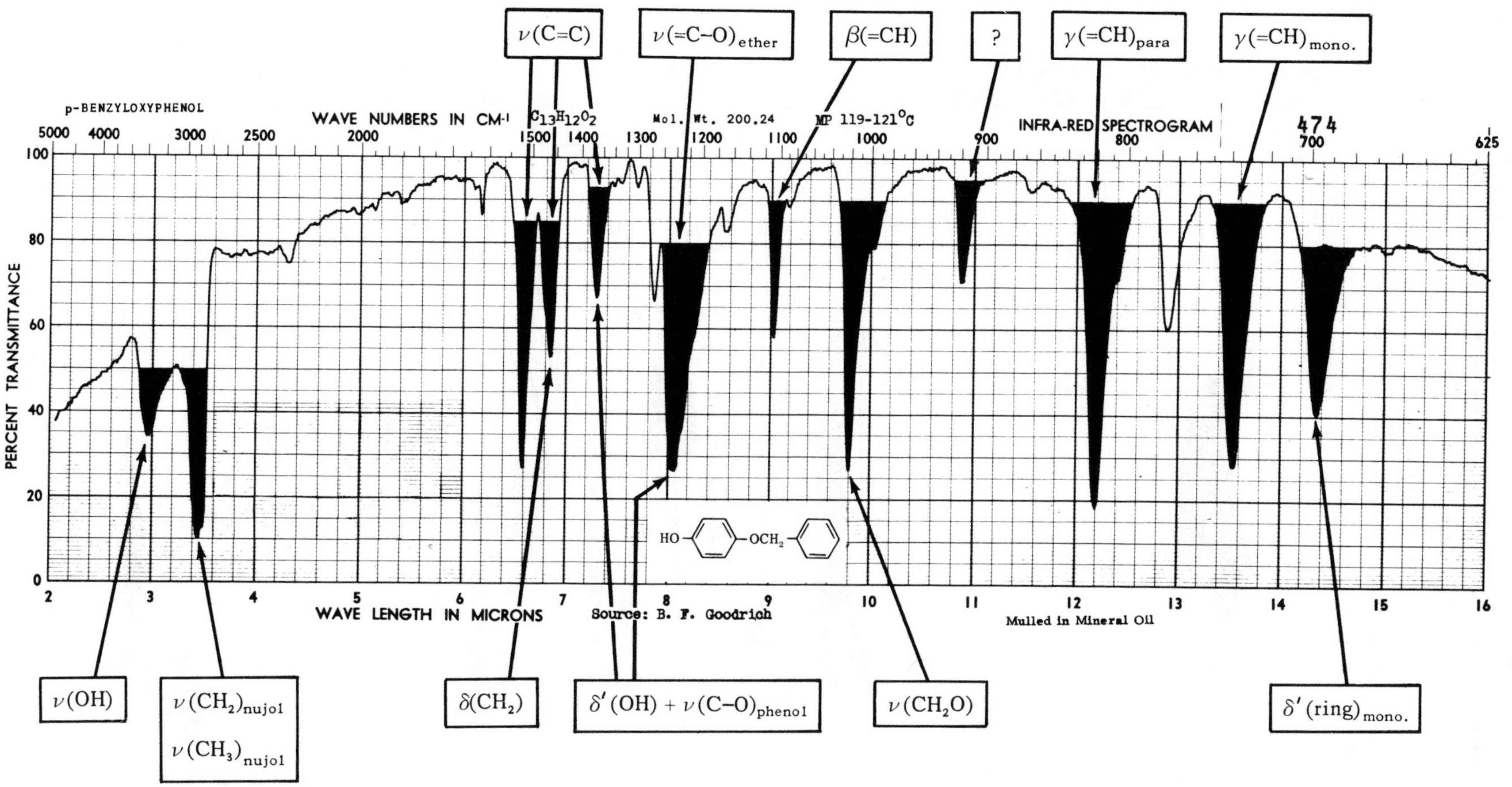

64. This compound combines a phenol with an ether, and we find the ν(=C–O) ether vibration coincides with the δ'(OH)+ ν(C–O) of the phenol. The $\nu(CH_2O)$ band is distinct, but at a low frequency of 1020 cm^{-1} unless the weaker 1100 cm^{-1} band is the correct assignment. This author prefers the lower position since the $CH_2C_6H_5$ group could remove electron density from the C–O group.

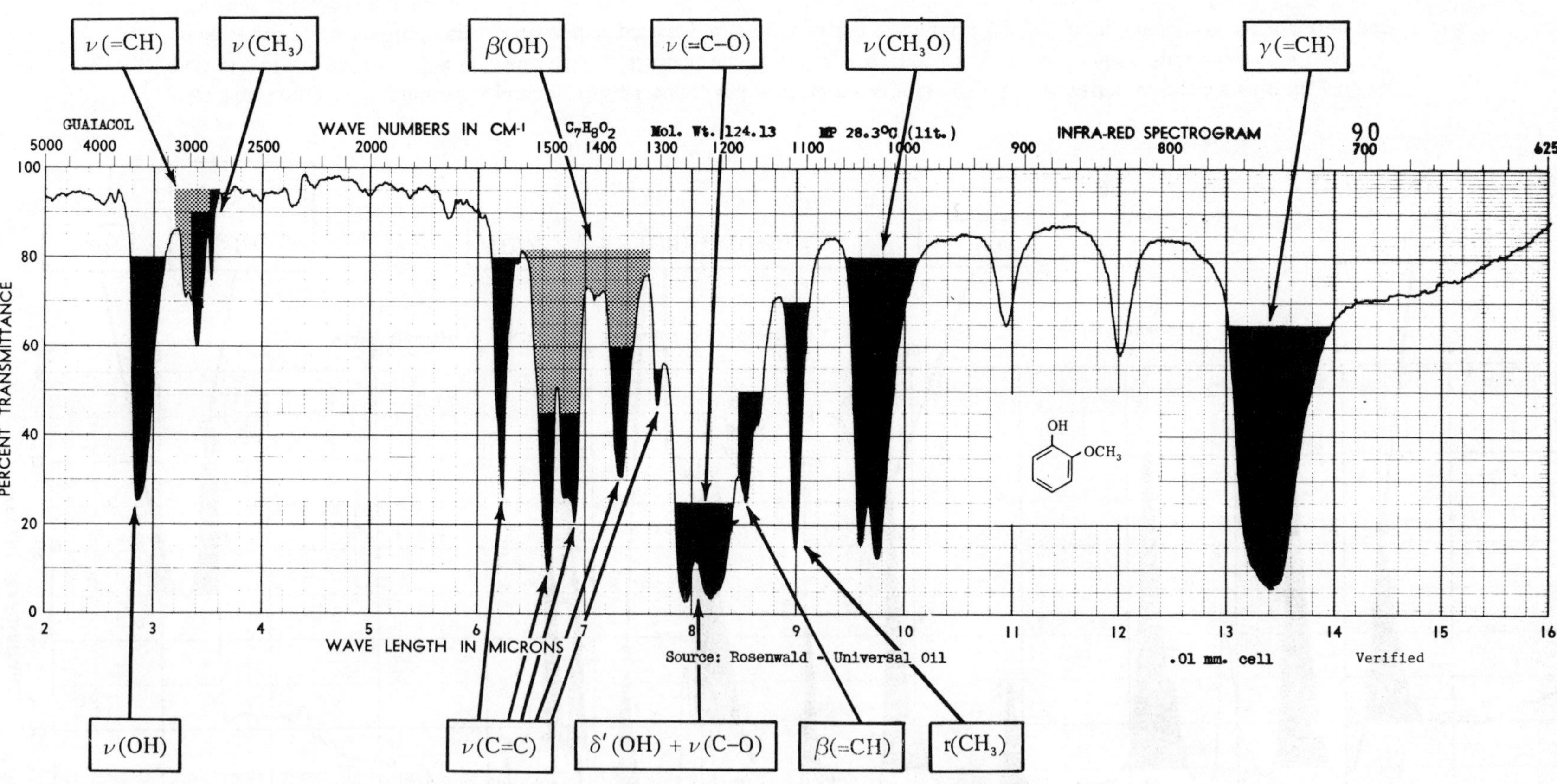

65. This compound combines the groups $=C-OH$ and $=C-OCH_3$. The phenolic group frequencies are distinct, except for the $\delta'(OH)+\nu(C-O)$ which coincides with the $=C-O$ of the anisole group. The $\nu(CH_3O)$ is at 1020 cm^{-1}, a little lower than for other molecules, probably reflecting the unusual environment of the OCH_3 group in this molecule. Reference should be made to the previous anisole spectra.

66 NONCYCLIC ETHERS

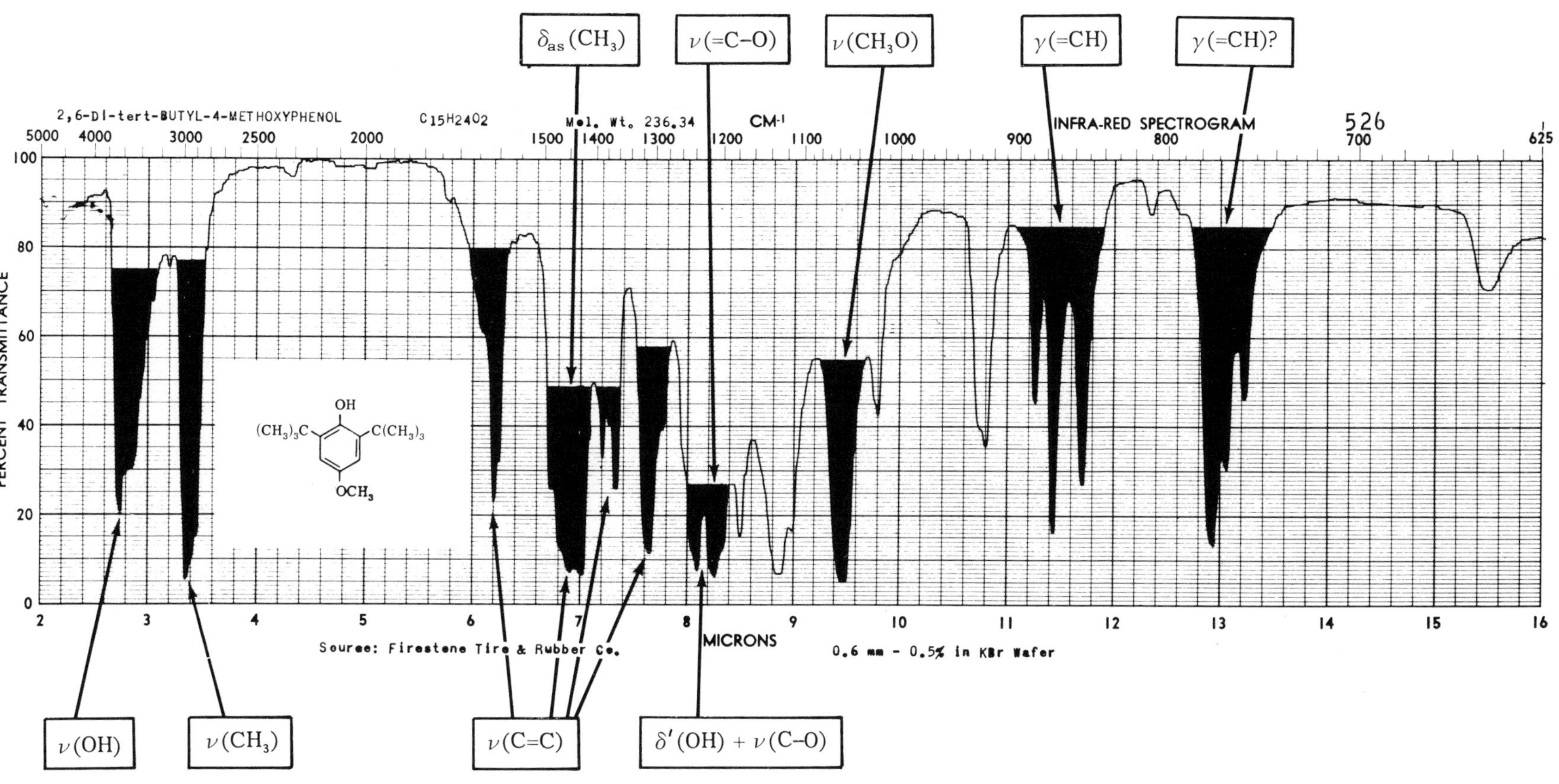

66. This compound is a hindered phenol with an OCH_3 in the para position. The 1250 cm^{-1} is assigned to the $\delta'(OH)$ + $\nu(C-O)$ of the phenol and $\nu(=C-O)$ of the ether. The two bands in the 900-700 cm^{-1} region are assigned to the $\gamma(=CH)$, although usually only the 900-860 cm^{-1} band is suggested in correction tables.

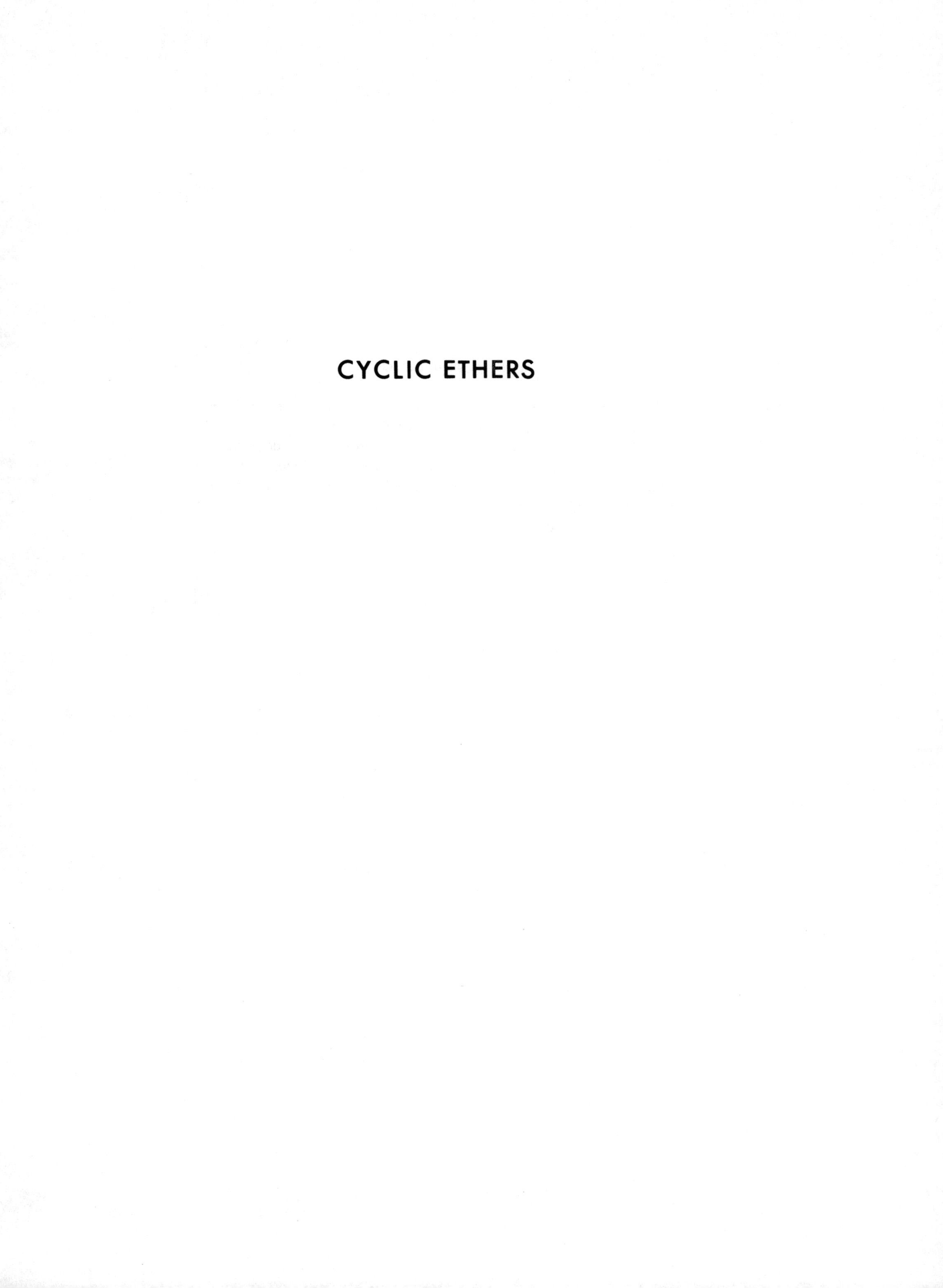

CYCLIC ETHERS

Cyclic Ethers

The cyclic ethers will be considered separately from the noncyclic, since the position of $\nu_s(C-O)$ and $\nu_{as}(C-O)$ are more variable for the noncyclic ethers. The smallest ring ether is ethylene oxide, and a large number of examples of derivatives of it will be examined. Attention should be directed to the $\nu_s(C-O)$ and $\nu_{as}(C-O)$ vibrations of the following analysis, since these vibrations are the ones which shall be utilized for group frequencies.

Vibrational Analysis

Ethylene Oxide

Source: G. Herzberg, "Infrared Spectra of Polyatomic Molecules," Van Nostrand, Princeton, 1945, p. 341.

Band, cm^{-1}		Fundamental and species	Assignment
infrared (vapor)	Raman (liquid)		
	3007	$\nu_1(a_1)$	$\nu(CH_2)$
1495	1487	$\nu_2(a_1)$	$\delta(CH_2)$
1263	1267	$\nu_3(a_1)$	$\delta'(C_2O)$ or $\nu_s(C-O)$
		$\nu_4(a_1)$	
808	806	$\nu_5(a_1)$	$\delta'(C_2O)$
	3061	$\nu_6(a_2)$	$\nu(CH_2)$
	1379	$\nu_7(a_2)$	$r(CH_2)$
	1023	$\nu_8(a_2)$	$t(CH_2)$
		$\nu_9(b_1)$	
1453	1469	$\nu_{10}(b_1)$	$\delta(CH_2)$
1151	1153	$\nu_{11}(b_1)$	$\delta'(CH_2)$
865	863	$\nu_{12}(b_1)$	$\delta'(C_2O)$ or $\nu_{as}(C-O)$
		$\nu_{13}(b_2)$	
1153	1151	$\nu_{14}(b_2)$	$r(CH_2)$
685	704	$\nu_{15}(b_2)$	$t(CH_2)$

Ethylene Oxide

Source: W. J. Potts, Spectrochim. Acta 21:511 (1965).

Band, cm^{-1}			Fundamental and species	Assignment
infared		Raman (liquid)		
CCl_4 and CS_2	vapor			
3056 S	3065 (forbidden)	3063	B_1	$\nu_{as}(CH_2)$
3000 S	3006	3005	A_1	$\nu_s(CH_2)$
1491W	1497.5	1490	A_1	$\delta(CH_2)$
1466 W	1471.5		B_1	$\delta(CH_2)$
1268 S	1270.5	1266	A_1	ν_s(ring), ring breathing or $\nu_s(C-O)$
868 VS	877.0	867	A_1	δ_s'(ring) or $\nu_{as}(C-O)$
	890		B_1	δ_{as}'(ring)
807 M	821.5	807	B_2	$r(CH_2)$
	860 (forbidden)		A_2	$r(CH_2)$
1118 W	1130	1120	A_1	$\omega(CH_2)$
	1151.0	1150	B_1	$\omega(CH_2)$
1142 M	1142.0		B_2	$t(CH_2)$
	1300 (forbidden)		A_2	$t(CH_2)$

CYCLIC ETHERS

$$\begin{array}{c} O \\ / \quad \backslash \\ H_2C - CH_2 \end{array}$$

Source: R. C. Lord, B. Nolin, J. Chem. Phys. No. 4, 24:656 (1956).

Band, cm^{-1}		Fundamental and species	Assignment
infrared (vapor)	Raman (liquid)		
3079 S(Q)	3063	ν_{13}	$\nu(CH_2)$
3058 S(P)			
3019 VSB	3005	ν_1, ν_9	$\nu(CH_2)$
2982 SSh	2961	ν_2, ν_2	
2945 S		combination	
2913 S	2916	ν_2,ν_{10}	
2276 MW (ctr)			
2266 MW (ctr)		$2\nu_4$, $2\nu_{14}$	
2253 MW (ctr)			
2045 MW		combination	
2008 M		"	
1998 MW		"	
1641 M (Q)		"	
1646 M (R)			
1635 M (Q)			
1629 M (ctr)		$2\nu_8$	
1624 M (Q)			
1616 M (P)			
1521 M			
1500 M (Q)			
1495 M (ctr)	1490	ν_2	$\delta s(CH_2)$
1487 M (R, Q)			
1470 MW (Q)			
1451 MW (P)		ν_{10}	$\delta s(CH_2)$
1289 S (R)			
1273 S (Q)			
1270 S (ctr)	1266	ν_3	ring breathing or $\nu_s(C-O)$
1266 S (Q)			
1252 S (P)			
1168 M (R)			
1153 M (Q)	1150	ν_{11}	$\omega(CH_2)$
1143 M (Q)			
1134 M (P)		ν_{14}	$t(CH_2)$
897 (R)			
892		ν_{12}	δ'(ring)
882 (Q)	867		
877 VS (ctr)		ν_5	δ'(ring) or $\nu_{as}(C-O)$
871 (Q)			
855 (P)			
839 S (R)			
821 (Q)		ν_{15}	$r(CH_2)$
800 Sh			
	807	ν_8	$r(CH_2)$
	1120	ν_4	$\omega(CH_2)$

CYCLIC ETHERS

O
/ \
$H_2C - CHCH_3$

Source: M. C. Tobin, Spectrochim. Acta 16:1108 (1960).

Infrared band (cm^{-1})		Raman band (cm^{-1})	Assignments
liquid	vapor		
3080 M		3065	$\nu(CH_2)$
3000 S		3006	$\nu(CH)$
3950 M	2960	2975	$\nu(CH_3)$
2900 Sh		2929	$\nu(CH_3)$
		2864	
1520 M			
1500 M	1450-1490		$\delta(CH_2)$
1450 S		1456	$\delta_{as}(CH_3)$
1408 S	1396 (P), 1407 (P), 1422 (R)	1406	$\delta_s(CH_3)$
1368 M		1368	$t(CH_2)$
1262 M	1258 (P), 1262 (Q), 1268 (R)	1263	δ'(ring), ν_s(ring), or $\nu_s(C-O)$
1162 W		1166	$\omega(CH_2)$
1142 M }	1120	1135	$\omega(CH)$
1132 M }			$r(CH_2)$
1103 M		1102	$\nu(ring-CH_3)$
1022 VS	1015, 1026	1023	$\omega(CH_3)$
948 VS	950, 964	950	$r(CH_3)$
895 M	888 (P), 895 (Q), 905 (R)	896	$r(CH_3)$, δ'(ring), or $\nu_{as}(C-O)$
825 VS	828 (P), 838 (Q), 848 (R)	828	δ'(ring) or $\nu_{as}(C-O)$
745 S	757, 770	745	δ'(ring) or $r(CH_2)$
		600	
		508	
	400 (P), 415 (Q), 425 (R)	416	$\delta(ring-CH_3)$
	355 (P), 367 (Q), 379 (R)	371	$\delta(ring-CH_3$
		277	$t(CH_3)$

Comparison of Vibrational Analyses of Ethylene Oxide and Propylene Oxide*

Source: M. C. Tobin, Spectrochim. Acta 16:1108 (1960).

$H_2C(O)CH_2$ (ethylene oxide)	$H_2C(O)CHCH_3$ (propylene oxide)	Assignment
3063, 3079	3065	$\nu(CH_2)$
	3006	$\nu(CH_3)$
	2975	$\nu(CH_3)$
	2929	$\nu(CH_3)$
	2846	$\nu(CH_3)$
1490	1500	$\delta(CH_2)$
	1456	$\delta(CH_3)$
	1406	$\delta(CH_3)$
1345	1368	$t(CH_2)$
1266	1263	δ'(ring) or $\nu_s(C-O)$
1153	1166	$\omega(CH_2)$
1143	1142	$\omega(CH)$
1120	1132	$r(CH)$
	1102	$\nu(ring-CH_3)$
	1023	$\omega(CH_3)$
	950	$r(CH_3)$
892	896	$r(CH_2)$ or δ'(ring)
877	828	δ'(ring) or $\nu_{as}(C-O)$
807, 821	745	δ'(ring) or $r(CH_2)$
	416	$\delta(ring-CH_3)$
	371	$\delta(ring-CH_3)$
	227	$t(CH_3)$

*In comparing the assignments for ethylene oxide and propylene oxide, it is noted very little shifting of bands occurs except of course for motions of the CH_3 group.

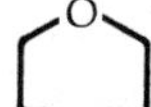

Source: A. Palm, E. R. Bissell, Spectrochim. Acta 16:459 (1960).

Infrared band, cm^{-1}		Raman band, cm^{-1}	Assignment
liquid	solid*		
2977 VS	2947 VS	2975	$\nu_{as}(CH_2)$
	2924 VS	2938	$\nu_{as}(CH_2)$
2861 VS	2849 VS	2865	$\nu_s(CH_2)$
2680 M	2694 VS	2717	combinations
1972 M	1935 M		"
	1889 W		"
	1723 W		"
1461 S	1487 M	1486	$\delta(CH_2)$
	1466 M	1452	"
	1441 S		"
	1421 WSh		
1364 M	1368 M		$\omega(CH_2)$
1333 W	1339 W		
	1323 M		$\omega(CH_2)$
1289 M	1307 M		$\omega(CH_2)$
1234 M	1241 S	1234	
1177 S	1179 VS	1174	ν_{as}(ring)
	1150 W		
	1108 WSh	1104	$t(CH_2)$
1067 VS	1058 VS	1071	ν_{as}(ring) or $\nu_{as}(C-O)$
1030 MSh	1043 VS	1028	$r(CH_2)$
	980 W		
	954 S	964	$r(CH_2)$
908 VS	921 S	913	ν_s(ring) or $\nu_s(C-O)$
	908 S		ν_s(ring) or $\nu_s(C-O)$
	891 S		
	871 S		
	838 VS		
	725 W		
654 S	662	651	$r(CH_2)$
		596	δ_β(ring)
		276	δ_γ(ring)
		215	δ_γ(ring)

*at −180°C.

CYCLIC ETHERS

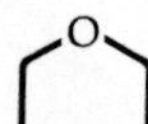

Source: A. R. Katritzky, Physical Methods in Heterocyclic Chemistry Vol. 2, Academic Press, 1963.

Infrared band, cm^{-1}	Species	Assignment
2958		$\nu(CH_2)$
2865		$\nu(CH_2)$
1460		$\delta(CH_2)$
1338 ?	A_1	$\omega(CH_2)$
1238	A_1	$\omega(CH_2)$
1367 ?	B_1	$\omega(CH_2)$
1290 ?	B_1	$\omega(CH_2)$
1238	A_2	$t(CH_2)$
1104	A_2	$t(CH_2)$
964	A_2	$r(CH_2)$
1174	A_1	ν(ring)
1028	A_1	ν(ring)
1071	B_1	ν(ring) or $\nu_{as}(C-O)$
913	A_1	ring breathing or $\nu_s(C-O)$
596	B_1	β(ring)
215	B_2	ring
276	A_2	ring

Source: A. R. Katritzky, Physical Methods in Heterocyclic Chemistry Vol. 2, Academic Press, 1963.

Band, cm^{-1}	Species	Assignment
3124	A_1	$\nu(CH)$
3163	B_1	$\nu(CH)$
1586	B_1	$\nu(C=C)$
1490	A_1	$\nu(C=C)$
1460	B_1	$\nu(C=C)$
1384	A_1	$\nu(C=C)$
1268	B_1	$\beta(=CH)$*
1140	A_1	$\beta(=CH)$
1067	A_1	$\beta(=CH)$
1181	B_1	$\beta(=CH)$
995	A_1	ring breathing
838	B_2	$\gamma(=CH)$
1030 ?	A_2	$\gamma(=CH)$
744	B_2	$\gamma(=CH)$
660	A_2	$\gamma(=CH)$
874	B_1	β(ring)
720	A_1	β(ring)
601	B_1	γ(ring)
550	A_2	γ(ring)

*A band here could be considered as $\nu_{as}(C-O)$.

Source: L. W. Pickett, J. Chem. Phys. 10:660 (1942).

Band, cm^{-1}			Species	Assignment
infrared		Raman		
vapor	liquid			
3164 S		3154 (P)		
2963 VW		3121 (P)		
2915 VW		3089 (P)		
2673 W				
2604 MW				
2440 MW				
2360 MW				
2246 W				
2188 VW				
2105 W				
2040 MW				
2012 VW				
1906 W				
1712 MW				
1580 S			B_1	$\nu(C=C)$
1490 VS	1495 VS	1483 (P)	A_1	$\nu(C=C)$
1387 M	1375 M	1380 (P)	A_1	$\nu(C=C)$
1264 W	1249 W	1270 (P)	A_1	$\delta_s(CH)$
		1200 (P)		
1189 S	1176 M	1171(DP)	A_1	ring or $\nu_{as}(C-O)$
		1137 (P)		
1073 S	1052 W	1061 (P)	A_1	$\delta_s(CH)$
		3014 (DP)		
999 VS	990 VS	986 (P)	B_1	$\delta_{as}(CH)$?
872 S	864 S	871 (DP)	B_2	ring
763 S		839 (DP)	B_2	$\delta_{as}(CH)$
725 S	740 VS	724 (P)	A_1	ring
624 S	648 W		B_1	ring
584 S	601 VS	601 (DP)		

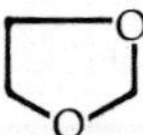

Source: A. R. Katritzky, Physical Methods in Heterocyclic Chemistry Vol. 2, Academic Press, 1963.

Infrared bands, cm^{-1}	Species	Assignment*
2889 S	A_1	$\nu(CH_2)_{4,5}$
2857 S	A_1	$\nu(CH_2)_2$
2998 M	B_1	$\nu(CH_2)_2$
2964 S	B_1	$\nu(CH_2)_{4,5}$
2889 S	B_2	$\nu(CH_2)_{4,5}$
1509 S	A_1	$\delta(CH_2)_2$
1480 S	A_1	$\delta(CH_2)_{4,5}$
1480 S	B_2	$\delta(CH_2)_{2,4}$
1361 S	A_1	$\omega(CH_2)_{4,5}$
1397 S	B_2	$\omega(CH_2)_2$
1327 W	B_2	$\omega(CH_2)_{4,5}$
1251 W	A_2	$t(CH_2)_2$
1208 W	A_2	$t(CH_2)_{4,5}$
1286 W	B_1	$t(CH_2)_{4,5}$
723 M	B_1	$r(CH_2)_2$
921 VS	B_1	$r(CH_2)_{4,5}$
1087 VS	A_1	ν(ring) or $\nu_{as}(C-O)$
1030 VS	A_1	ν(ring) or $\nu_{as}(C-O)$
1158 VS	B_2	ν(ring) or $\nu_{as}(C-O)$
961 S	B_2	ν(ring) or $\nu_s(C-O)$
939 VS	A_1	ring breathing or $\nu_s(C-O)$
680 M	B_2	β(ring)

*2, 4, 5 refer to position of CH_2 in ring.

$$O\begin{matrix} CH_2-O \\ CH_2-O \end{matrix}CH_2$$

Source: W. R. Ward, Spectrochim. Acta 21:1311 (1965).

Band, cm^{-1}		Fundamental and species	Assignment
infrared (CCl_4 and CS_2)	Raman (liquid)		
3018 M	3020 VS		$\nu(CH_2)$
2950 W	2950 VVW		overtone
2869 M	2869 S	a_1	$\nu(CH_2)$
2793 M	2794 S	a_1	$\nu(CH_2)$
2765 W	2742 M		$\nu(CH_2)$
2090 M			combination
1995 M			combination
1860 M			overtone
1497 M	1493 VW	a_1	$\delta(CH_2)$
1477 M	1474 S		$\delta(CH_2)$
1453 W			combination
1412 S	1411 M		$\omega(CH_2)$
1309 S	1308 S		$t(CH_2)$
1274 W			combination
1229 S			combination
1168 S	1163 WB		δ'(ring) or $\nu_{as}(C-O)$
1068 VS	1070 WB		δ'(ring) or $\nu_{as}(C-O)$
1050 SSh	1051 WB		$r(CH_2) + \delta'$(ring)
970 VS	962 VS	a_1	ring breathing or $\nu_s(C-O)$
935 VS	931 MB	a_1	δ'(ring)
749 W	748 SSh	a_1	$r(CH_2)$
612 W	612 VVW		overtone
524 S	523 SSp	a_1	δ'(ring)
476 SB	472 W		δ'(ring)
	307 W		δ'(ring)

```
H3CHC – O
     /      \
    O        CHCH3
     \      /
H3CHC – O
```

Source: W. R. Ward, Spectrochim. Acta 21:1311 (1965).

Infrared band, cm^{-1} (CCl_4 and CS_2)	Fundamental and species	Assignment
2999 VS		$\nu_{as}(CH_3)$
2941 M	a_1	$\nu_{as}(CH_3)$
2893 W		overtone
2905 MW		?
2848 SSh		combination
2842 VS	a_1	$\nu_s(CH_3)$
2836 SSh		$\nu_s(CH_3)$
2815 W		combination
2781 W	a_1	$\nu(CH)$
2755 W		combination
2732 W		combination
1454 S	a_1	$\delta_{as}(CH_3)$
1425 VW		combination
1396 S	a_1	$\gamma(-CH)$
1371 S	a_1	$\delta_s(CH_3)$
1344 S		$\beta(-CH)$
1329 Sh		combination
1184 VS		$r_\beta(CH_3)$
1174 VS		ring
1121 MWSh	a_1	$r_\gamma(CH_3)$
1105 VS		ring
951 VS	a_1	ring
946 MSSh		overtone
857 MS		$\nu(CH_3-ring)$
838 M	a_1	$\nu(CH_3-ring)$
758 M		$\delta_\beta(CH_3 - ring)$
748 W	a_1	ring
574 W		$\gamma(CH_3 - ring)$
527 W	a_1	ring
474 W		ring

$H_7C_3HC - O$
$/ \quad \backslash$
$O \qquad CHC_3H_7$
$\backslash \quad /$
$H_7C_3HC - O$

Source: W. R. Ward, Spectrochim. Acta 21:1311 (1965).

Band, cm^{-1}		Fundamental and species	Assignment
Infrared (CCl_4)	Raman		
2990 VS	2977 S		
2950 VS	2948 VS		
2880 S	2885 VS		
2830 S	2832 MW		
2765 M			
1467 S			
1460 Sh	1461 VS		
1432 Sh	1443 VS		
1393 MS	1391 W		γ(CH)
1357 VS	1359 M		β(CH)
1317 MW			
1306 M	1307 M		
1273 M	1273 VB		
1261 M			
1172 VS	1173 M	ν_7, ν_{11}	ν_{as}(C−O)
1148 VS			
1127 S			
1109 Sh			
1101 VS	1080 M		
1087 Sh			
1079 Sh			
1042 S			
1025 S			
1011 S			
1000 Sh			
970 S			ν_s(C−O)
964 Sh			
952 MS	953 MW		
919 MS	922 M		
752 Sh			
747 W		ν_3	
743 Sh			
527 VW	525 MS	ν_2	
506 VW	502 W		
472 VW	470 MW	ν_6, ν_{10}	ring
446 VW	445 M		
	392 W		
	370 W		
	324 MS	ν_8, ν_{12}	
	242 MS		

CYCLIC ETHERS

Source: A. R. Katritzky, Physical Methods of Heterocyclic Chemistry Vol. 2, Academic Press, 1963.

These compounds have many strong bands in the 1150-1000 cm^{-1} region and overtones of medium intensity near 2000 cm^{-1}. A band near 800 cm^{-1} is assigned as a ring breathing vibration.

Source: J. J. Mannion, T. S. Wang, J. Mol. Spectr. 990 (1960).

The cyclic ether

$$\begin{array}{ccc} (CH_2)_4-O-(CH_2)_4 \\ \begin{array}{ccc} | & \quad\quad & | \\ C & & C \\ ||| & & ||| \\ C & & C \\ | & & | \end{array} \\ (CH_2)_4-O-(CH_2)_4 \end{array}$$

is reported. A very strong band appears at 1110 cm^{-1}, similar to the straight-chain ethers.

Source: A. R. Katritzky, Physical Methods in Heterocyclic Chemistry Vol. 2, Academic Press, 1963.

The derivatives of this compound have bands as follows. The 2, 3 derivative has bands at 1585, 1481, 1474 and 1450 cm^{-1}; the 2, 5 derivative at 1580, 1481 and 1455 cm^{-1}.

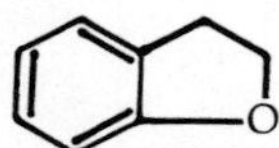

Band, cm^{-1}	Assignment
3100-3000	$\nu(=CH)$
2950-2850 S	$\nu(CH_2)$
2000-1650	combination
1640-1602 W, 1500-1480 S	$\nu(C=C)$
1485-1445	$\delta(CH_2)$
1260-1210 S	$\nu(=C-O)$
1000-985 S, 950-943 M	aromatic ring
900-650 S	$\gamma(=CH)$

Infrared Spectra of Epoxy Compounds

Source: O. D. Shreve, M. R. Heether, H. B. Knight, D. Swern, Anal. Chem. 23:277 (1951).

The infrared absorption spectra of some epoxy compounds are reported. It is pointed out that, based on the spectra of eight oxirane compounds, one group of workers conclude that only the 1250 cm^{-1} band can be identified with reasonable certainty as characteristic for the oxirane run. Some of these spectra are included in this volume.

Correlation Tables

In examining the previous vibrational analysis, it can be noted that the position of the $\nu_{as}(C-O)$ and $\nu_s(C-O)$ varies with ring size. The following positions can be noted.

Ring size	$\nu_{as}(C-O)$, cm^{-1}*	$\nu_s(C-O)$, cm^{-1}*
6-member	1098	813
5-member	1071	913
4-member	983	1028
3-member	839	1270

Usually one of these bands is strong and can be utilized as a group frequency. For the ethylene oxide ring, a 1280-1230 cm^{-1} ring-breathing vibration is quite strong and distinct, and is a useful group frequency. For ethylene oxide derivatives bands at 950-815 and 880-750 cm^{-1} are also ring vibrations, and are used as group frequencies. For monosubstituted rings, the 880-805 cm^{-1} band is quite distinct, while for 1,1 and 1,2 derivatives the band appears in the 850-775 cm^{-1} region. The trisubstituted derivatives have a strong band in the 770-750 cm^{-1} range. A number of other correlations are suggested in the following correlation table.

*In the spectra which follow we note these bands as ν_{as}(ring) and ν_s(ring) to agree with the vibrational analyses listed for these compounds. Some authors point out that ν_s(ring) can be referred to as a ring-breathing vibration, where the C—C and C—O parts of the ring move in and out in phase as the ring enlarges and collapses.

Epoxy Compounds

Vibration	Symbol	Band, cm^{-1}	Intensity
CH stretch of epoxy ring	ν(CH)	3050-3000	M-S
Torsion of CH_2	$t(CH_2)$	1370-1320	MSp
Symmetric stretching of rings	ν_s(ring)	1280-1230	Variable
Asymmetric stretching of ring	ν_{as}(ring)	950-815	Variable
ring deformation	δ'(ring)		Variable
A. monosubstituted		880-805	
B. 1, 1 derivatives		850-775	
C. 1, 2 derivatives		850-775	
D. trisubstituted		770-750	

CYCLIC ETHERS

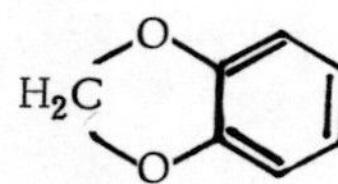

Methylene Dioxy Compounds

Vibration	Symbol	Band, cm^{-1}	Intensity
CH_2 symmetric stretch	$\nu_s(CH_2)$	2780	S
C–O stretch*	ν(C–O)	925	M-S
No assignment		720	M (can be a shoulder band)
Steroidal epoxy bands		900-800 or 1035-1000	Variable

*Confusion will arise with vibration assignments of epoxy rings with a nearby band assigned as ν_{as}(ring). Both notations are acceptable; however, ν_{as}(ring) more clearly describes the motion.

Spectra of Cyclic Ethers

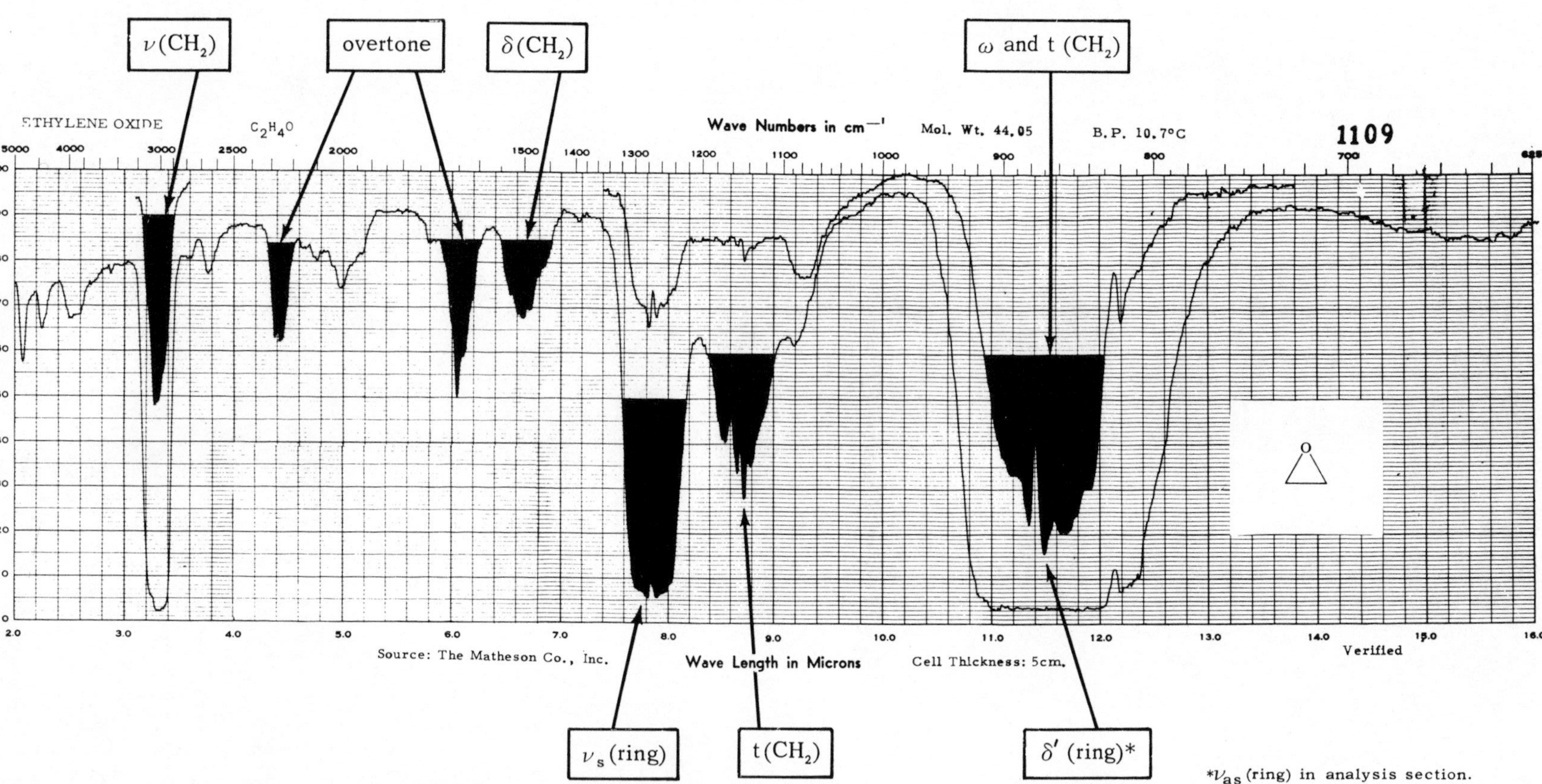

*ν_{as} (ring) in analysis section.

1. The spectrum of ethylene oxide is presented as the first member of the epoxy series. The assignments are based on the vibrational analyses presented in the Correlation section. In our correlation table we have used the symbols ν_{as}(ring) and ν_s(ring). To be consistent in all the following spectra we have used this notation although we could possibly use ν(C−O) for the band near 900 cm^{-1}. This notation would be more consistent with that used for noncyclic ethers. Note that three bands are useful in recognizing these derivatives. These are ν_s(ring) near 1250 cm^{-1}, ν_{as}(ring) near 880 cm^{-1}, and δ'(ring) near 800 cm^{-1}.

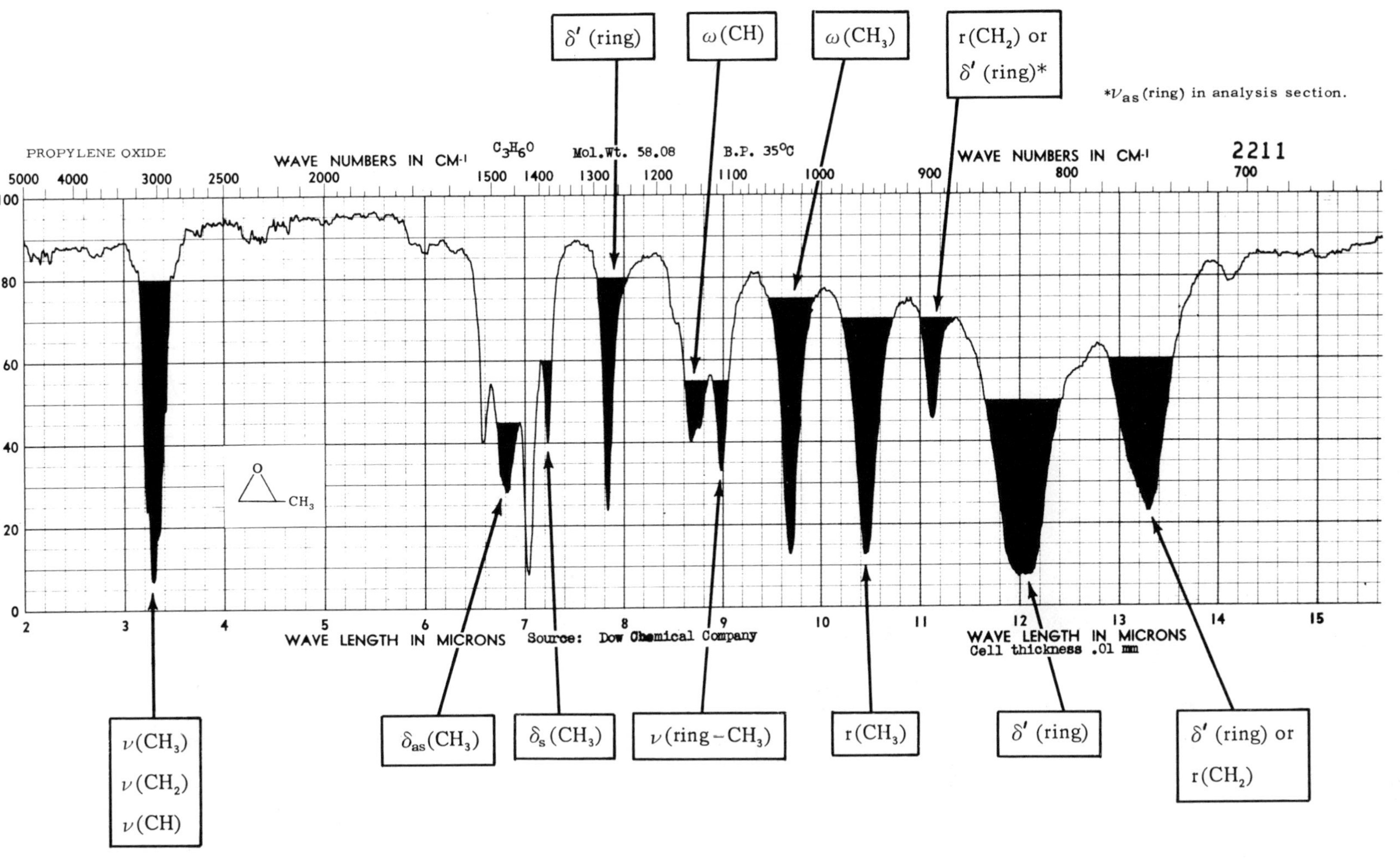

2. Propylene oxide liquid spectrum is presented here. The assignments are based on the vibrational analysis presented previously. Again the 1250, 880, and 800 cm^{-1} bands are found, and assigned as ν_s(ring), ν_{as}(ring), and δ'(ring) respectively.

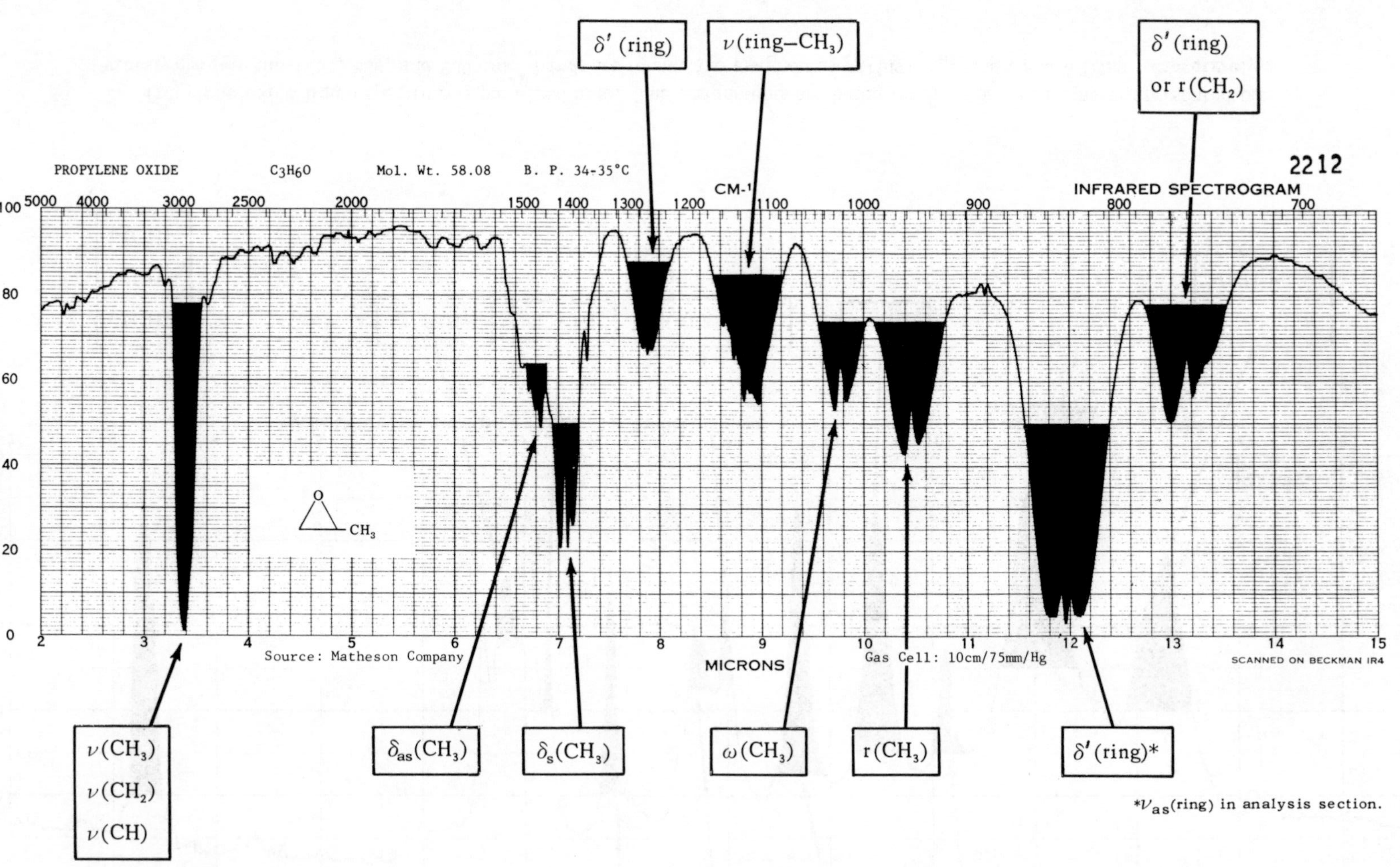

*ν_{as}(ring) in analysis section.

3. Propylene oxide gas spectrum can be compared to the liquid state spectrum just presented. The gas state spectrum has broader bands than the liquid, except in the 1550-1400 cm^{-1} region, where apparently one of the bands is not present and the region is sharper. The broadness of the bands are due to the presence of P, Q, and R branches in the bands. For example, the band near 840 cm^{-1} has distinct P, Q, and R branches. Note the absence of a band at 1520 cm^{-1} in this spectrum, compared to the first. This band may have been due to an impurity.

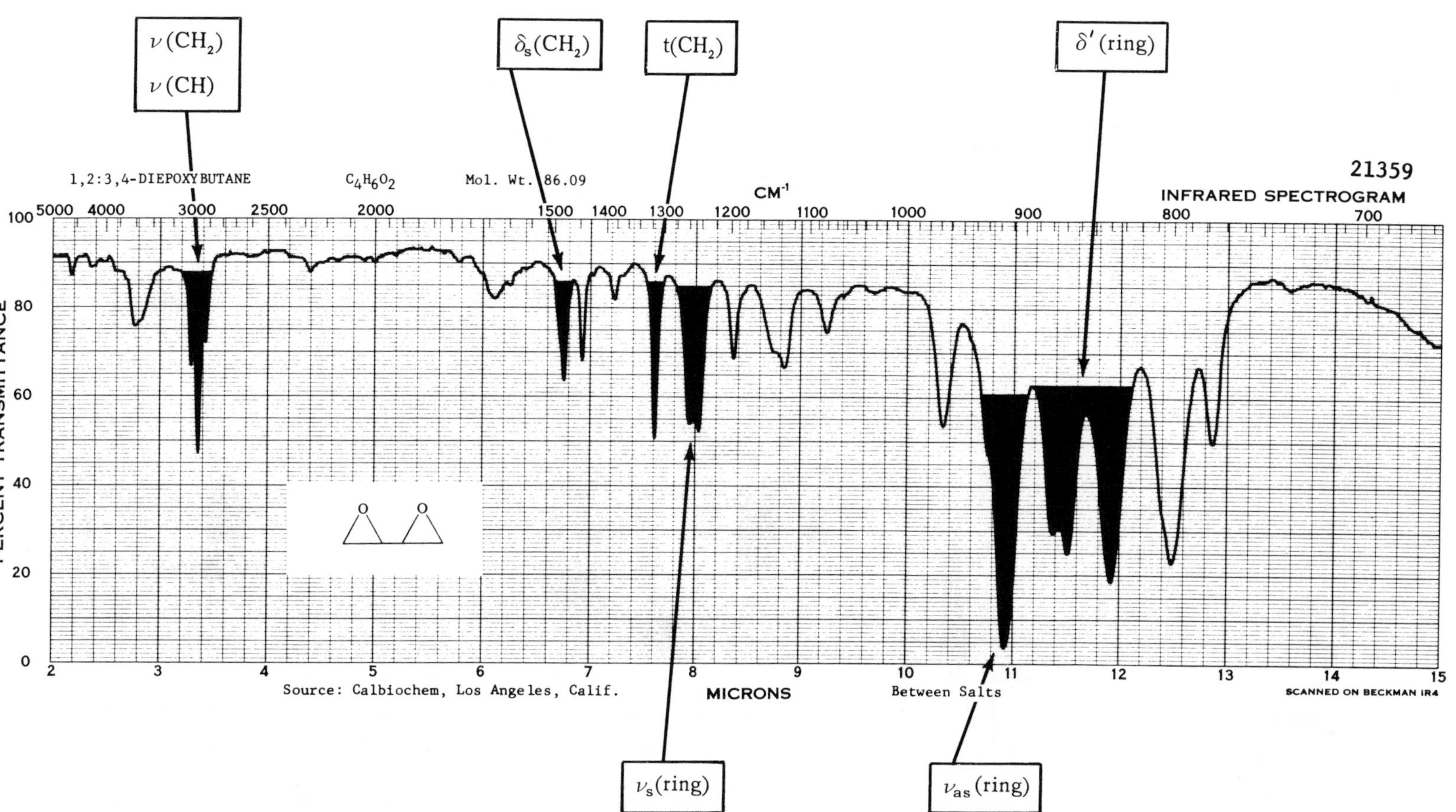

4. Combining two epoxy rings gives the compound 1, 2: 3, 4-diepoxybutane. The spectrum is presented here. The strongest band is near 910 cm^{-1}, and is assigned as ν_s(ring). The δ'(ring) assignment can be made in the 900-800 cm^{-1} region, but three bands occur here. We make an arbitrary choice of two of these bands.

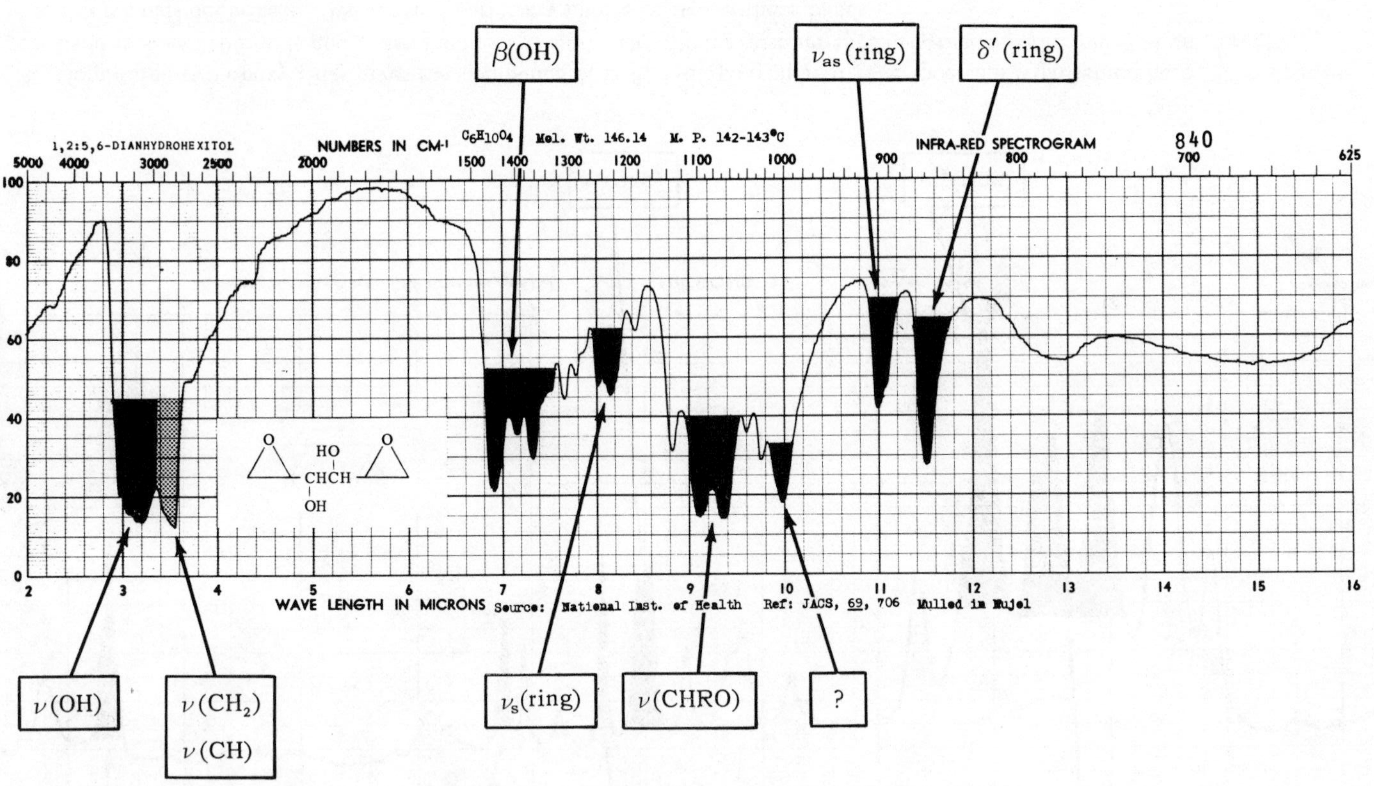

5. This compound combines an epoxy ring with an alcoholic group. The alcoholic group is secondary, so the ν(CHRO) should be near 1100 cm^{-1}. The band near 1080 cm^{-1} is therefore assigned as this vibration. The β(OH) of the alcohol results in the broadness near 1400 cm^{-1}. The epoxy grouping is similar to the previous spectrum. The ν_{as}(ring) band is weaker here and shifted slightly, if we have correctly assigned it at the position near 900 cm^{-1}. A strong band near 1000 cm^{-1} is not easily assigned, unless some primary alcohol is present.

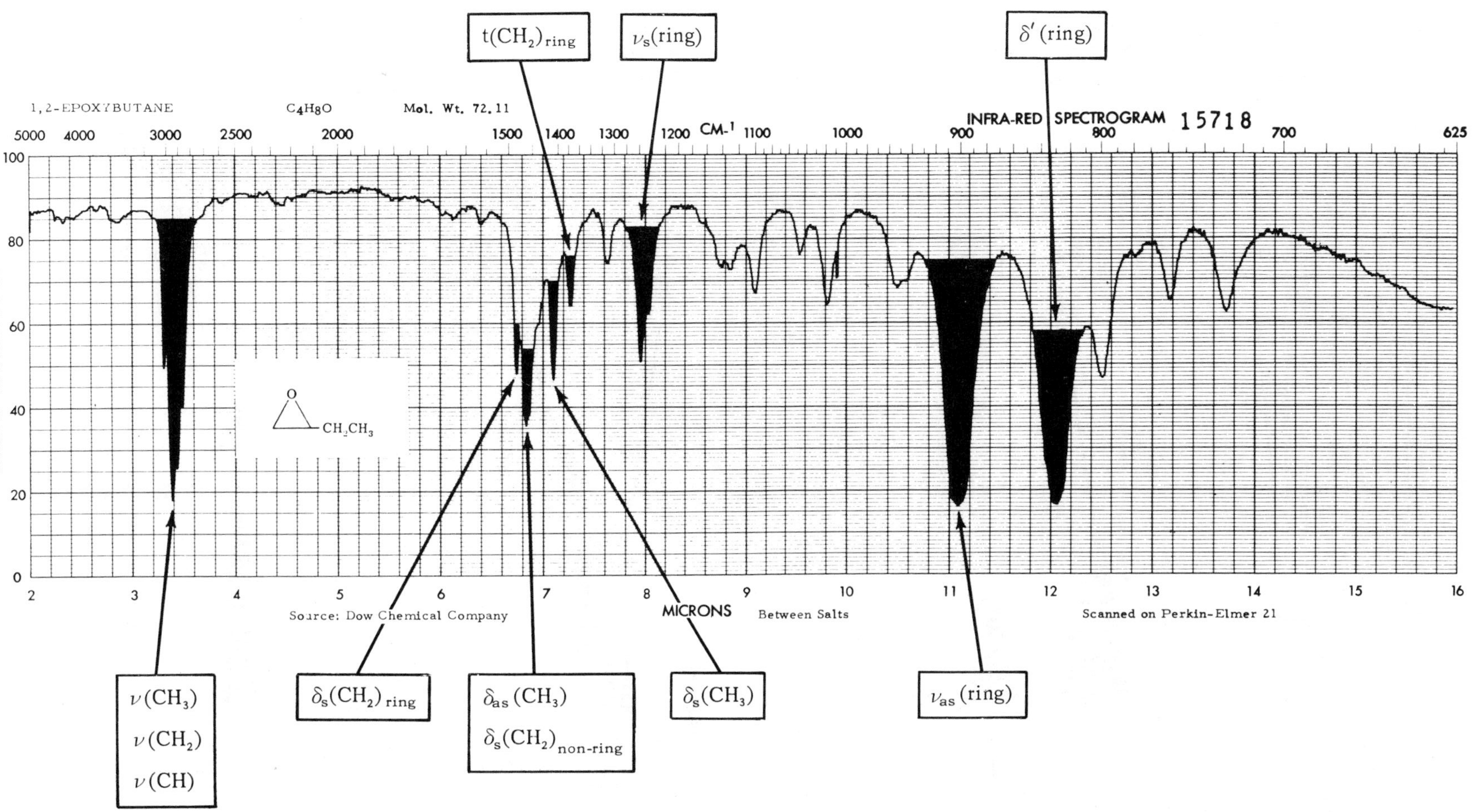

6. 1, 2-Epoxybutane has the three group frequencies we associate with the epoxy group. These are the two strong bands near 900 and 820 cm^{-1} and the medium intensity band near 1250 cm^{-1}. The other bands can be assigned without difficulty to stretch and deformations of the chain and ring CH groups.

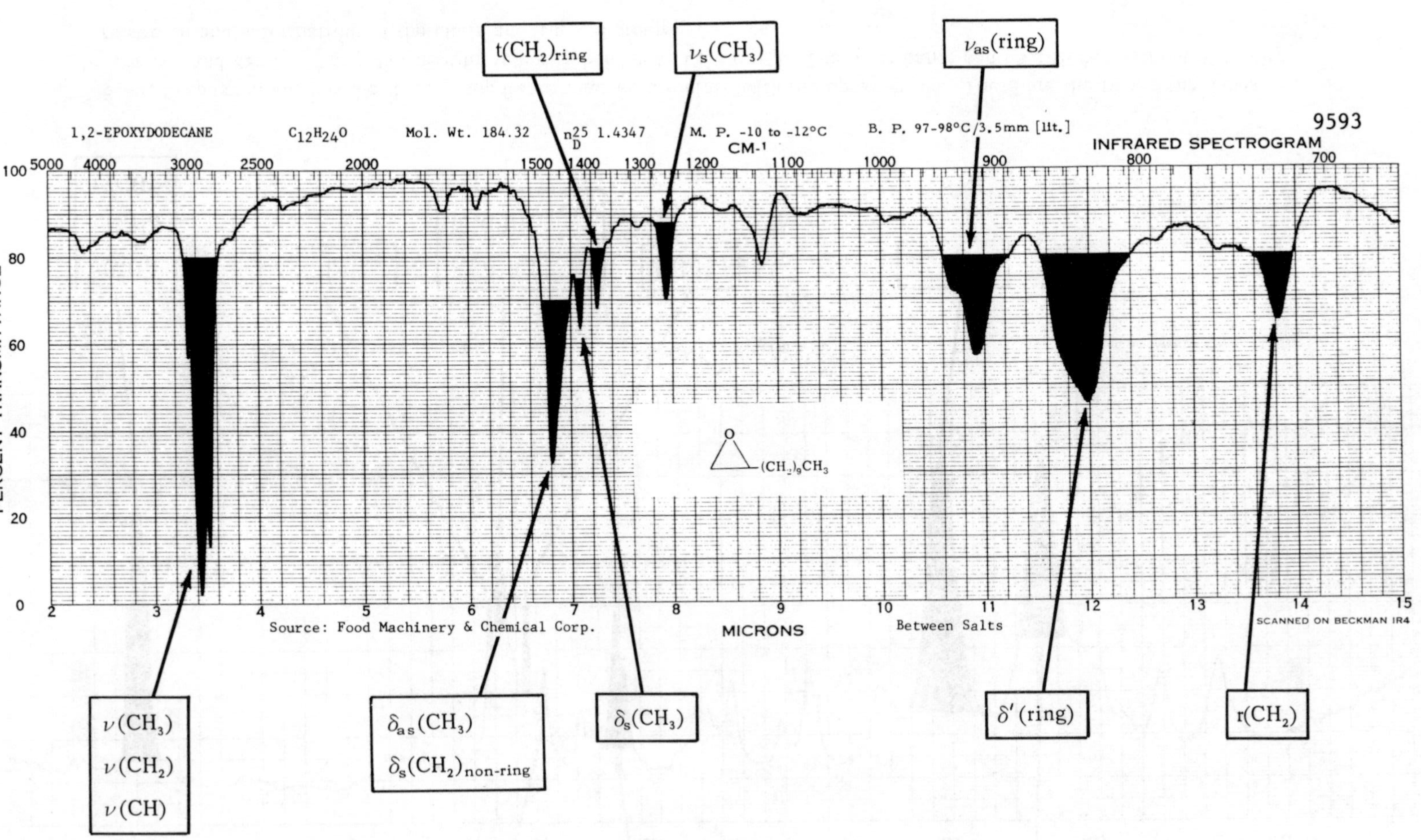

7. This compound has a longer alkyl chain on the ring, as compared to the previous spectrum. Both spectra, however, have similar strong bands in about the same position. The 900 cm^{-1} band is shifted in this spectrum compared to the previous one. The $\delta(CH_2)$ band is very strong here, indicating the larger number of CH_2 groups here compared to the previous compound.

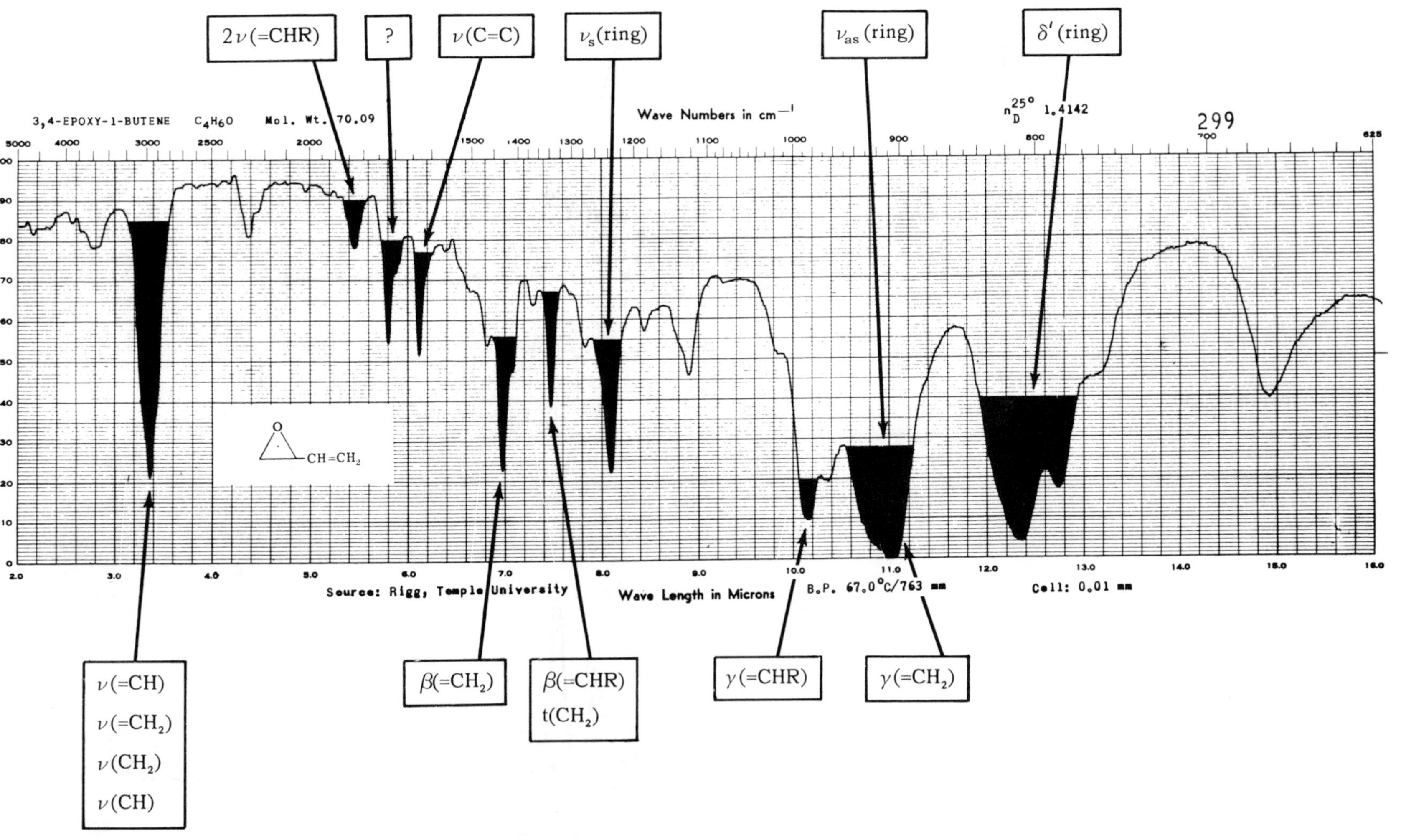

8. This compound is the first example of an olefin attached to the epoxy ring. The vinylic $\gamma(=CH)$ band interferes to some extent with the epoxy ring. However, it would be possible to identify these two groups as being present. There is a puzzling band near 1700 cm^{-1}; it could be a $\nu(C{=}C)$, but this is a very high position.

Reproduced from Anal. Chem. 23:277 (1951).

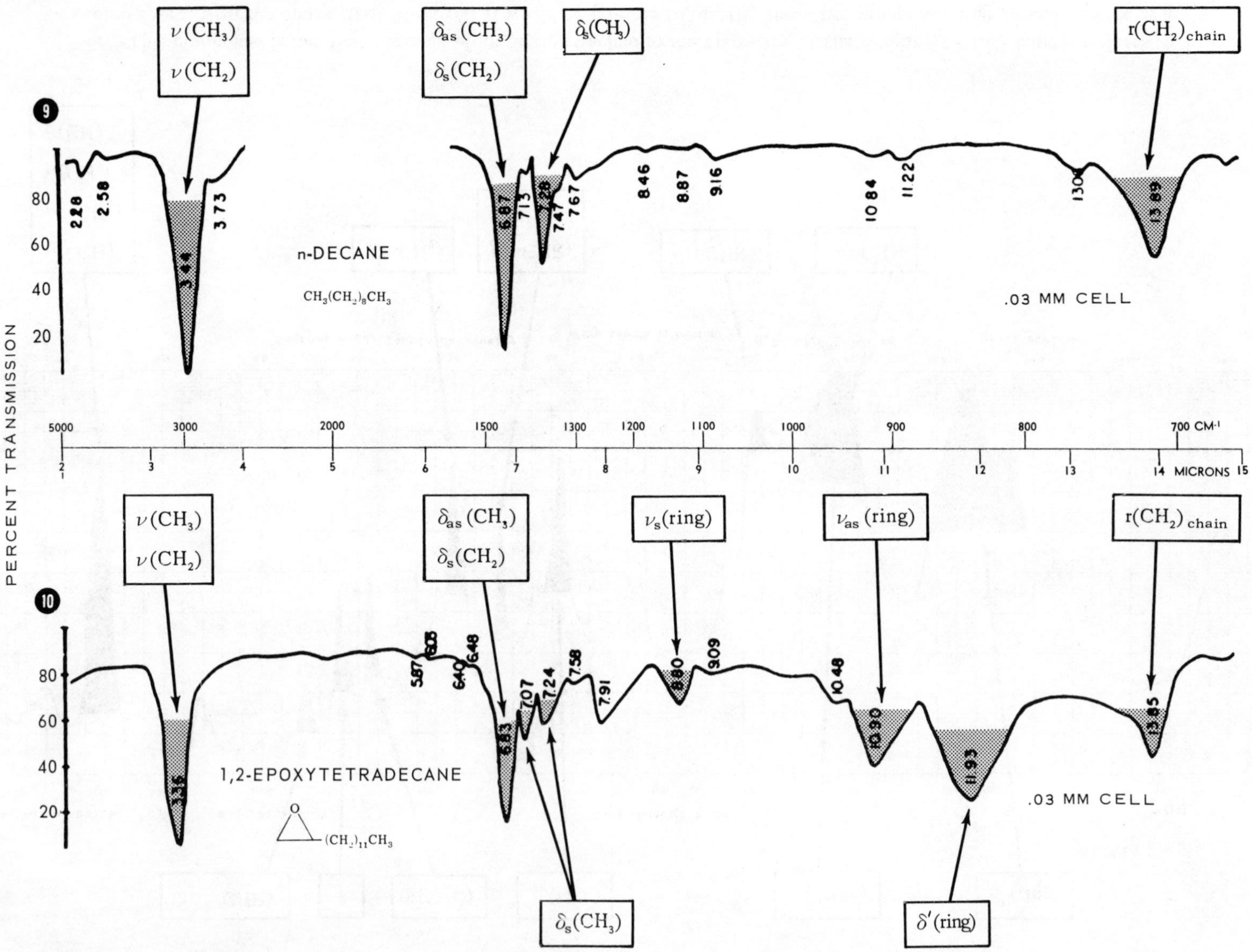

9 n-DECANE

$CH_3(CH_2)_8CH_3$

.03 MM CELL

$\nu(CH_3)$ $\nu(CH_2)$

$\delta_{as}(CH_3)$ $\delta_s(CH_2)$

$\delta_s(CH_3)$

$r(CH_2)_{chain}$

10 1,2-EPOXYTETRADECANE

$(CH_2)_{11}CH_3$

.03 MM CELL

$\nu(CH_3)$ $\nu(CH_2)$

$\delta_{as}(CH_3)$ $\delta_s(CH_2)$

$\delta_s(CH_3)$

$\nu_s(\text{ring})$

$\nu_{as}(\text{ring})$

$\delta'(\text{ring})$

$r(CH_2)_{chain}$

PERCENT TRANSMISSION

MICRONS

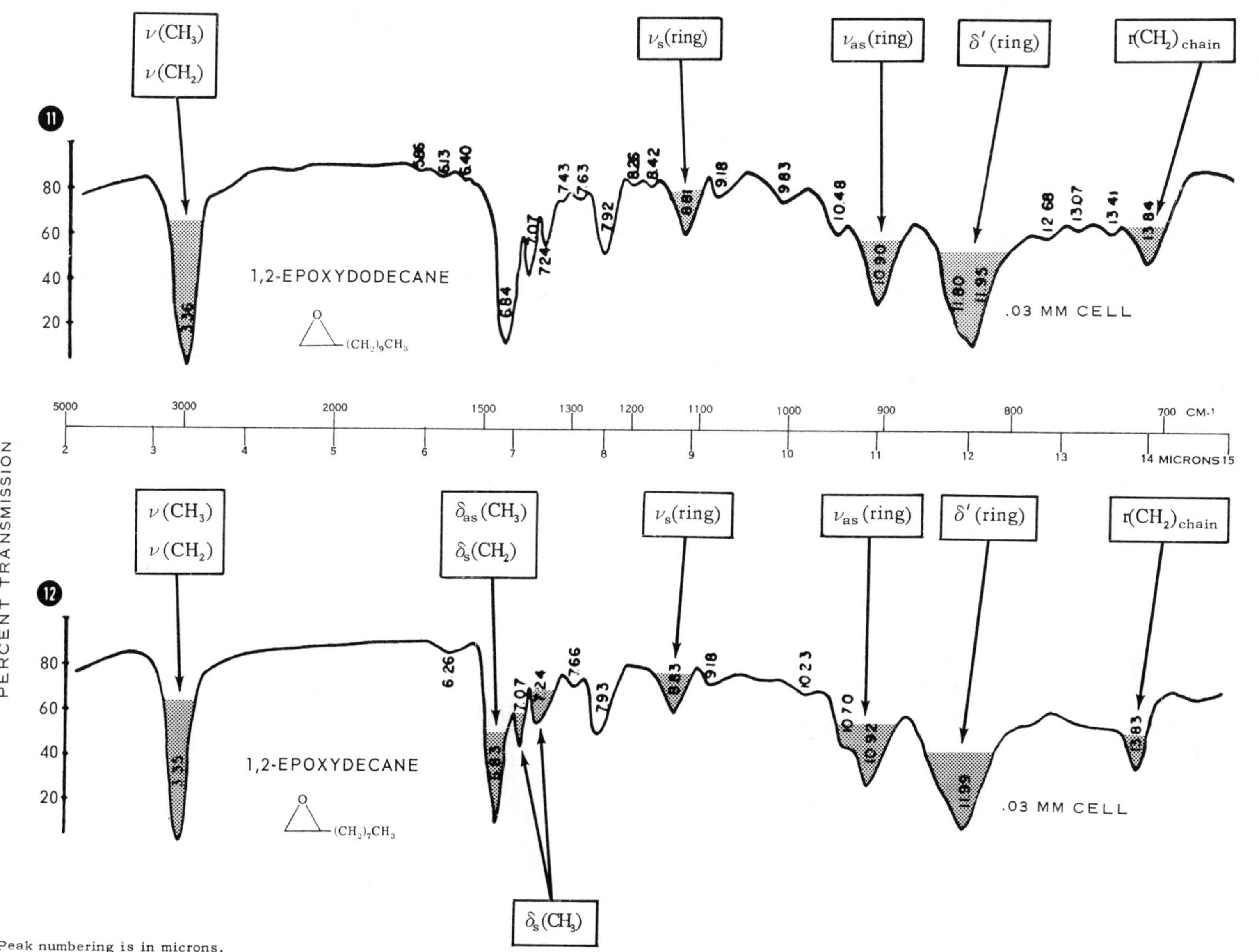

Peak numbering is in microns.

9-12. The above compounds, except the first, have an epoxy ring. It is noted the epoxy compounds have bands near 1430, 1265, 1135, 920, and 840 cm^{-1} that the hydrocarbon does not. The authors assign the first three to C−O and the last two to motions of the ring as a unit. We prefer to assign them as we have the previous spectra: δ′(ring) near 850, ν_{as}(ring) near 910, and ν_s(ring) near 1250 cm^{-1}.

Reprinted from Anal. Chem. 23 : 277 (1951).

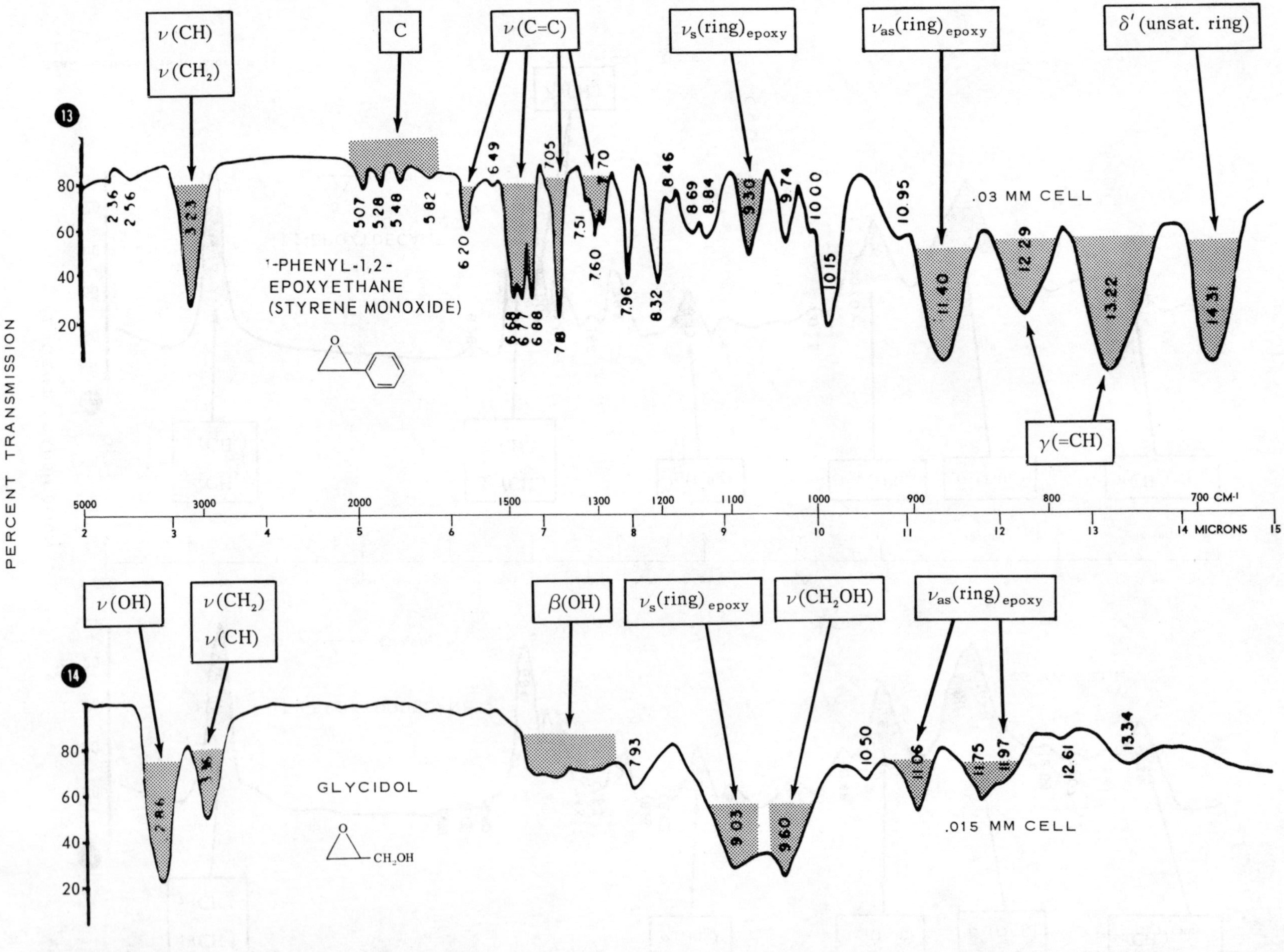

13
ν(CH)
ν(CH2)
C
ν(C=C)
νs(ring)epoxy
νas(ring)epoxy
δ′(unsat. ring)
γ(=CH)
2.36
2.56
3.23
5.07
5.28
5.48
5.82
6.20
6.49
6.68
6.77
6.88
7.05
7.18
7.51
7.60
7.70
7.96
8.32
8.46
8.69
8.84
9.30
9.74
10.00
10.15
10.95
11.40
12.29
13.22
14.31
.03 MM CELL
1-PHENYL-1,2-
EPOXYETHANE
(STYRENE MONOXIDE)
PERCENT TRANSMISSION
80
60
40
20
5000
3000
2000
1500
1300
1200
1100
1000
900
800
700 CM-1
2
3
4
5
6
7
8
9
10
11
12
13
14 MICRONS
15
14
ν(OH)
ν(CH2)
ν(CH)
β(OH)
νs(ring)epoxy
ν(CH2OH)
νas(ring)epoxy
2.86
7.93
9.03
9.60
10.50
11.06
11.75
11.97
12.61
13.34
GLYCIDOL
CH2OH
.015 MM CELL

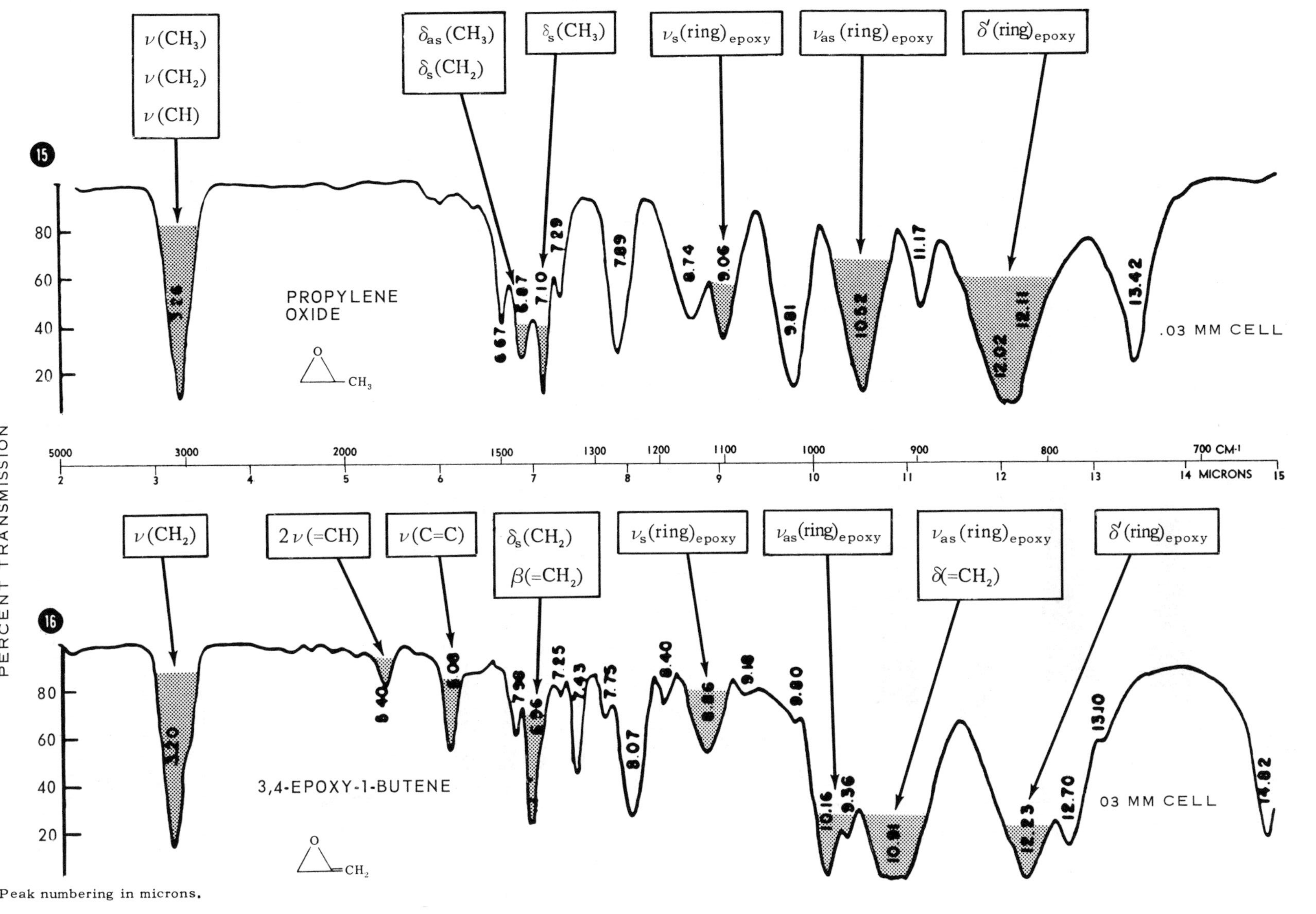

13-16. Comparison of the Spectra of Styrene monoxyide, glycidol, propylene oxide and 3, 4 epoxy-1-butene.

The above compounds have an epoxy ring. Bands near 910 and 850 cm^{-1}, suggested as ring vibrations for alklane epoxy compounds, also appear in these spectra. From the vibrational analysis reported in the correlation section for propylene oxide we know bands near here are ring vibrations. We therefore assign, as before δ'(ring) at 850, ν_{as}(ring) at 910, and ν_s(ring) at 1250 cm^{-1}. The olefinic compound has the δ'(ring) band nearer 810 than 850 cm^{-1}, apparently due to the unsaturation adjacent to the ring. The $\gamma(=CH)$ aromatic ring vibrations appear in the expected positions.

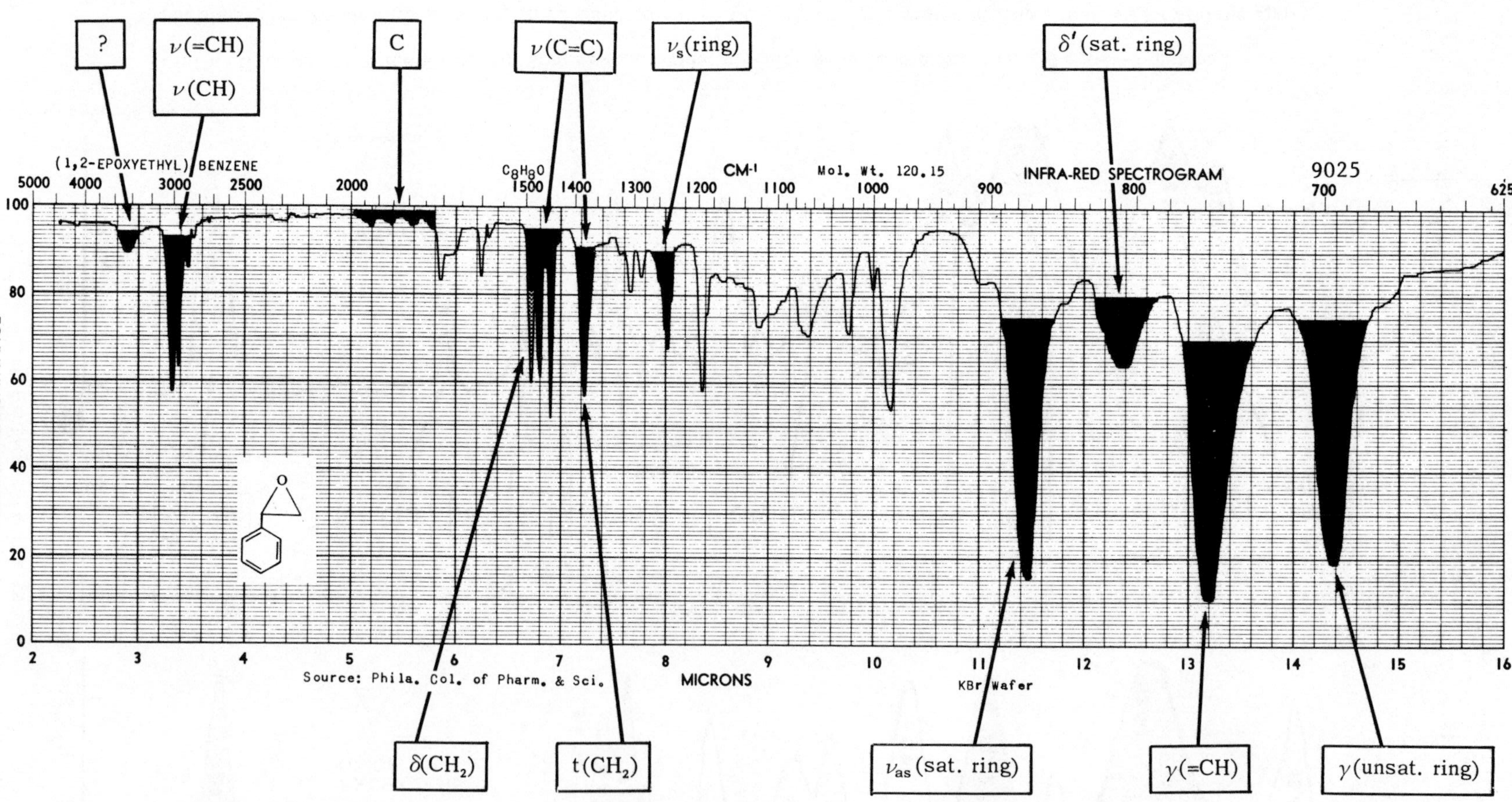

17. This spectrum is the first example of an aromatic ring attached to the epoxy ring. We can first note the 1250, 900, and 810 cm^{-1} bands which are typical for the epoxy ring. We note the 1250 and 810 cm^{-1} bands are fairly weak, and only the band near 890 cm^{-1} assigned as the ν_{as} of the epoxy ring, is strong. In the aliphatic epoxy compounds we have examined thus far the 810 cm^{-1} band was not this weak. This should be noted by the reader, as it occurs for these aromatic epoxy compounds.

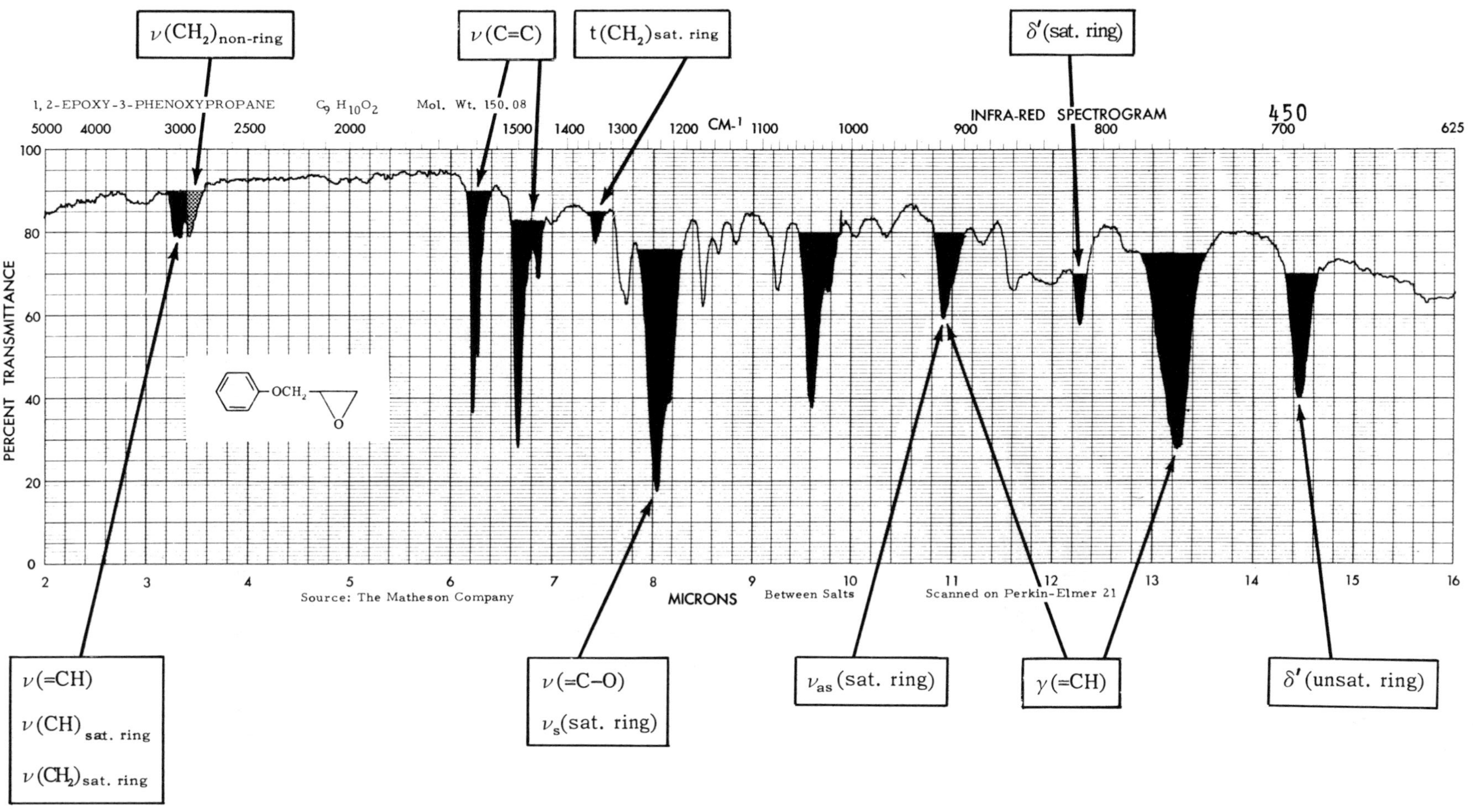

18. This compound combines the groups $=C-O$, $-CH_2O$, and the epoxy ring. We find bands occur in the correct region for each of these groups. The $\nu(=C-O)$ near 1200 cm^{-1}, the $\nu(CH_2O)$ near 1030 cm^{-1}, and the 900 and 810 cm^{-1} bands for the epoxy ring. The 1250 cm^{-1} epoxy band is covered by the $\nu(=C-O)$.

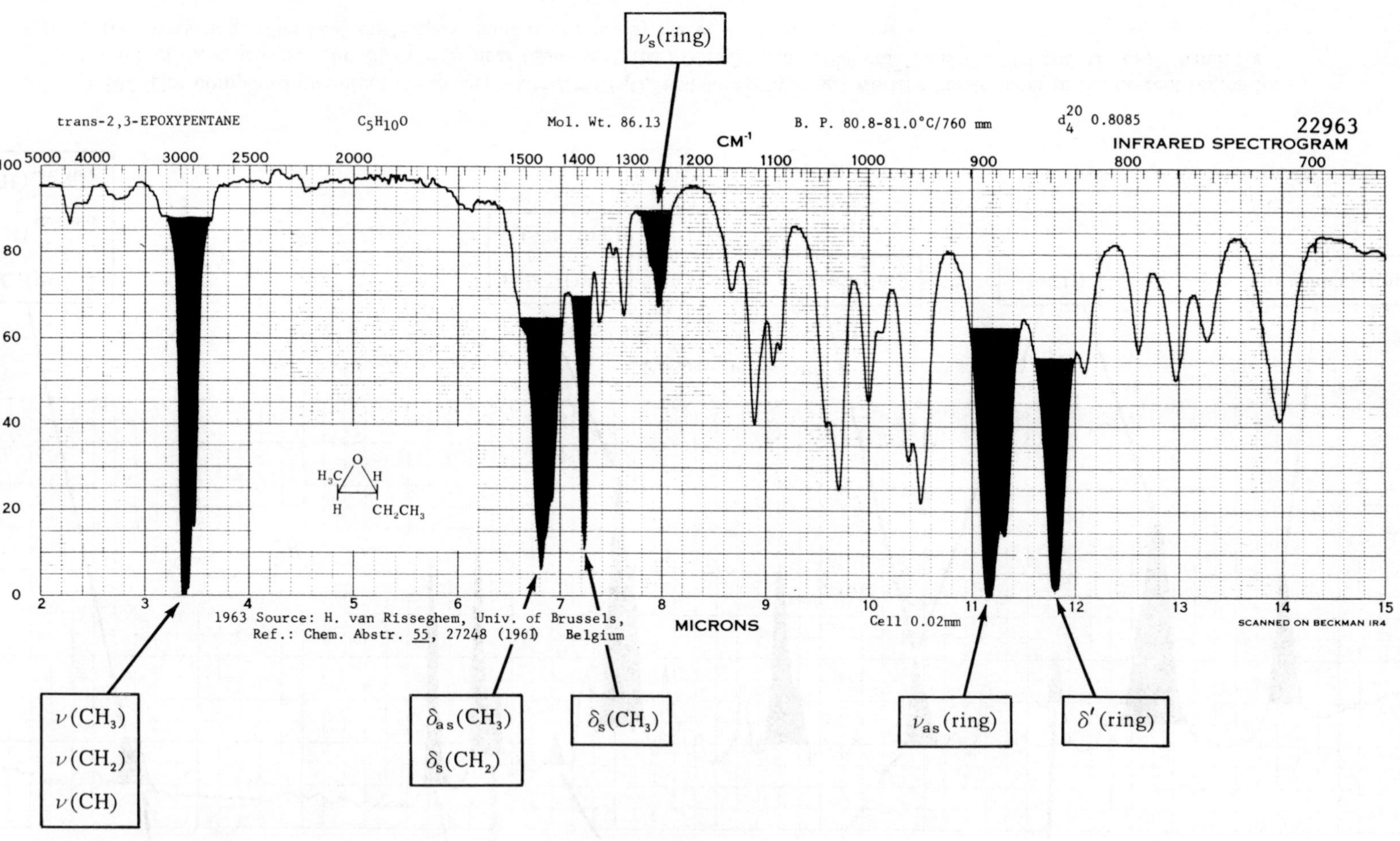

19. This is the first example of a 1, 2 derivative of the epoxy ring. We expect a strong band in the 850-775 cm^{-1} region for these derivatives, and a band is found near 840 cm^{-1}. The 890 cm^{-1} band is the ν_{as}(ring) and is strong, while the 1250 cm^{-1} band is fairly weak. The 1450 cm^{-1} band is very strong here, but since the ν_{as}(ring) band is bottoming out, it is probable the sample thickness was too great.

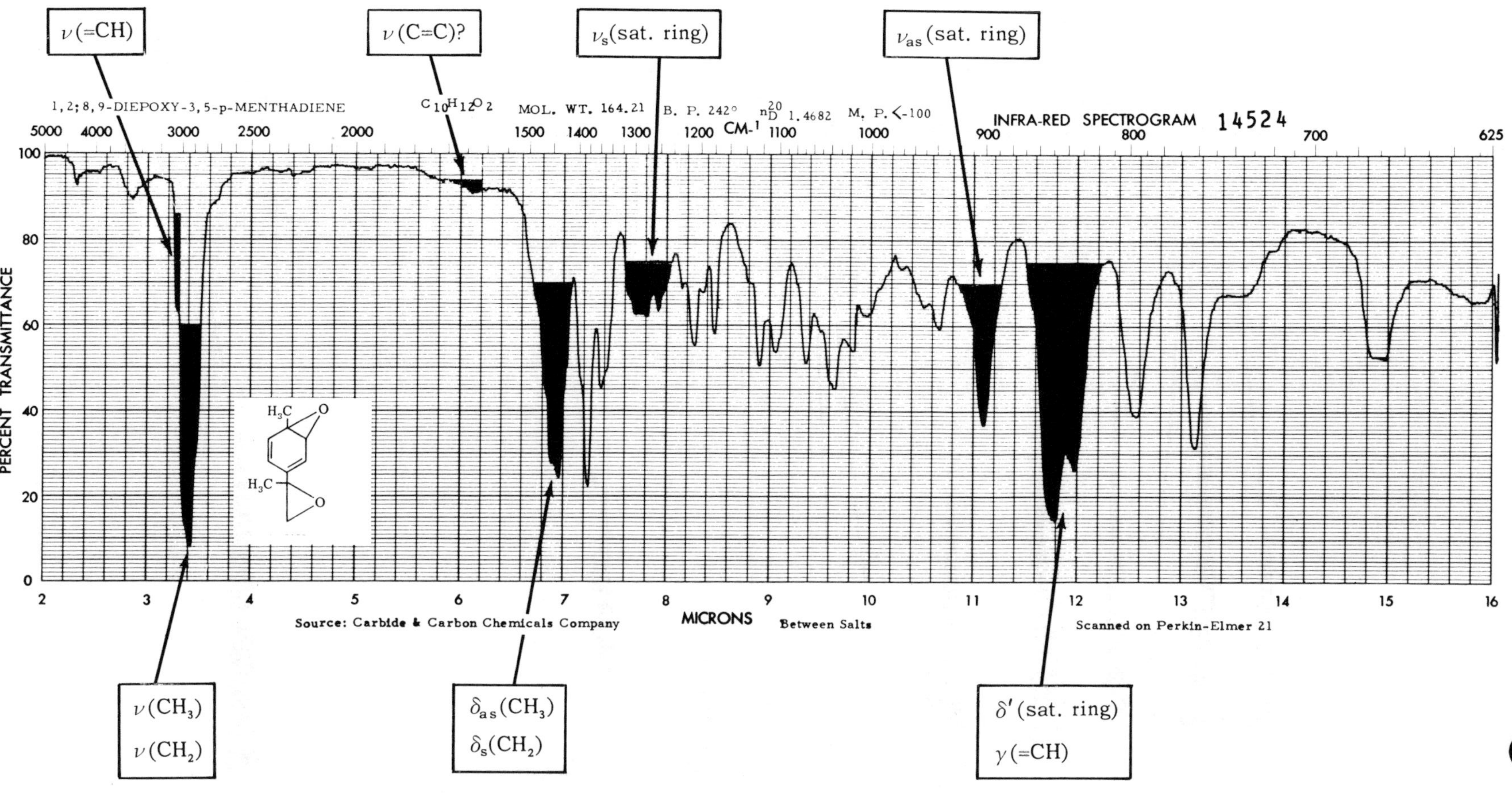

20. This compound is the first of a series where the COC ring is attached to two positions on another ring. We do not have correlations suggested for this type of compound, but shall attempt to locate bands near 1250, 900, and 810 cm^{-1} as we did for previous epoxy rings. In this spectrum a band occurs near 900 cm^{-1} which is assigned as ν_{as}(ring). The 810 cm^{-1} band is interfered with by a γ(=CH) vibration, so it cannot be easily identified. The 1250 cm^{-1} region is complex, and cannot be used to identify the presence of the COC ring. It appears, therefore, that it would be difficult to identify the COC or the epoxy ring.

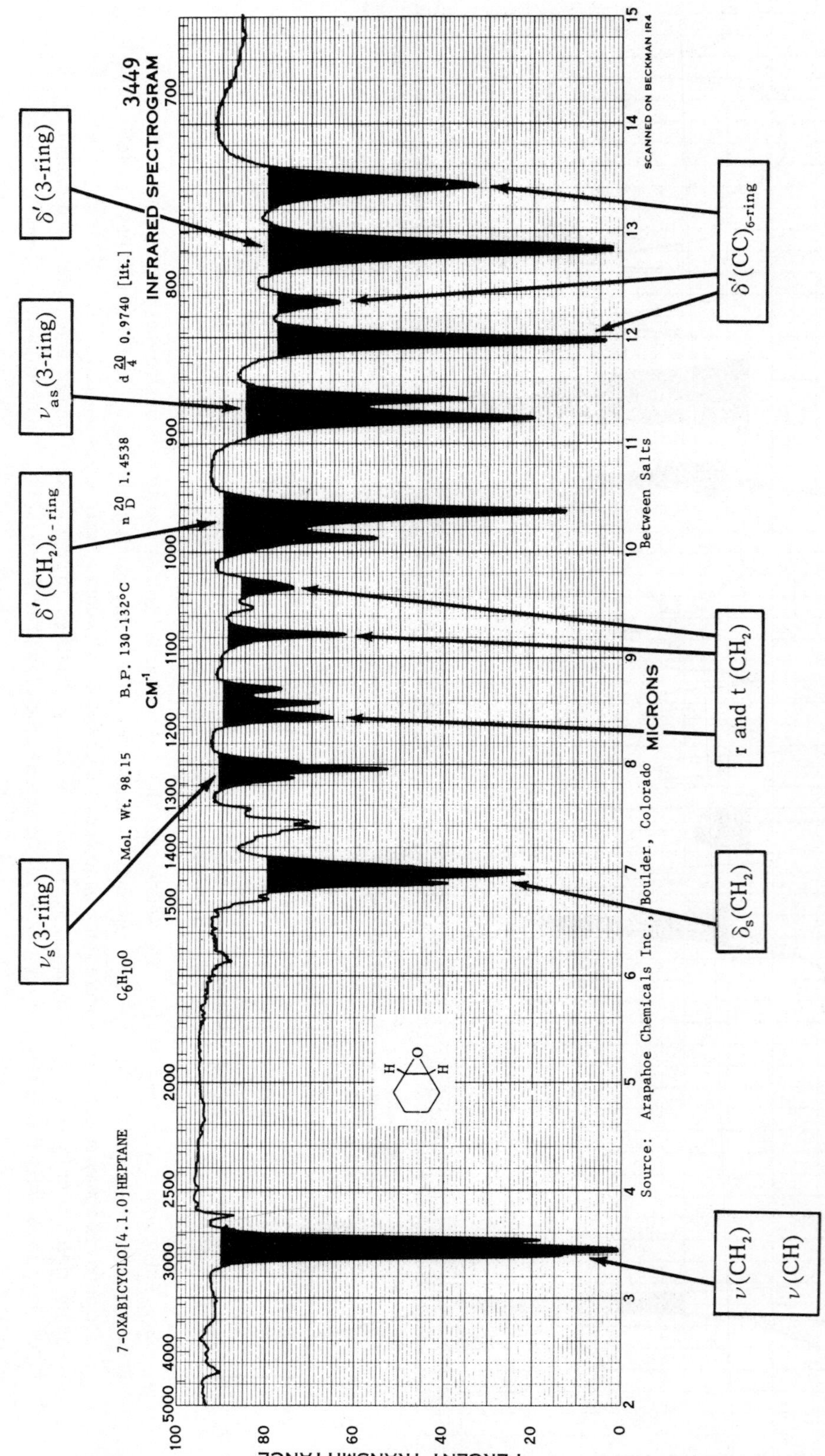

21. This compound has the epoxy ring attached to a saturated ring. Again it would be difficult to identify that a COC ring is present here, if this spectrum were presented as an unknown compound. The saturated ring vibrations occur in a similar region as the COC. We can make the assignments since we know the groups which are present, and the assignments are so listed.

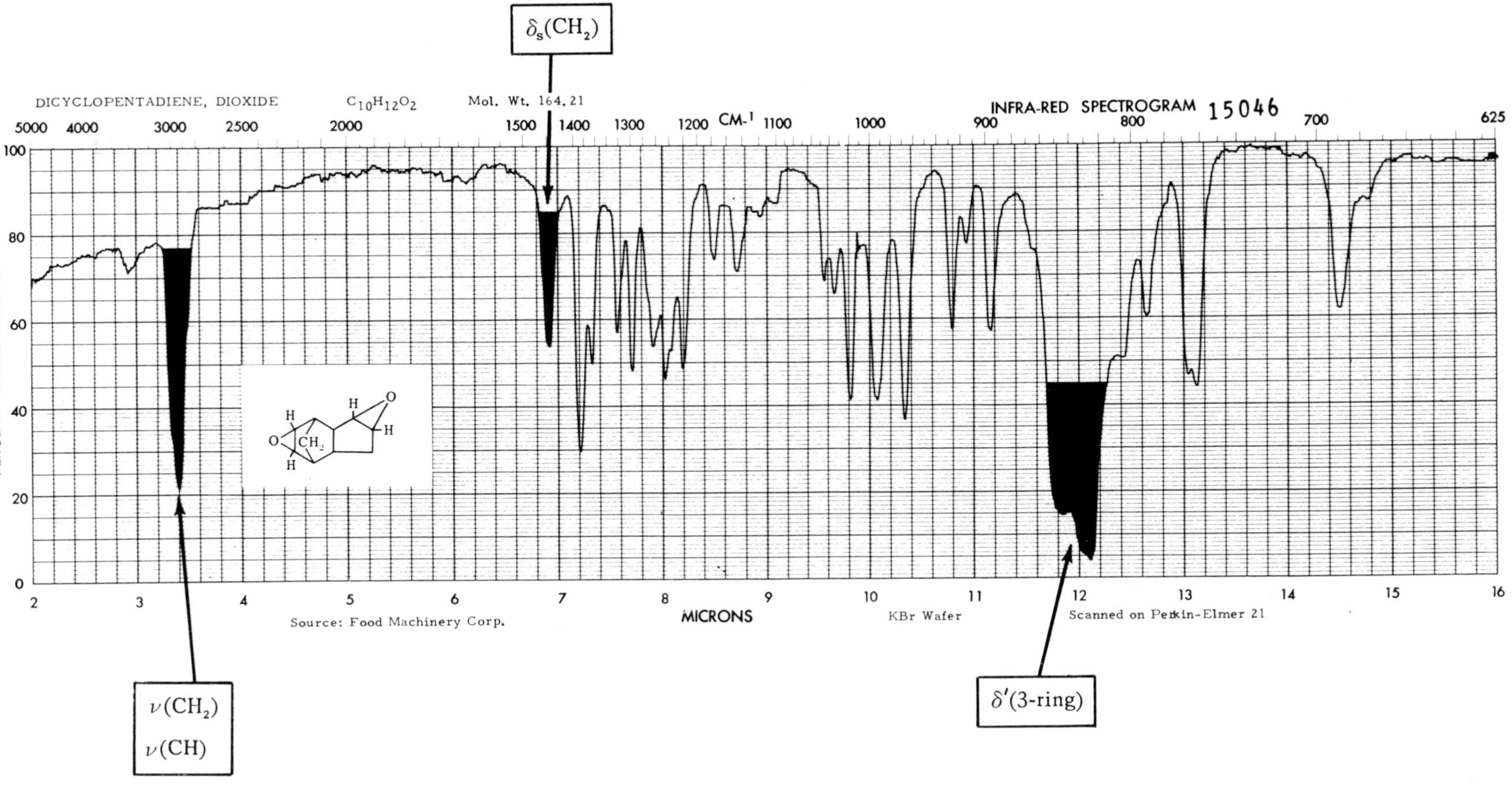

22. This compound has two COC rings attached to a saturated ring. We find a strong 810 cm^{-1}, but only a weak series of bands near 900 cm^{-1}. We cannot therefore assign the presence of the COC ring for spectra of unknown compounds of this type. We make no attempt to assign many of the bands, since these are not considered good group frequencies. The reader might wonder if for these compounds the strong 820 cm^{-1} band is diagnostic for the COC ring. We shall see it does not always appear in spectra of compounds of this type.

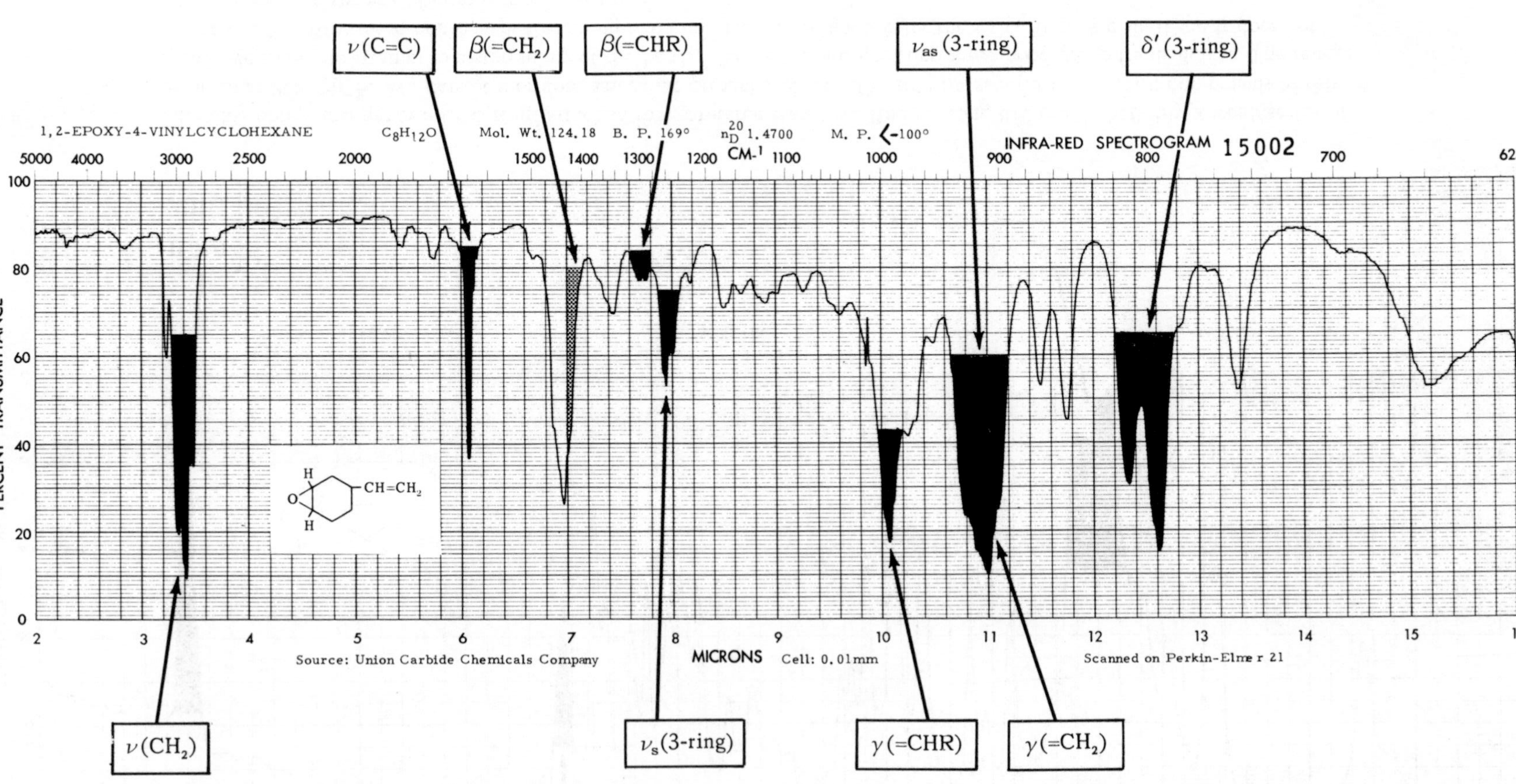

23. This compound has a COC ring similar to the last several ones examined; however, a vinyl group is now present. This results in interference of the COC vibrations with the vinylic (see for example the 910 and 810 cm^{-1} region), and makes it almost impossible to find distinct group frequencies for the COC ring. We must conclude in an unknown spectrum it would not be possible to identify the COC ring on these compounds.

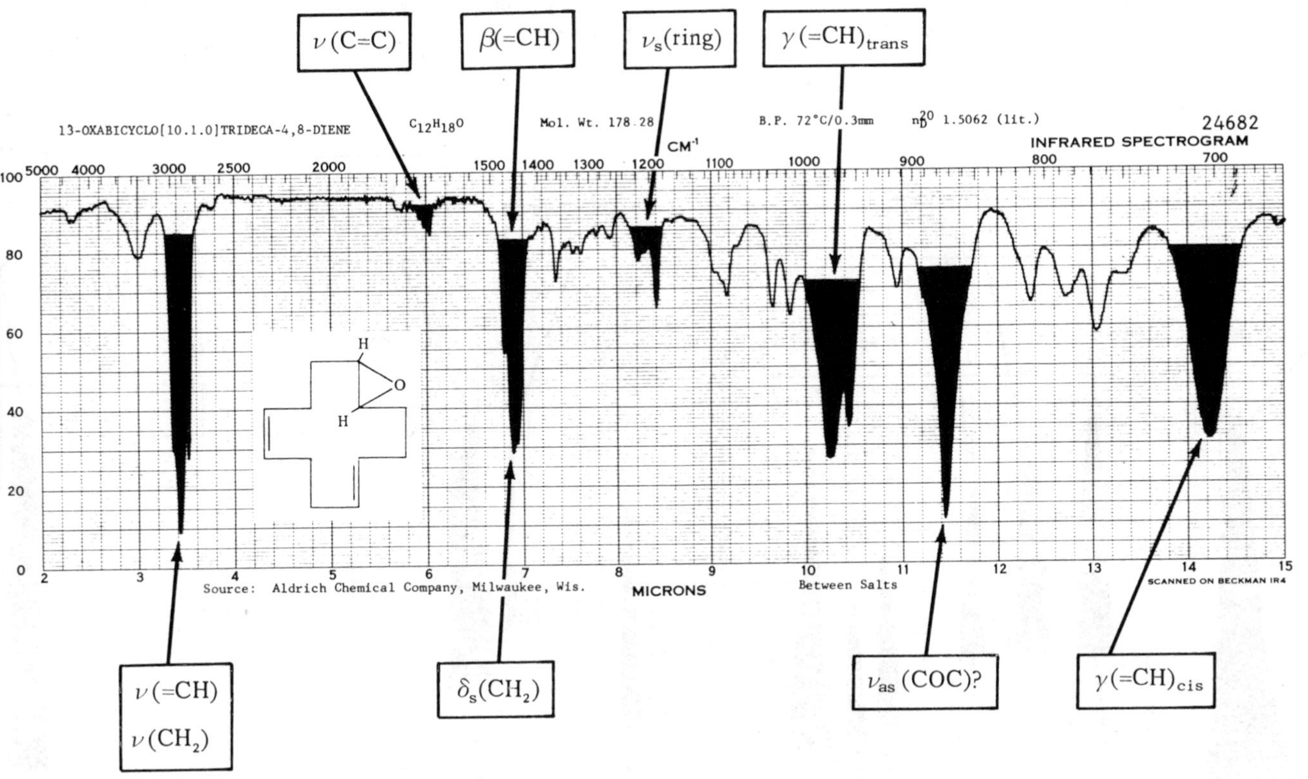

24. This compound has a COC ring in a large ring. Since very little is known about the group frequencies of these very large rings, we cannot be certain that the strong band near 875 cm^{-1} is due to the COC ring. We have assigned it tentatively as the $ν_{as}$(COC). The unsaturation should place the olefinic hydrogens cis to each other, and a strong band is found near 700 cm^{-1} which can be assigned as $γ(=CH)_{cis}$. There is a band, however, at the correct position for $γ(=CH)_{trans}$, and so we must assign this band as this vibration.

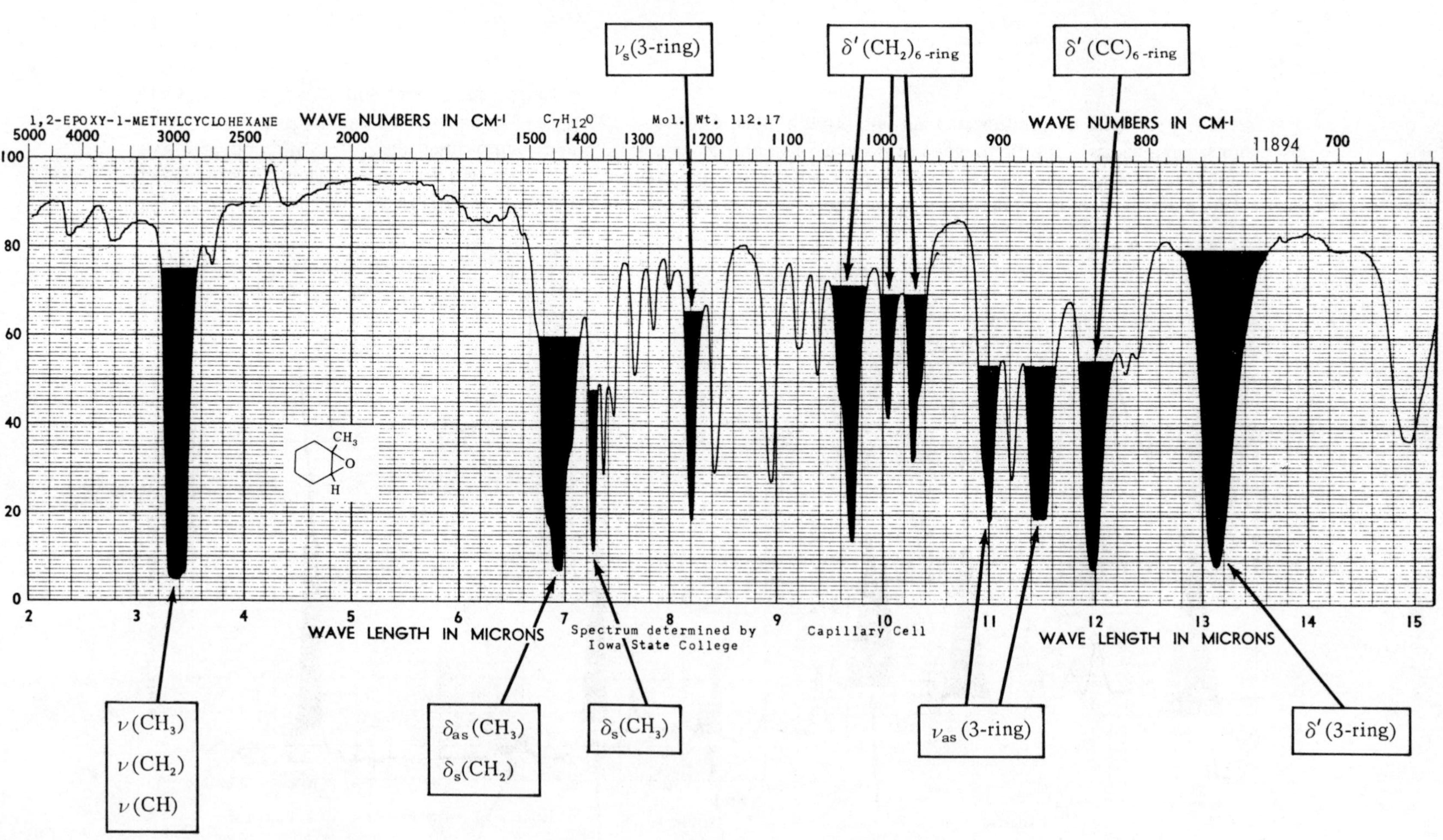

25. This compound has a COC ring similar to several others we have just examined; however, one of the hydrogens of this ring has now been replaced by a CH_3 group. There are many strong bands from 1500 to 700 cm^{-1}, and it is very unlikely that the correct assignments could be made, even knowing the structure. For an unknown spectrum we could not identify the COC ring as being present for this class of compound.

26 CYCLIC ETHERS

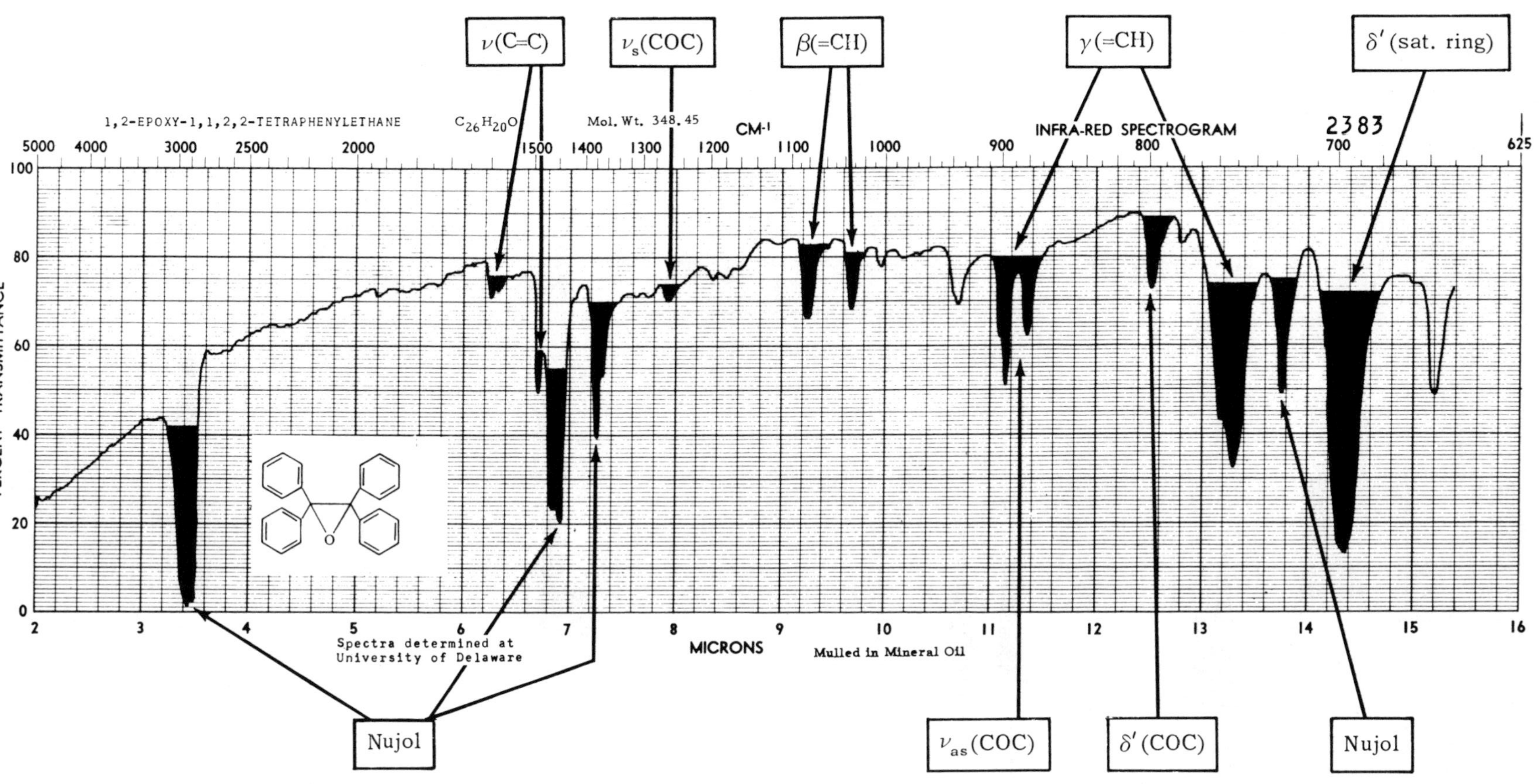

26. This compound has the COC ring with aromatic rings in place of the four hydrogens. Again we want to know if it is possible to identify the COC ring if the spectrum were run as an unknown. The answer is no. The only bands would be the ones near 900 and 800 cm^{-1}, and these could be aromatic ring vibrations as well as COC.

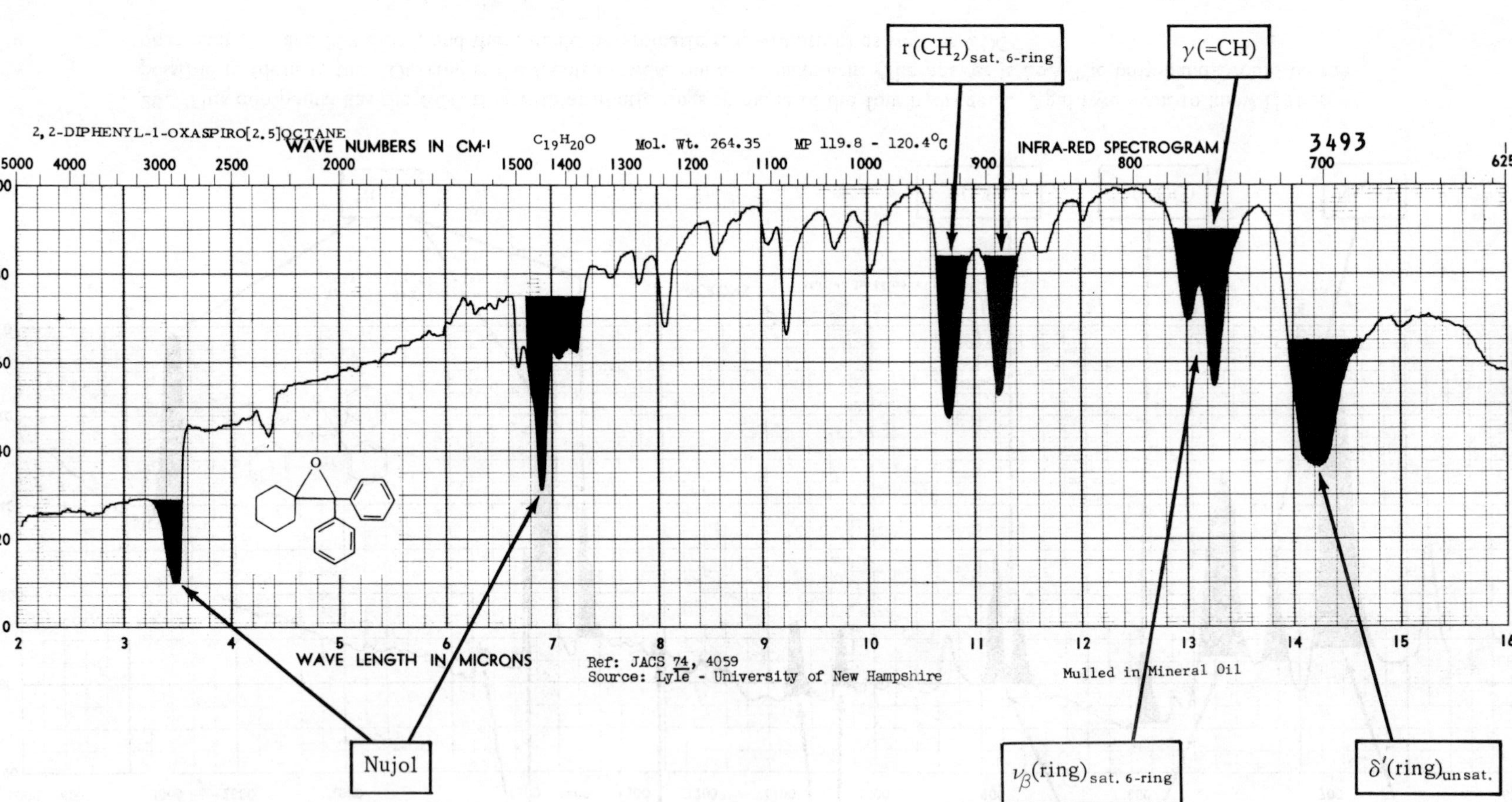

27. This compound has two aromatic and one saturated ring attached to the COC ring, and again it would be very difficult to assign the COC ring vibrations. The assignments of the bands are those based on group frequencies for both aromatic and unsaturated rings.

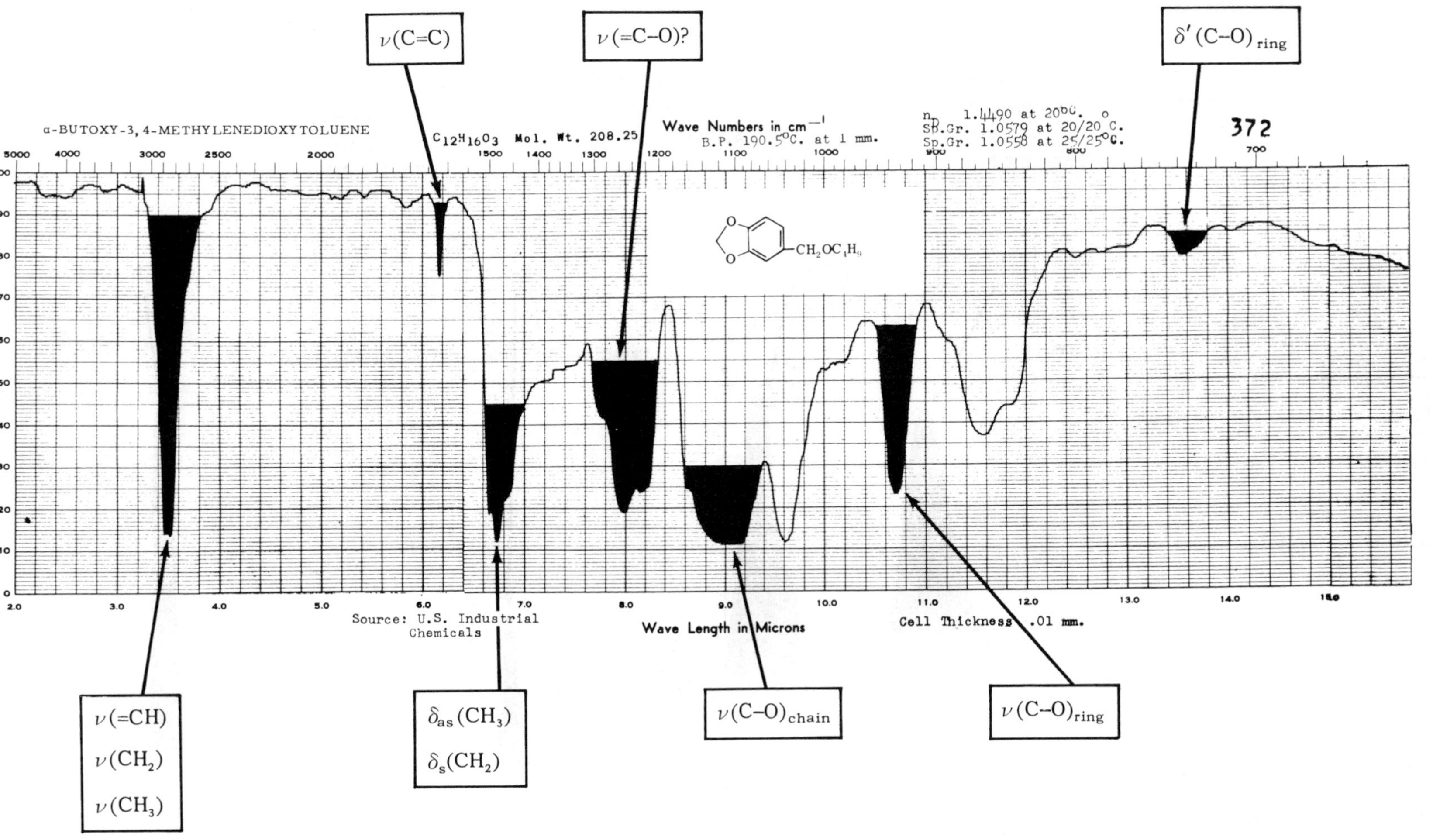

28. This compound has a $COCH_2OC$ ring attached to an aromatic ring. Compounds of this general type, labeled methyl dioxy compounds, are considered in the correlation section, and group frequencies are suggested. The only band which appears of sufficient diagnostic value is the ν(C–O), which appears near 920 cm^{-1}. There is such a band in this spectrum, which is so assigned. A band near 720 cm^{-1} is also assigned to this type of dioxy compound, but it is so weak that it has little diagnostic value. There is also present a CH_2O group, and this is assigned as a broad band near 1090 cm^{-1}.

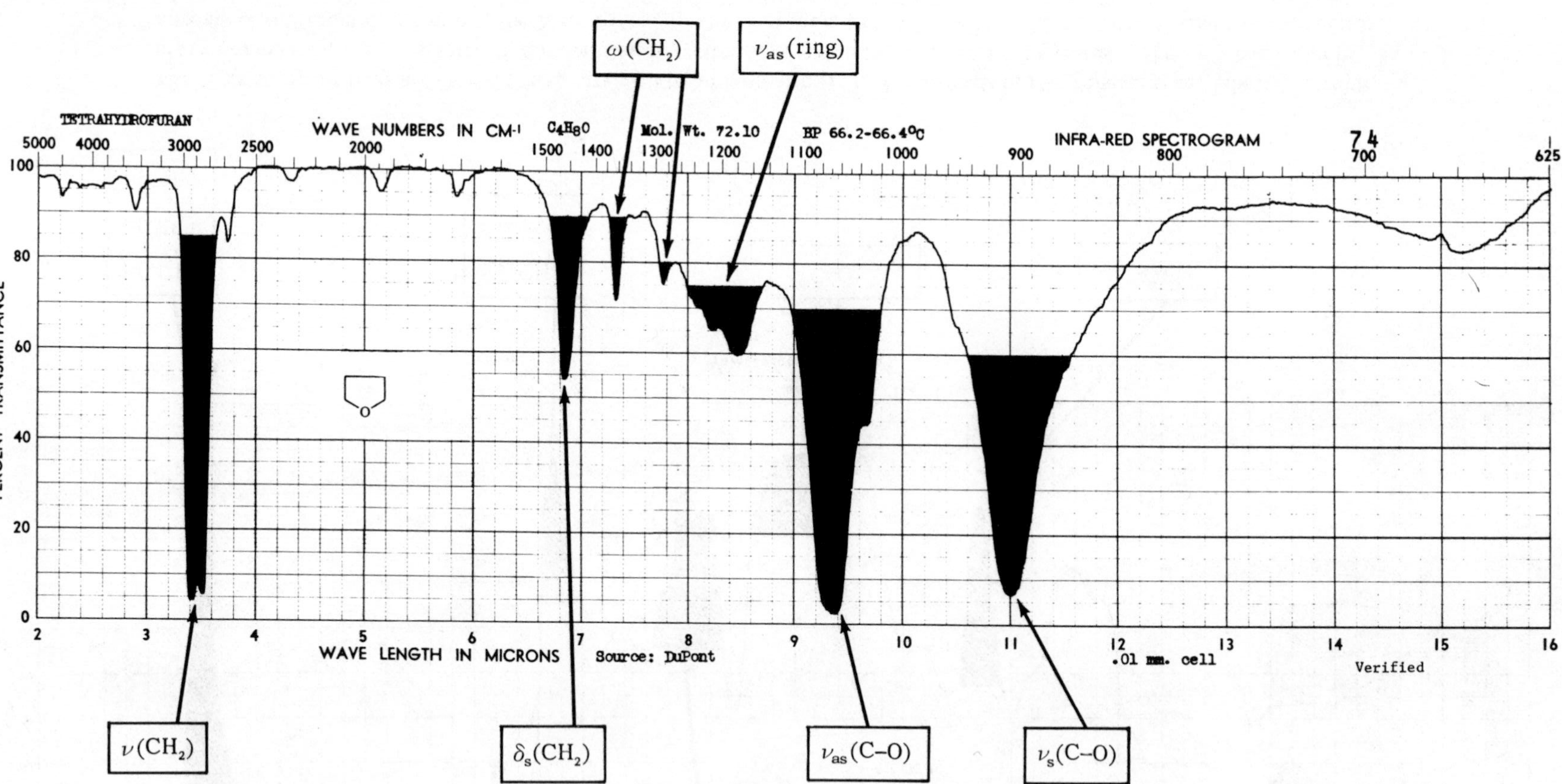

29. We have presented a vibrational anaylsis for tetrahydrofuran in an earlier section and the bands of this spectrum are assigned from this analysis. Note the ν_{as}(C−O) and ν_s(C−O) are now closer to each other and very strong. We have pointed out that as the ring size increases the ν_{as} shifts to higher frequency and ν_s to lower, and this ring size represents the case where they are near each other. For a large ring such as this we can now refer to the two ring vibrations as ν_{as}(C−O) and ν_s(C−O).

㉚ CYCLIC ETHERS

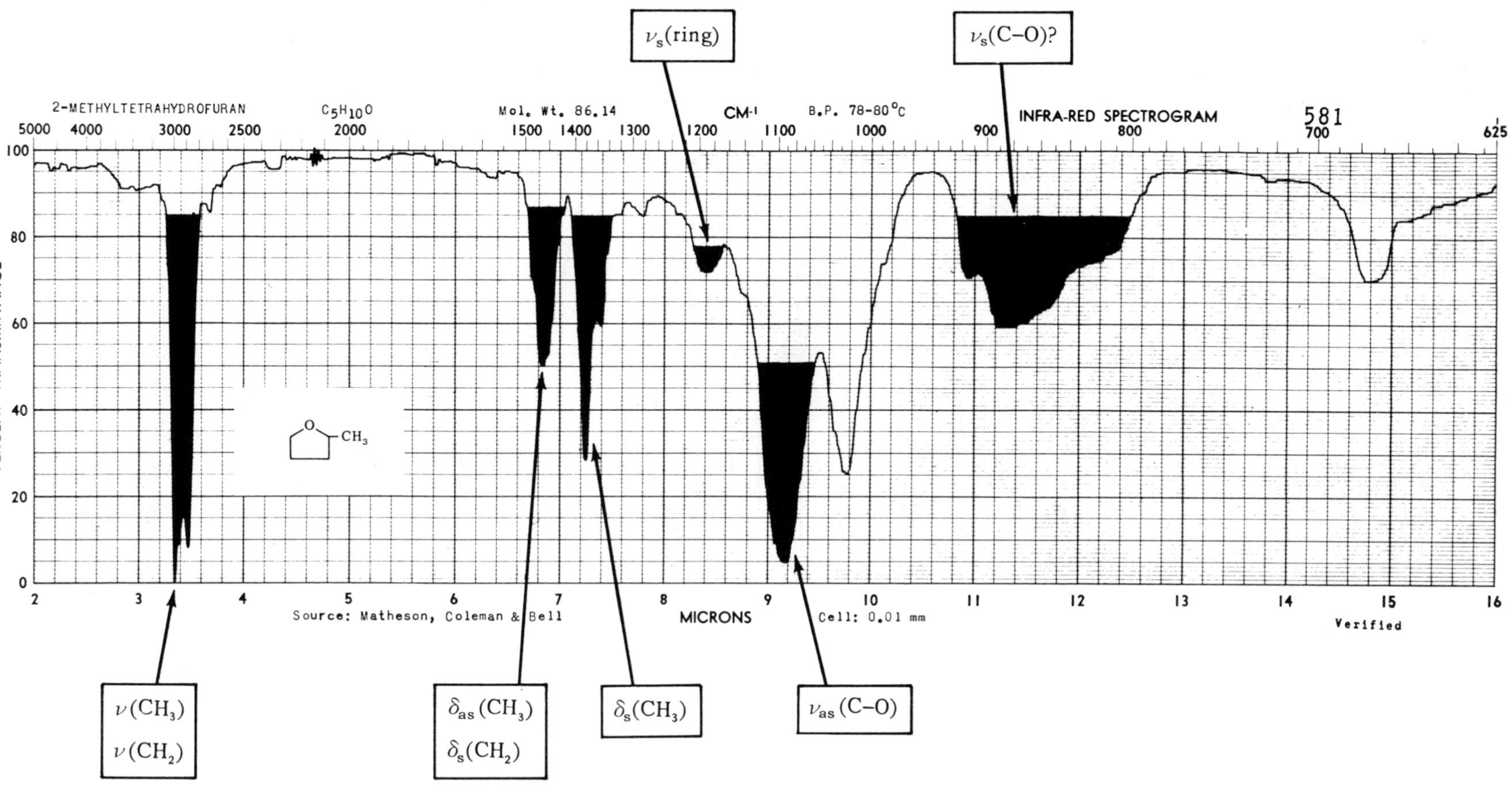

30. Substituting a CH_3 group on the tetrahydrofuran ring changes the spectrum of the furan quite radically. We can still identify the ν_{as}(C–O) as a strong band near 1085 cm^{-1}, but the ν_s(C–O) assignment is not as obvious. A 1020 cm^{-1} band is not easily assigned to any group.

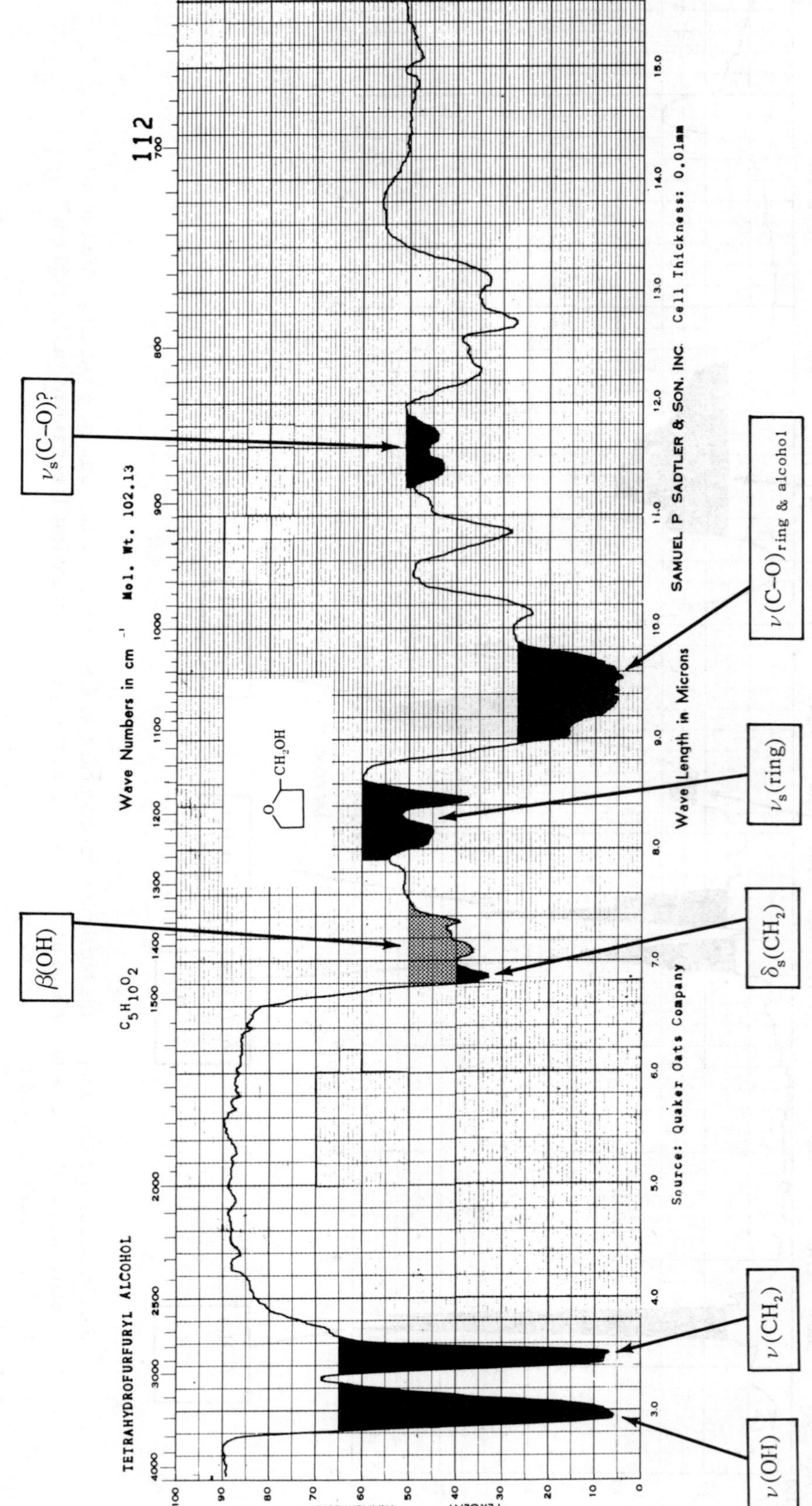

31. If a CH_2OH is now substituted on the tetrahydrofuran ring the spectrum has a number of strong broad bands, as seen in this spectrum. The $\nu(C-O)_{ring\ \&\ alcohol}$ results in a broad band near 1050 cm^{-1}. It is doubtful if the ring could be identified from the bands present in this spectrum.

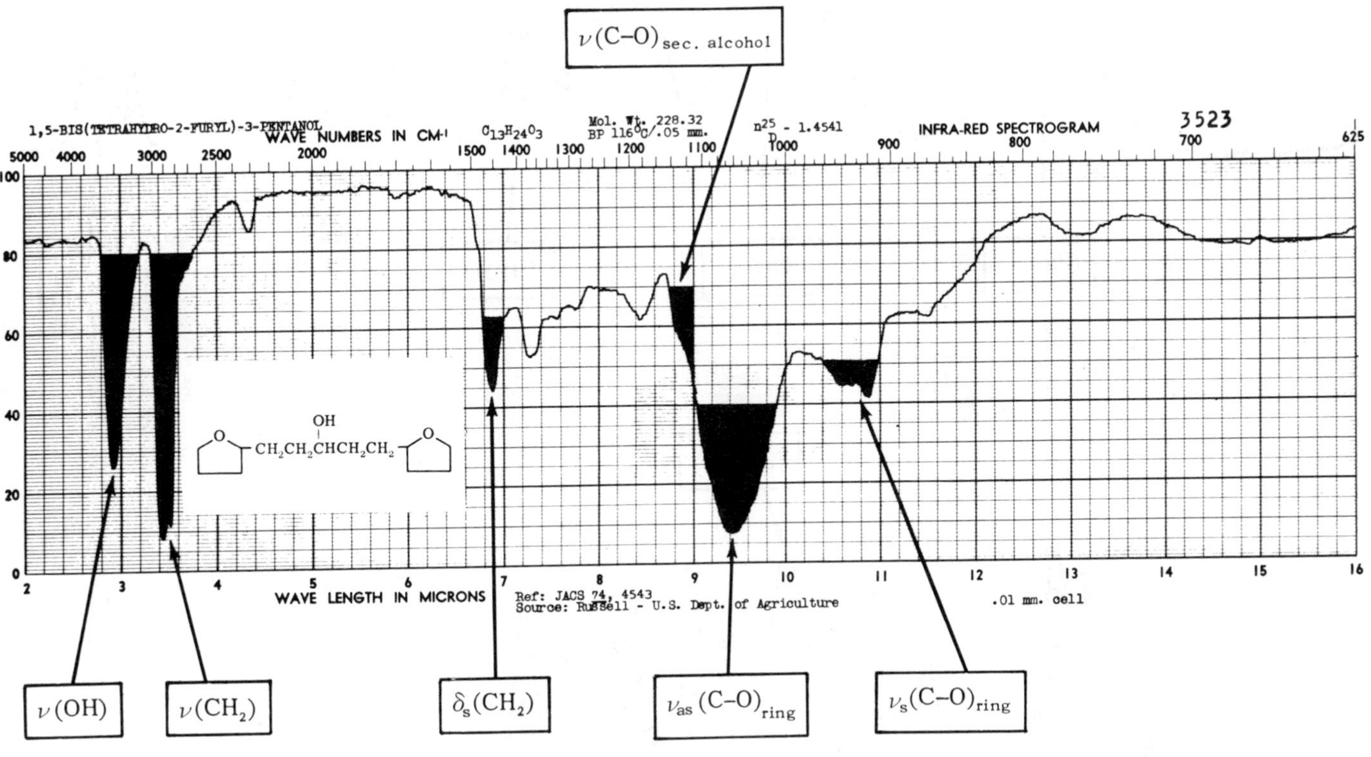

32. The combination of a ring ether and a secondary alcoholic group is illustrated in the structure of this compound. The secondary alcoholic group gives rise to a C–O stretch near 1100 cm^{-1}, while the $\nu_{as}(C-O)_{ring}$ is near 1050 cm^{-1}. It is unfortunate the bands are not resolved, as this would illustrate how group frequencies do appear in the expected region.

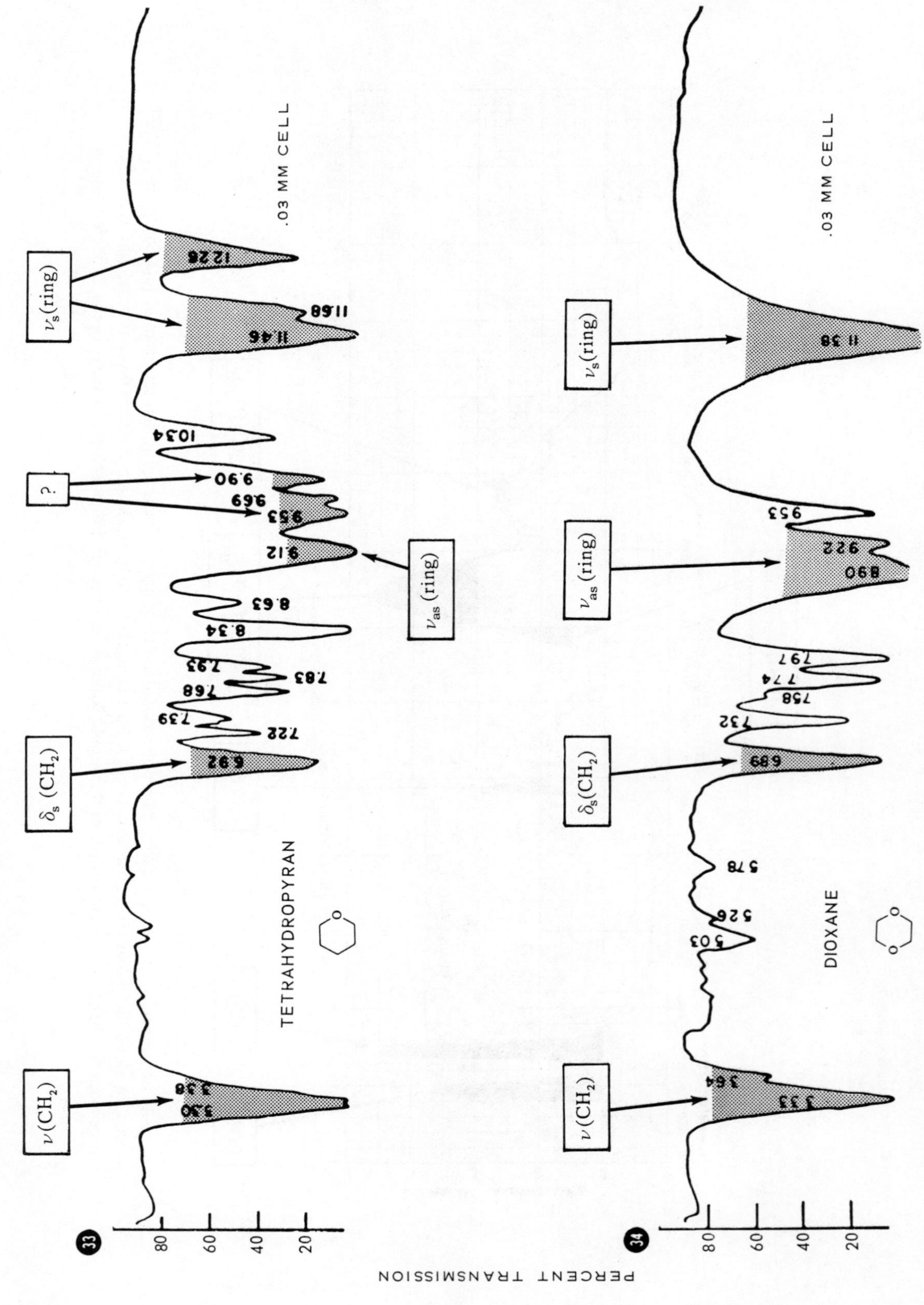

Reprinted from Anal. Chem. 23:277 (1951).

33

TETRAHYDROPYRAN

.03 MM CELL

$\nu(CH_2)$ — 3.38, 3.50

$\delta_s(CH_2)$ — 6.92

7.22, 7.39, 7.68, 7.83, 7.93, 8.34, 8.63

ν_{as} (ring) — 9.12

? — 9.53, 9.69, 9.90

10.34

ν_s(ring) — 11.46, 11.68, 12.26

34

DIOXANE

.03 MM CELL

$\nu(CH_2)$ — 3.33, 3.64

5.03, 5.26, 5.78

$\delta_s(CH_2)$ — 6.89

7.32, 7.58, 7.74, 7.97

ν_{as} (ring) — 8.90, 9.22

9.53

ν_s(ring) — 11.38

PERCENT TRANSMISSION

80 60 40 20

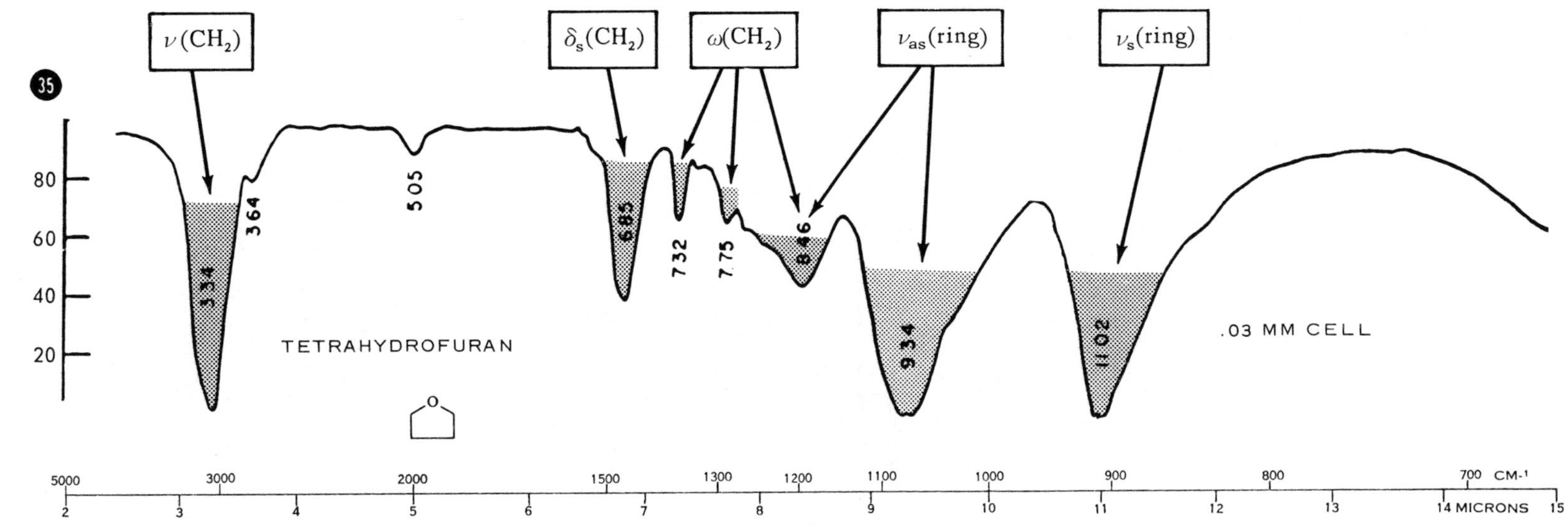

33-35. Comparison of the spectra of tetrahydropyran, dioxane and tetrahydrofuran.

The above compounds are saturated ring ethers and their spectra are compared here. The workers reporting these spectra point out that all have a strong band in the 1110 cm^{-1} region, similar to all saturated ethers. They further suggest that for six-member rings a band near 880 cm^{-1} is characteristic, while the band near 910 cm^{-1} is characteristic for five-member rings. Other workers suggest that the ν_{as}(ring) and ν_s(ring) for six-member rings appear near 1100 and 815 cm^{-1} respectively. For five-member rings these are near 1070 and 915 cm^{-1}. We therefore assign ν_{as}(ring) and ν_s(ring) to bands near these positions. Note the six-member rings have strong bands in the same region, while the five-member ring does not.

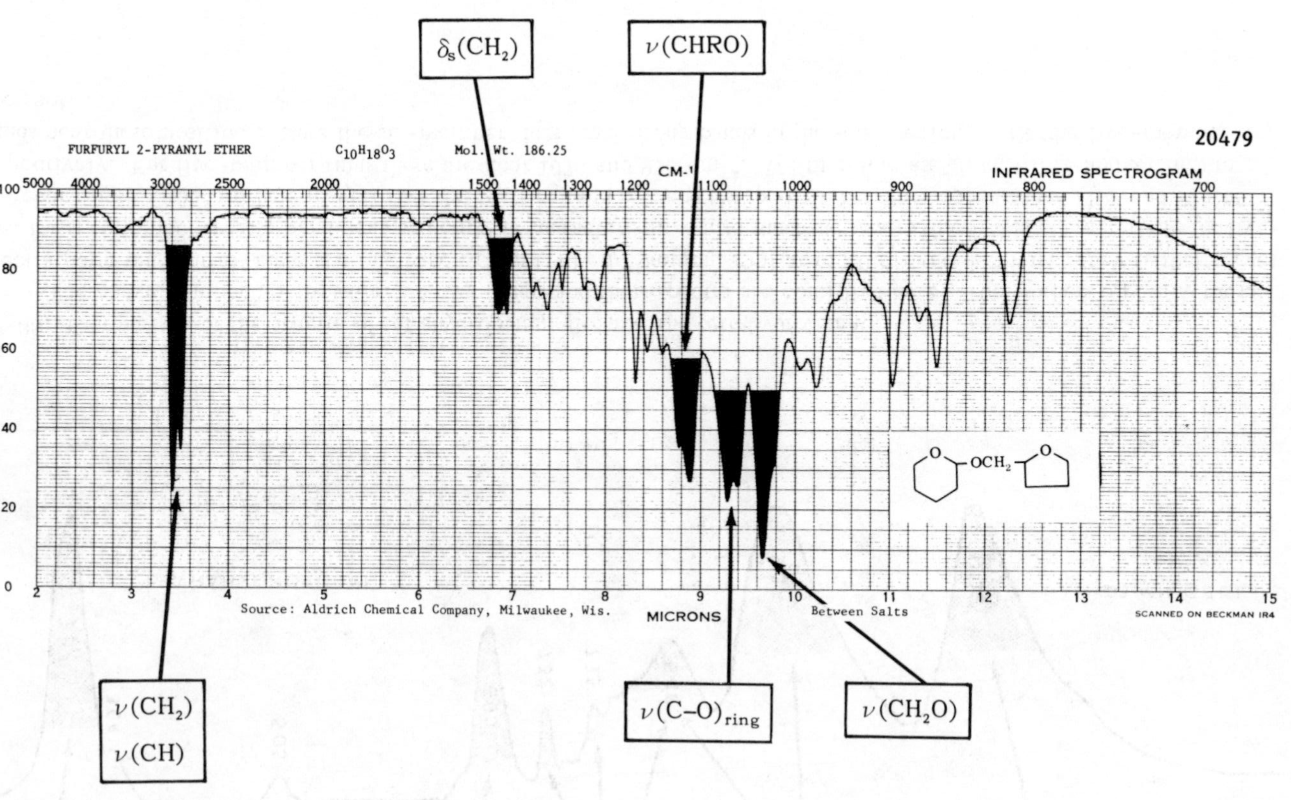

36. The groups present here are the five- and six-member ring ethers as well as a straight-chain ether. We predict bands near 1110, 1030, and 1080 cm^{-1} for the groups CHRO, CH_2O, and the ring C−O groups. These are observed. Apparently both the five- and six-member ring give the ν(C−O) band near 1100 cm^{-1}, as we have seen in their spectra presented in this series. Note however the band is doubled, which possibly means the bands are at slightly different positions for the rings.

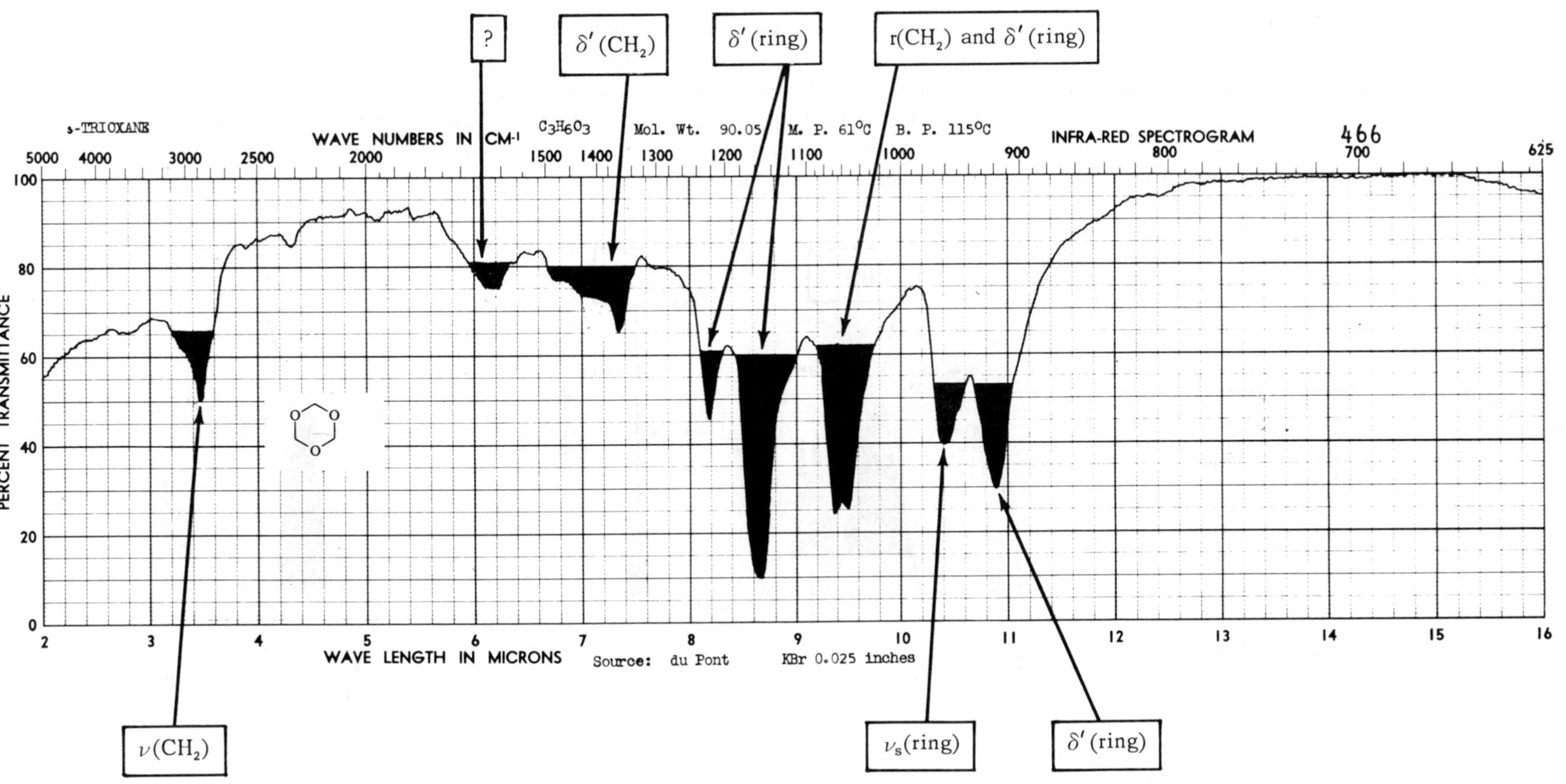

37. In the correlation section we presented the vibrational analysis of the trioxanes, so the assignments here are based on this analysis. The author would like, however, to refer to the band near 1050 cm^{-1} as the $\nu(CH_2O)$, since we have seen this band appears quite consistently in all the spectra having this group.

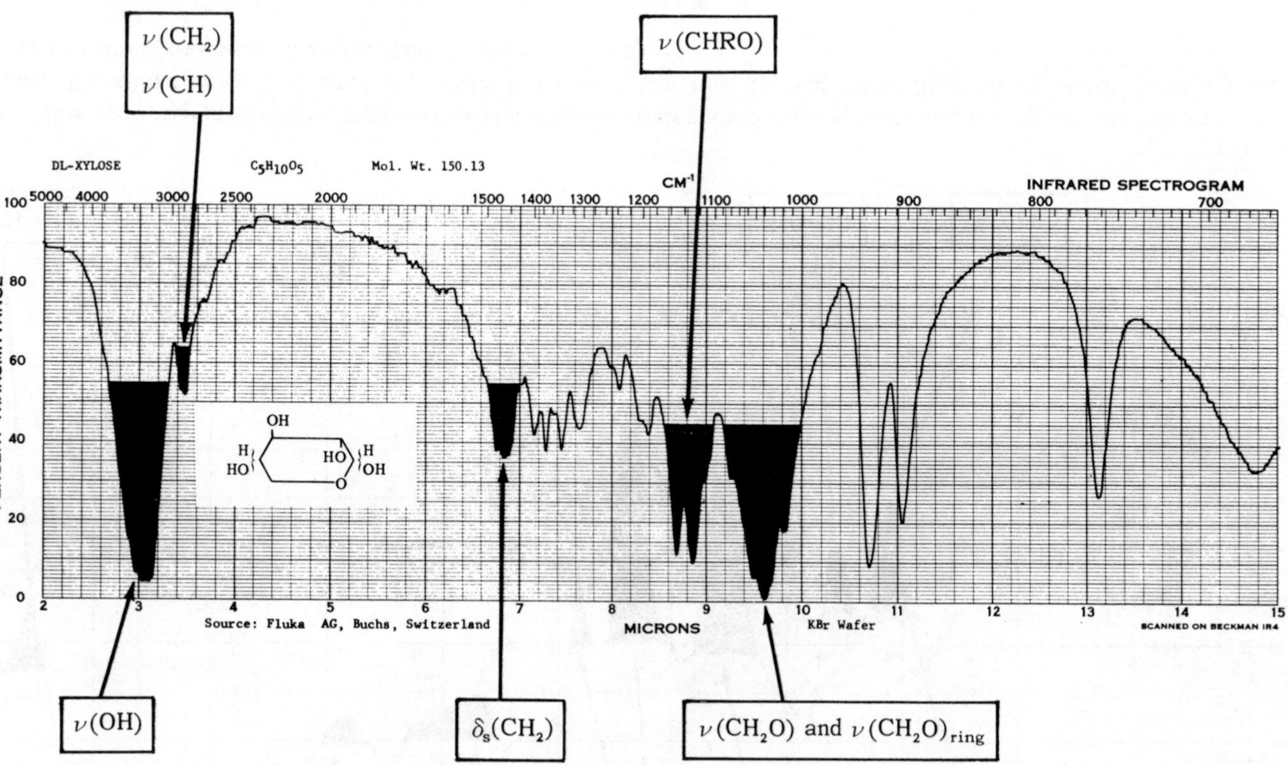

38. This spectrum is presented here to remind the reader that many complex compounds such as sugars, celluloses, etc., have C—O groups, and our simple correlations are still applicable. However, to do an adequate analysis the reader should compare a related series of spectra of these compounds so slight changes of structure can be noted from slight changes in spectral bands. For this spectrum we identify ν(CHRO) and $\nu(CH_2O)$ bands in the expected positions. The doubling of the ν(CHRO) may be expected, if we note two environments for the CHRO groups. The ring C—O stretch adds to the broad 1050 cm^{-1} band. The other bands are assigned from previous correlations; however, the 920 cm^{-1} doublet is puzzling, unless it is the ν_s(C—O) of the ring.

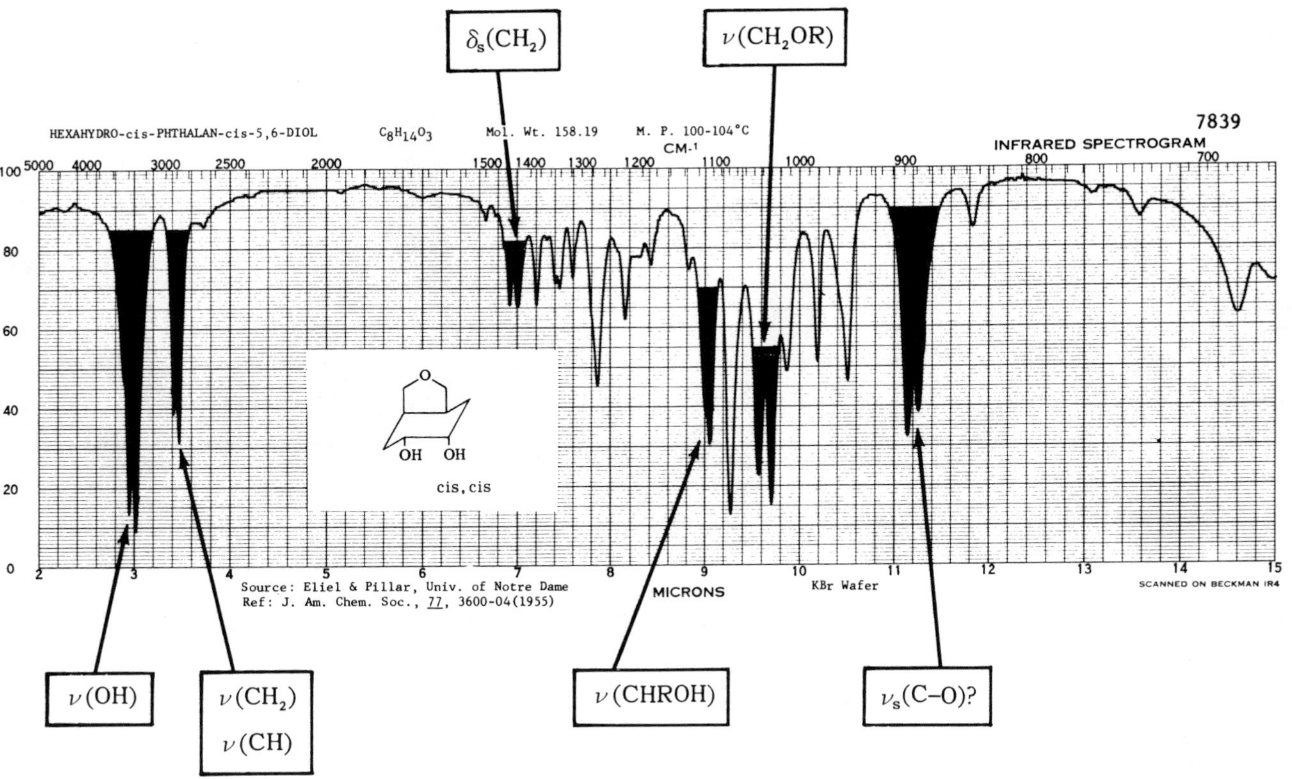

39. This very complex ring ether can be analyzed if we note the groups and their expected positions are: $\nu(CH_2OCH_2)$, 1030 cm^{-1}; $\nu(CHROH)$, 1110 cm^{-1}. Bands are found at these positions, and are assigned to these groups. The complexity of the 1120-1000 cm^{-1} region, however, suggests that either we have a number of isomers for this compound or impurities are present. Note the suggestion of the $\nu_s(C{-}O)$ of the ring ether near 900 cm^{-1}.

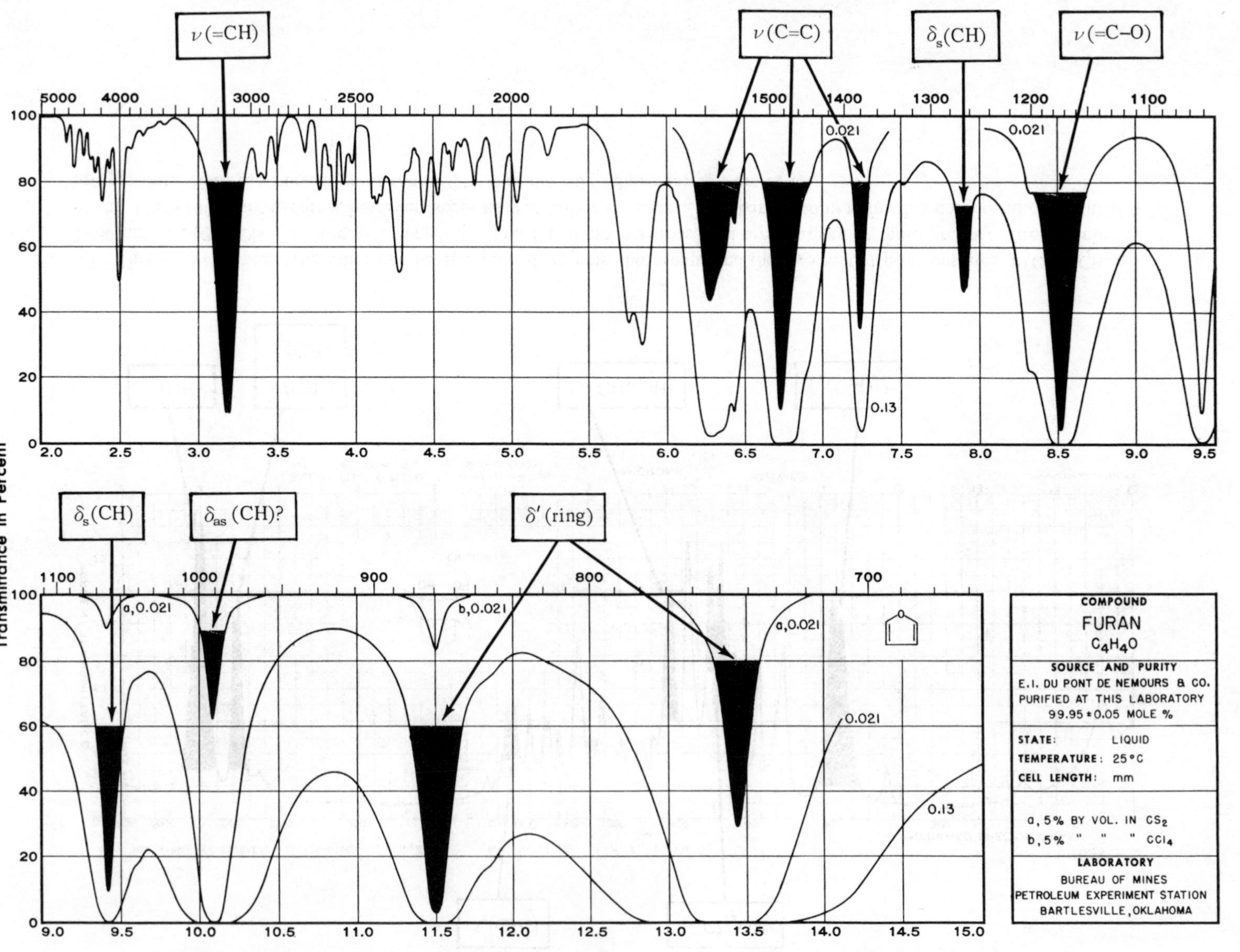

40. The vibrational analysis of furan was presented in the correlation section. The assignments in this spectrum are based on the analysis. We pose the question for the reader if a band near 1200 cm^{-1} is expected because the structure $=C-O$ occurs here? The answer is not obvious, as one of the vibrational analyses reported a band at 1198 cm^{-1} as a ring vibration while a second reported $\beta(=CH)$. This author feels that if the ring is not strained, the position of the C−O stretch should be similar to that of the non-ring ethers. Therefore, the 1189 cm^{-1} band can be assigned as $\nu(=C-O)$.

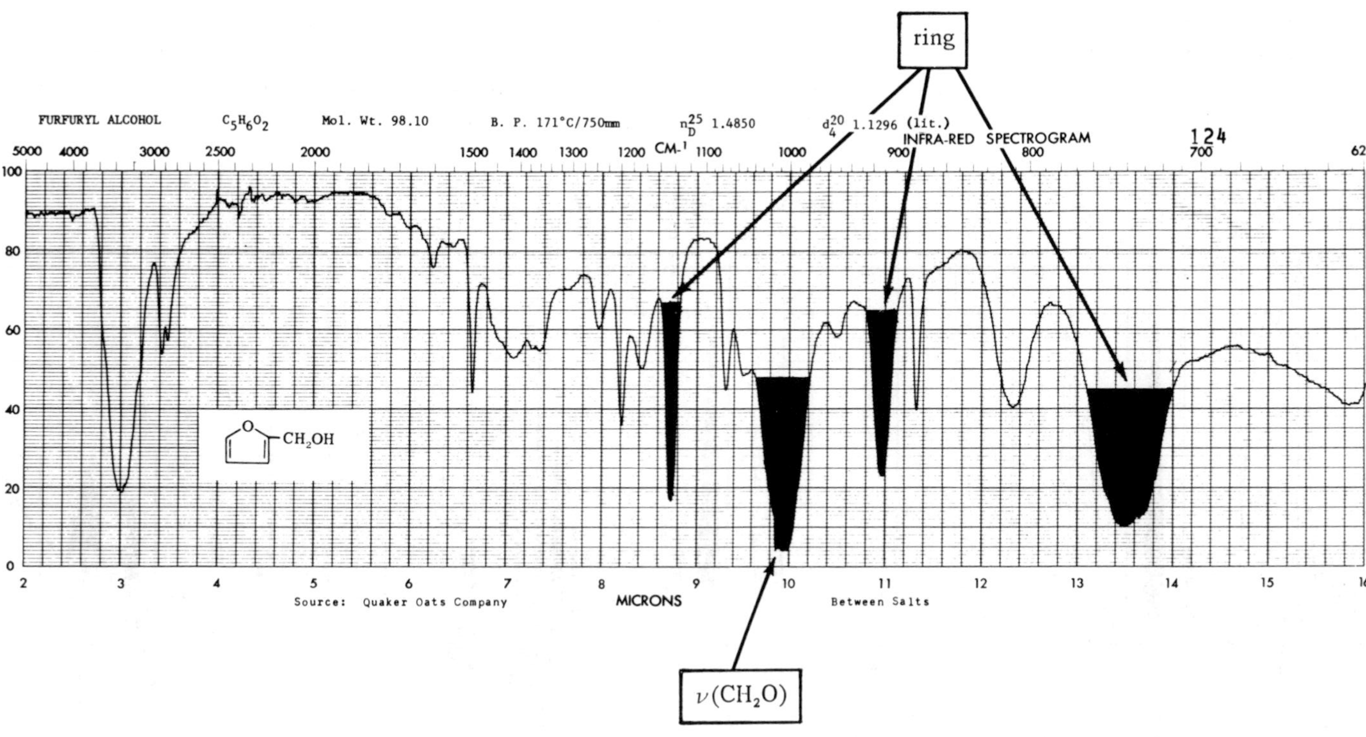

41. Furfuryl alcohol has the furan ring and a primary alcohol. The alcoholic C—O stretch is at 1010 cm^{-1}. This lower position is expected if we compare this position to that for $C_6H_5CH_2OH$ (see Volume 2) and $C_6H_5CH_2OC_6H_5$ (see p. 105). The ring pulls electrons from the C—O band, and this lowers its frequency from 1035 for CH_3CH_2OH to 1010 cm^{-1} here. The furan ring gives rise to bands near 1150, 910, and 740 cm^{-1}. These are assignments based on the vibrational analysis of furan.

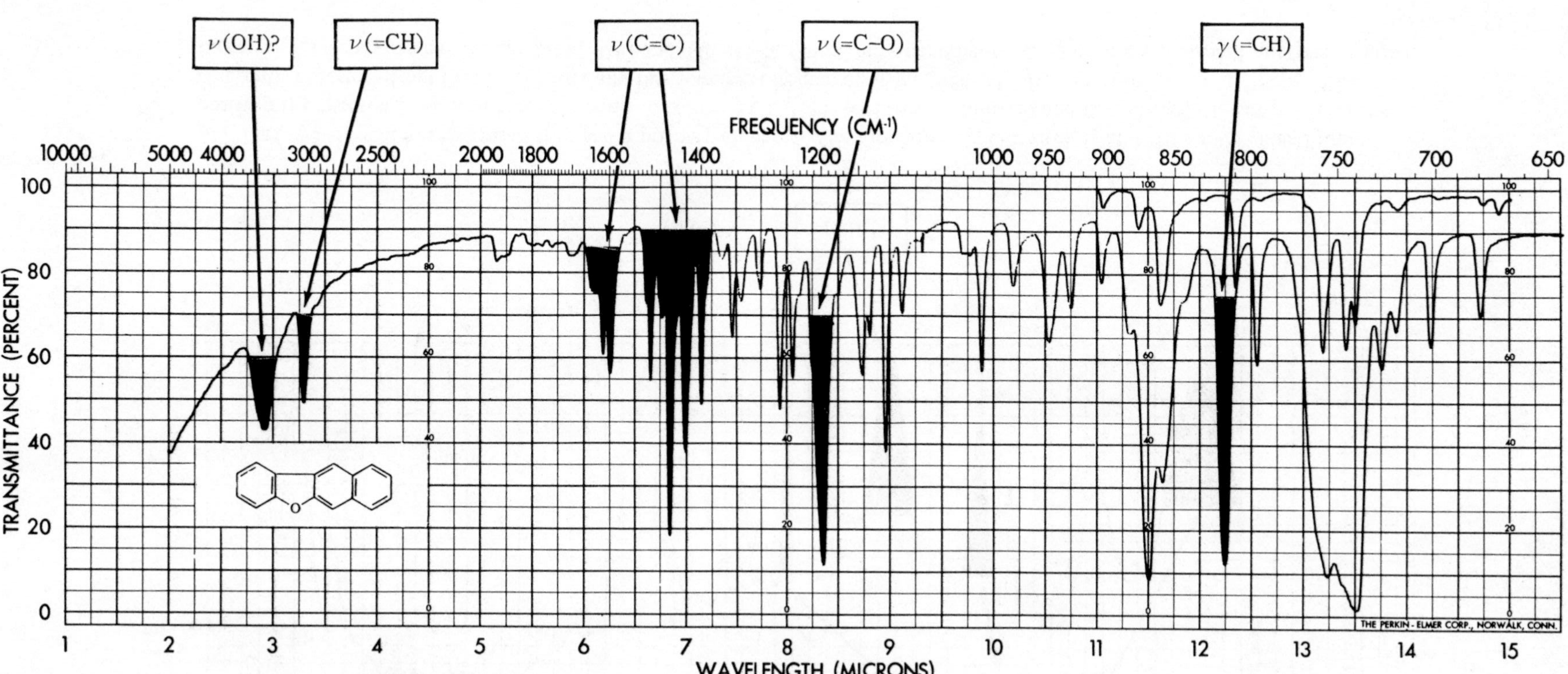

42. This complex compound has the equivalent of a furan ring in an aromatic series of rings. Note the strong 1200 cm^{-1} band which we expect for the ν(= C–O) vibration if we accept the assignment suggested for spectrum 40. The other assignments are the expected ones. We do not assign isolated ring vibrations to the furan part of the molecule, since it is part of the aromatic ring system, and the long wavelength region of the spectrum consists mostly of γ(= CH) bands of the aromatic ring.

PEROXIDES

PEROXIDES

Vibrational Analysis

The Oxidation of Methyl Radicals at Room Temperature

Source: P. L. Haust, J. G. Calvert, J. Phys. Chem. 63:71 (1959).

The spectra of dimethyl peroxide and methyl hydroperoxide are discussed in the above reference. These spectra are presented in the last part by this section.

Dialkyl Peroxides

Source: F. Welch, H. R. Williams, H. S. Mosher, J. Am. Chem. Soc. 77:557 (1955).

In this reference a table of absorption bands for dialkyl peroxides is presented. All are primary peroxides except two— the t-butyl and secondary butyl peroxides.

Organic Peroxides

Source: G. J. Minkoff, Proc. Roy. Soc. Lond. A224:176 (1954).

Infrared spectra of over thirty organic peroxides are reported. It is concluded that the ν(O—O) band occurs in the region from 1000 to 850 cm^{-1}. It is of medium intensity for hydroperoxide, and weak in peroxides. No specific rules are given for dialkyl and diacylperoxide. It is of interest to call attention to the paragraph in this article reporting two serious explosions that occurred for workers studying hydroxyethyl hydroperoxide and dihydroxyethyl peroxide. It is very difficult to purify the lower members of the peroxide series as they are unstable. Some of these spectra are presented in this section.

Infrared Absorption Spectra of Some Hydroperoxides, Peroxides, and Related Compounds

Source: O. D. Shreve, M. R. Heether, H. B. Knight, D. Swern, Anal. Chem. 23:282 (1951).

In comparing the spectra of $(CH_3)_3COH$ and $(CH_3)_3COOH$ it was noted that a band at 910 cm^{-1} for the alcohol disappeared, and a new strong band at 850 cm^{-1} appeared. Since other hydroperoxides have this band, it is assigned as a vibration of the OOH group.

Infrared Absorption Spectra of Tertiary Peroxides

Source: A. R. Philpotts, W. Thain, Anal. Chem. 24:638 (1952).

Bands in the 915-830 cm^{-1} region are associated with the $(C)_3C—O—$group rather than the O—O linkage. These bands occur in ethers as well as peroxides having the C_4O group. If the ν(O—O) band does occur in the 915-830 cm^{-1} region, it is weak and will probably be interfered with by other vibrations

Infrared Absorption Frequencies of the Tert-Butoxy Group

Source: H. A. Ory, Anal. Chem. 32:509 (1960).

Several peroxide compounds are included in this study.

Infrared Spectra of Alkyl Hydroperoxides

Source: H. R. Williams, H. S. Mosher, Anal. Chem. No. 4, 27:517 (1955).

The infrared spectra of 17 alkyl hydroperoxides are presented in this paper. Several of the spectra are included in this text. The authors assign the ν(O—O) stretch to the region near 900 cm^{-1}, and report it as a weak band. All of the compounds examined show absorption near 830 cm^{-1}.

PEROXIDES

$(F_3C)_2O_2$

Source: A. J. Arvia and P. J. Aymonino, Spectrochim. Acta 18:1299 (1962).

Band cm^{-1} (vapor)	Assignment
480 M	$\delta'_{as}(F_3C)$
556 W	$\delta'_{as}(F_3C)$
606 S	$\delta'_{as}(F_3C)$
625 S	$\delta'_{as}(F_3C)$
673 M	$\delta'_{s}(F_3C)$
821 W	$\nu(O-O)$
886 M	$\nu(C-O)$
974 W	$\nu(C-O)$
1062 M	combination
1122 S	$\nu_s(CF_3)$
1167 WSh	$\nu_s(CF_3)$
1238 VS	$\nu_{as}(CF_3)$
1265 VVS	$\nu_{as}(CF_3)$
1285 VVS	$\nu_{as}(CF_3)$
2141 M	combination
2540 M	combination

$(FCO)_2O_2$

Source: A. J. Arvia and P. J. Aymonino, Spectrochim. Acta 18:1299 (1962).

Band cm^{-1} (vapor)	Assignment
582 S 586 S 592 S	$\delta_s(F-C-O)$
660 M	r(F−C−O)
749 S	γ(OCFO)
912 M	$\nu(O-O)$
954 S	$\nu(C-O)$
1016 M	$\nu(C-O)$
1178 VVS	$\nu(C-F)$
1221 S	$\nu(C-F)$
1319 M	overtone
1899 VS 1905 VS	$\nu(C=O)$
1934 VS	$\nu(C=O)$
2028 M	overtone
2177 M	combination
2401 M	combination
3800 M	overtone
3820 M	combination

$C_2H_5OOC_2H_5$

Source: C. F. Kettering, W. W. Sleator, Phys., No. 2, 4:39 (1933).

Band, cm^{-1} (vapor)
2940 S
1740 M
1460 SSh
1350 VS
1235 W
1065 VVS
945 MWSh
880 VS
860 VSSh
795 W
725 W
670 M (Q branch)

Correlation of Peroxides

Group Frequencies for Peroxides

The group frequencies of peroxides should be similar to those found for ethers, for those peroxides of the type R_1OOR_2; and those of the type ROOH should be similar to the group frequencies of alcohols. In the following correlation tables these two divisions of peroxides are followed. If we examine the table for group frequencies for peroxides of the type ROOH the following points can be noted.

A. Primary and secondary alkyl hydroperoxides have their bonded ν(OH) band about 30 cm^{-1} higher than for the corresponding alcohol.
B. The grouping CH_2OOH shows shoulder bands at 1488 and 1435 cm^{-1} on the 1465 cm^{-1} $\delta(CH_2)$ band for those peroxides having alkyl chains of CH_2 groups.
C. The grouping =CH−OOH has a band in the 1352-1334 cm^{-1} region assigned as ω(CH).
D. The ν(C−O) of peroxides may appear about 10 cm^{-1} lower than for the corresponding alcohol or ether.
E. A weak band in the 880−845 cm^{-1} region may be assigned as ν(O−O), but it is of limited diagnostic value.
F. In normal alkyl hydroperoxide in the 835−800 cm^{-1} region it has been noted that, if an even number of carbon atoms are present, two bands near 827 and 807 cm^{-1} are observed. If the number is odd, then one band appears near 815 cm^{-1}.

Peroxides

Group frequency designation	Symbol	Position, cm^{-1}	Intensity
−O−O−stretch of aliphatic peroxides (see explanation in text)	ν(−O−O)	890-820	W
−O−O−stretch of aromatic peroxides	ν(O−O)	1000	W
C−O stretch	ν(C−O)	10-30 cm^{-1} lower than for corresponding ether or alcohol	
−O−O−H stretch	ν(−O−O−H)	3450	M-S
−CO−O−O−CO deformation of aliphatic peroxides	δ'(−CO−O−O−CO)	1820-1810 1800-1780	M-W M-W
−CO−O−O−CO deformation of aromatic peroxides	δ'(−CO−O−O−CO)	1805-1780 1785-1755	M-W M-W
deformation band of ozonides	δ'(ozonide)	1060-1040	M-W
bonded OH stretching frequency	ν(OH)	30 cm^{-1} higher than for corresponding alcohol	M-W
CH_2 bending frequency	$\delta(CH_2OOH)$	1488 and 1435	MSSh
CH wagging frequency	ω(CHOOH)	1352-1334	M-W

PEROXIDES

We shall present next the spectra of hydroperoxides and peroxides. Because these are unstable compounds it is difficult to find many spectra for them. In addition, those presented may have impurities present which give interfering or misleading bands. This author found it difficult to find the spectra he desired to illustrate the group frequencies of both types of O—O compounds. The following present the current literature of peroxide spectra, although some are not as sharp and distinct spectra as the author would like for a section such as this.

There is a simple set of correlations which can be listed for both hydroperoxides and peroxides: First, there seems to be no distinct ν(O—O) band, although we shall make a few tentative suggestions. Second, common to both hydroperoxides and peroxides is the group C—O—O, and its position depends to a great extent on what is attached to the carbon atom. The groups attached to the second oxygen atom appear not to influence band position.

The following general groups will show the position listed for the ν(C—O—O). It should be noted alcohols and ethers. have the same position.

Group	Position of ν(C—O—O)
H I ⋛C—C—O—O— I CH	1025 cm^{-1}
H I ⋛C—C—O—O— I C⋞	1110 cm^{-1}
C⋞ I ⋛C—C—O—O— I C /I\	1200 cm^{-1}
C ‖ C I C=C—C—O—O— I C ‖ C (C=C can be olefinic or aromatic)	1000 cm^{-1}

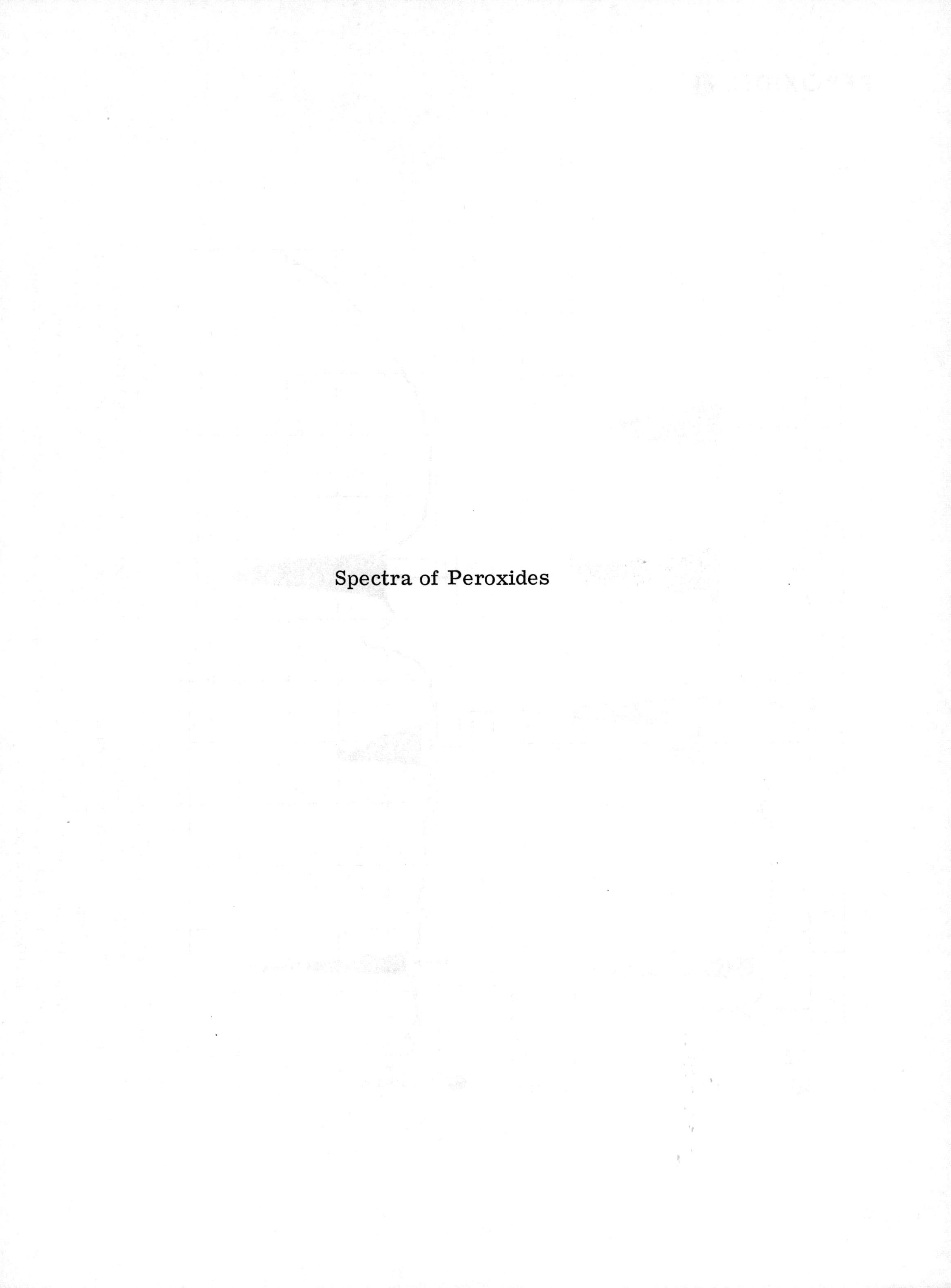

Spectra of Peroxides

PEROXIDES ❶

Reprinted from J. Phys. Chem. 63: 71 (1959).

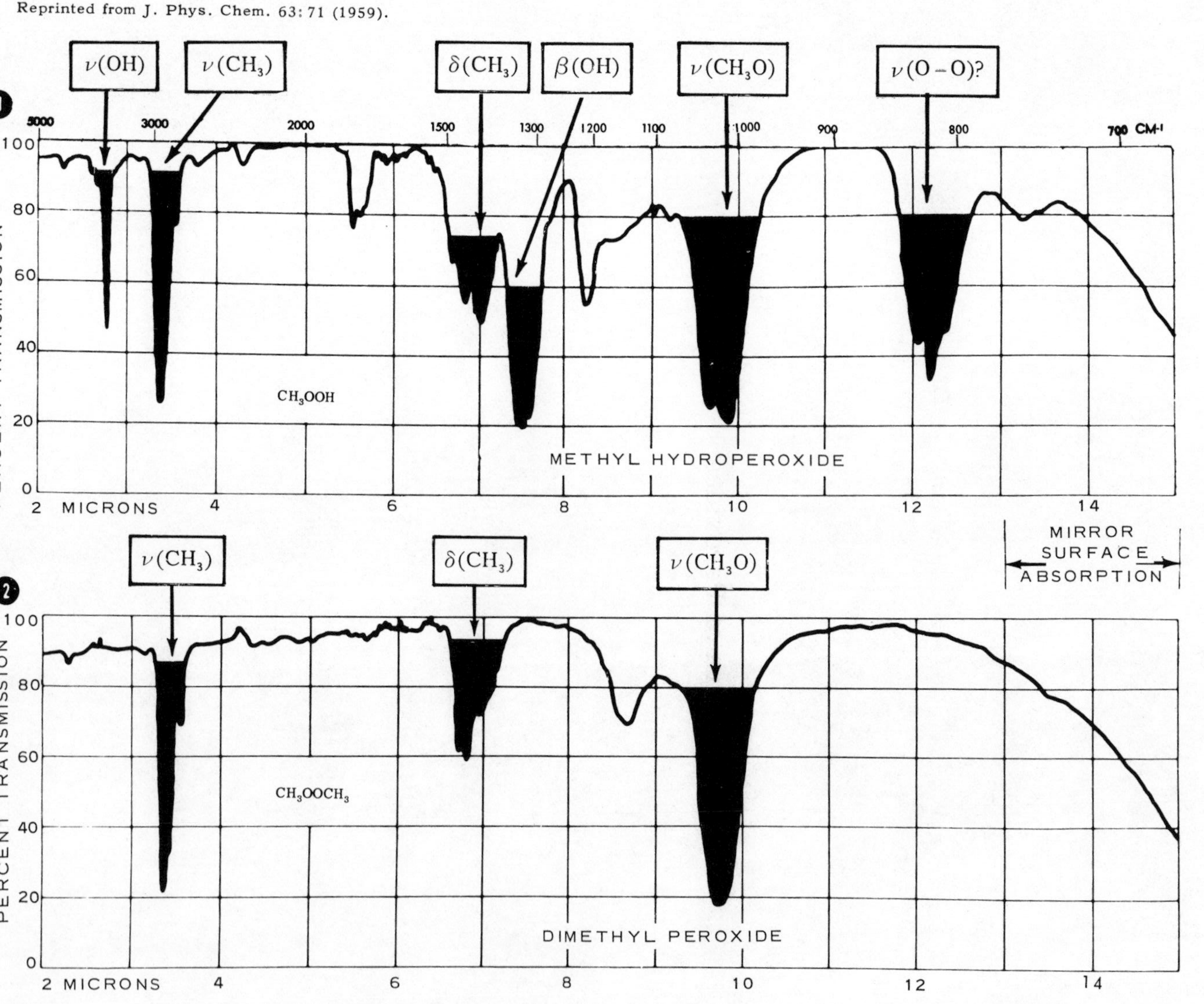

1,2. In the following section we shall consider first spectra of the hydroperoxides, and then the peroxides; however, here we can compare the two types to illustrate basic differences in them. The spectra of CH_3OOH and CH_3OOCH_3 are compared in this first figure. This is similar to comparing methanol and dimethyl ether. As a matter of fact, all four of these spectra are quite similar. All have a strong $\nu(C-O)$ band near 1020 cm^{-1}. The alcohols have a $\nu(OH)$ and $\beta(OH)$ vibration that does not appear in the ether. The strong band for the hydroperoxide near 840 cm^{-1} is not present in the peroxide nor in dimethyl ether. It is present in methanol and in many hydroperoxides, and is often assigned as $\nu(O-O)$. We therefore assign it here as $\nu(O-O)$, with a question mark.

Reprinted from Proc. Roy. Soc. London A224 : 176 (1954).

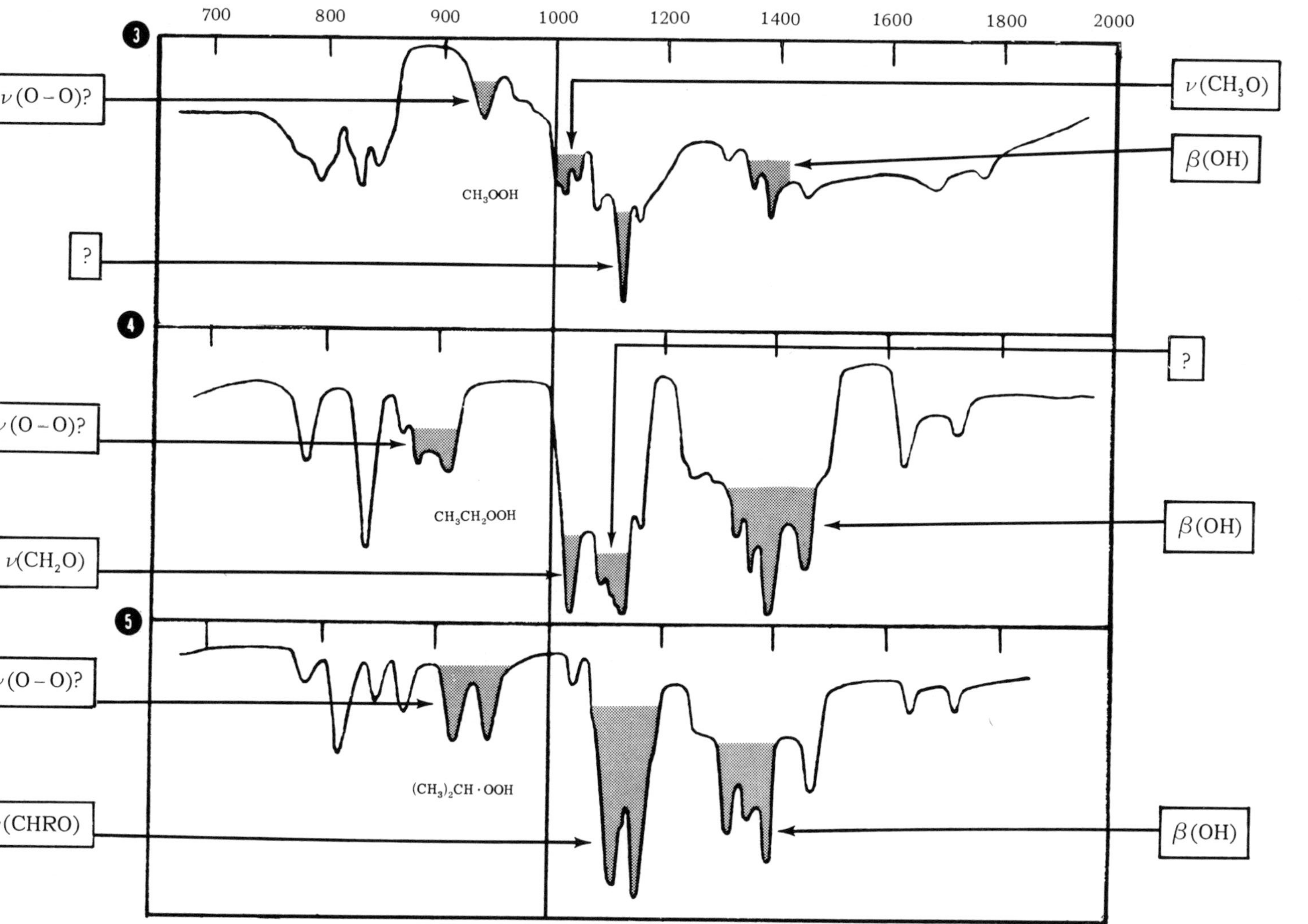

3, 4, 5. In this figure the spectra of the compounds CH_3OOH, C_2H_5OOH, and $CH(CH_3)_2OOH$ are compared. This reference is earlier than the previous one, and it will be of value to compare the spectrum of CH_3OOH presented here to the previous one. The spectra are similar except for the relative intensities of the $\nu(CH_3O)$ and $\beta(OH)$ vibrations. In the previous spectrum they are nearly equal, while in this figure the $\nu(CH_3O)$ is weaker. The compound CH_3CH_2OOH has the $\nu(CH_2O)$ and $\beta(OH)$ in similar positions as the methyl derivative. The compound $CH(CH_3)_2OOH$ has the $\nu(CHRRO)$ near 1150 cm^{-1}, where it nearly coincides with the $\beta(OH)$. This higher position is similar to what is observed for this band for $CH(CH_3)_2OH$, $CH(CH_3)_2OCH(CH_3)_2$, and probably for $CH(CH_3)_2OOCH(CH_3)_2$. There are bands near 800 cm^{-1} which might be $\nu(O-O)$, but since we have concluded that this assignment is dubious, we place it on the figure with a question mark.

Reprinted from Anal. Chem. 27 : 517 (1955).

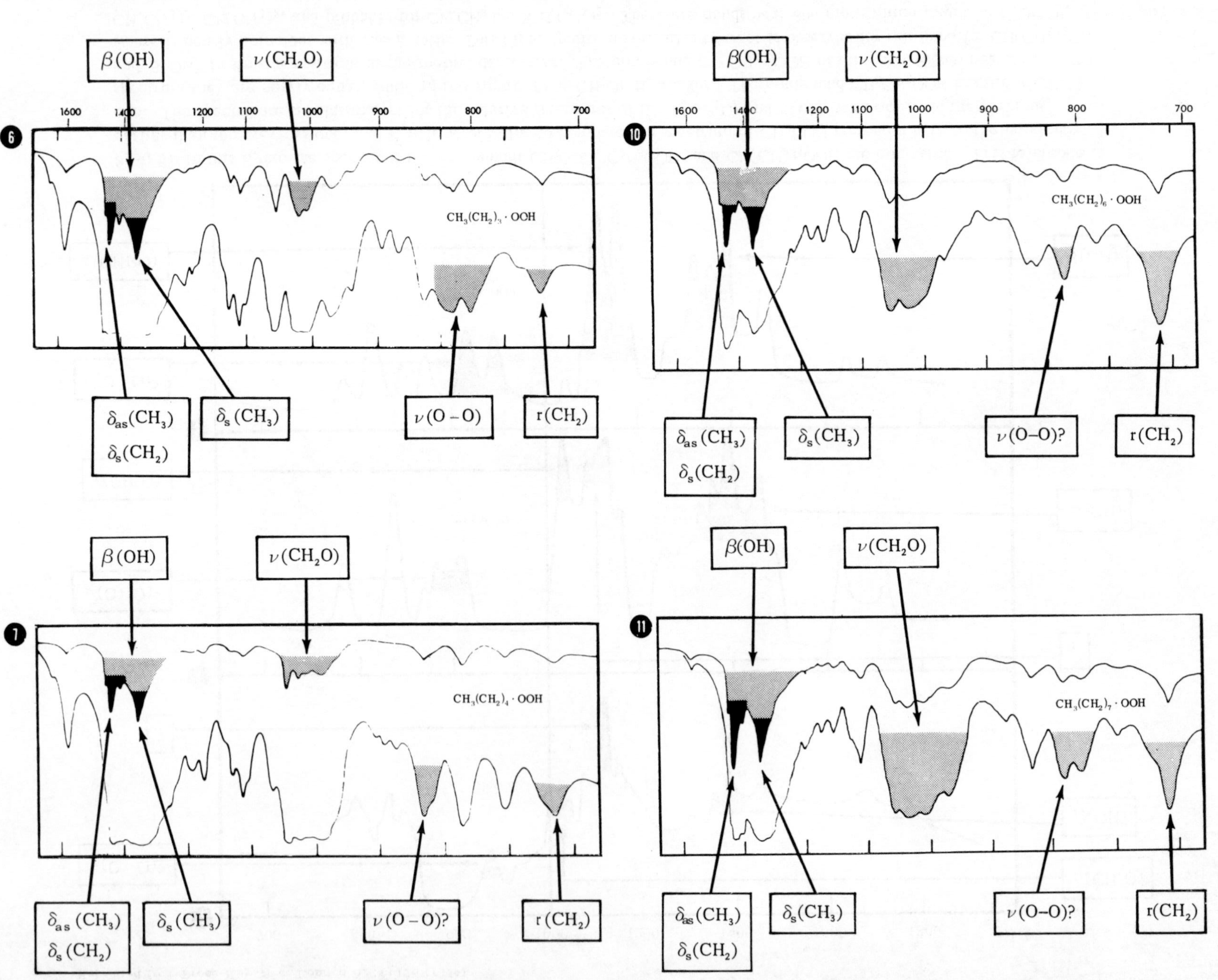

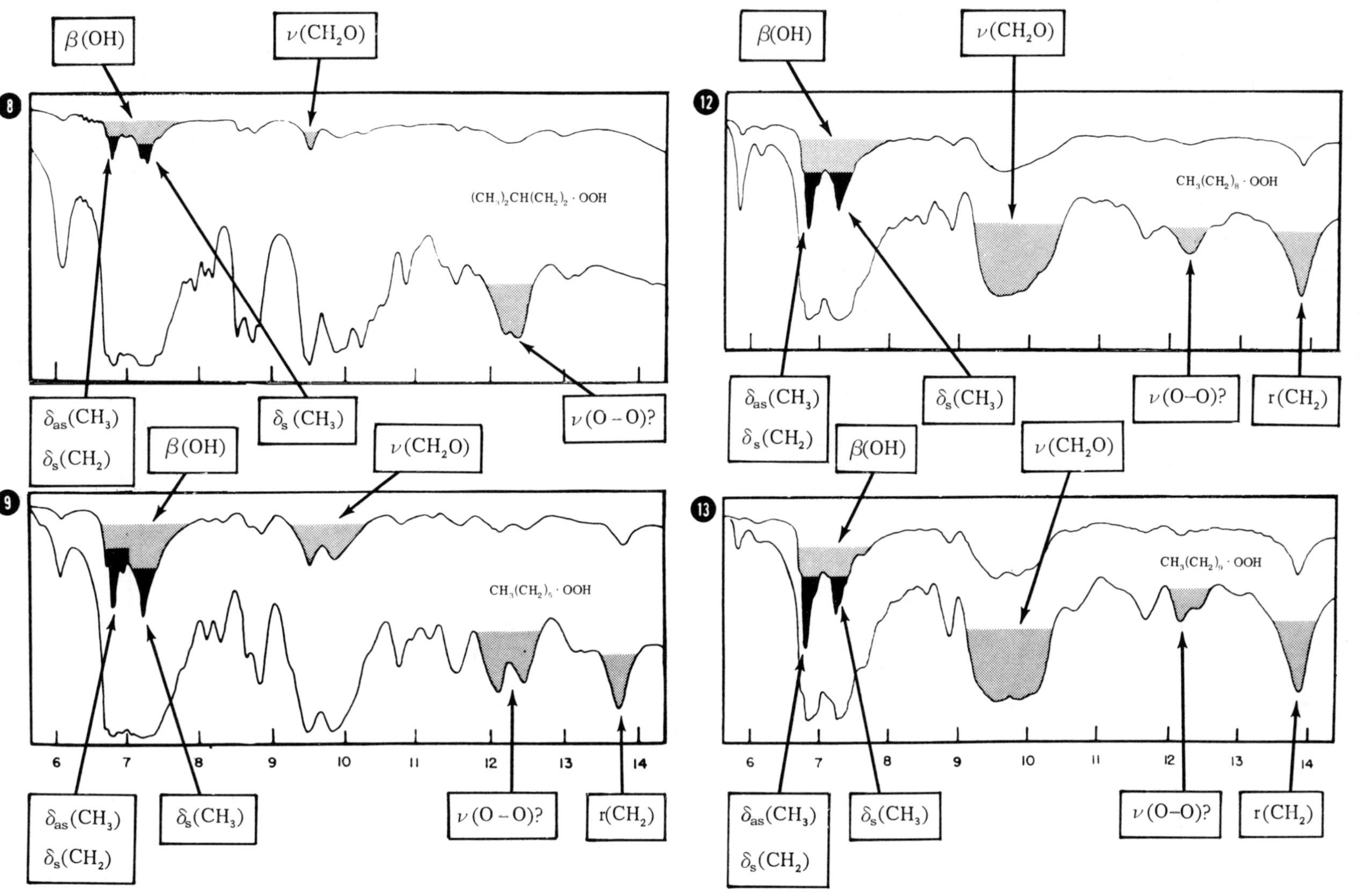

6-13. The spectra of a series of primary hydroperoxides is presented here. The $\nu(CH_2O)$ appears near 1025 cm^{-1} in all spectra, as expected. Note it is the only strong band in these aliphatic peroxides. We shall see for secondary peroxides the 1200-800 cm^{-1} region has more than one strong band; this makes the $\nu(C-O)$ assignment more difficult. The authors of these spectra suggests weak bands near 1490 and 1430 cm^{-1} can be used to identify primary hydroperoxides. The strong $\delta(CH_3)$ bands appear at 1470 and 1390 cm^{-1} and the weaker hydroperoxide bands may be shoulders on these bands. The $\nu(O-O)$ is a doubtful assignment in the 900-800 cm^{-1} region, but these authors suggest that straight-chain hydroperoxides having an even number of carbon atoms show two maxima at 825 and 805, while the odd-number compounds have only a singlet at 815 cm^{-1}.

Reprinted from. Anal. Chem. 27:517 (1955).

14

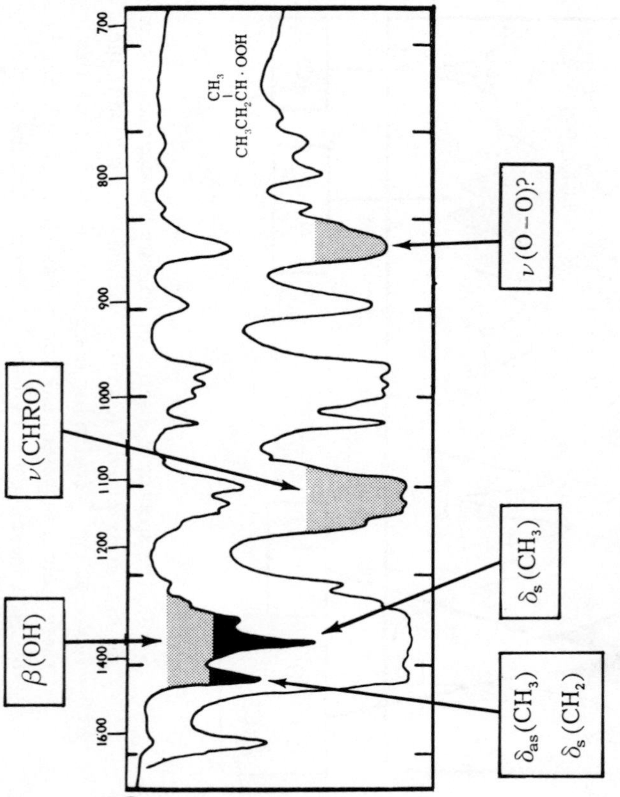

15

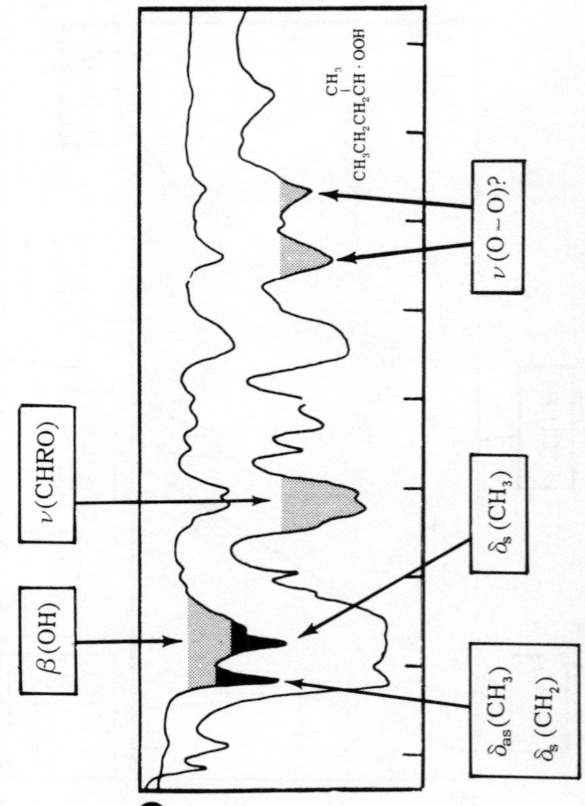

18

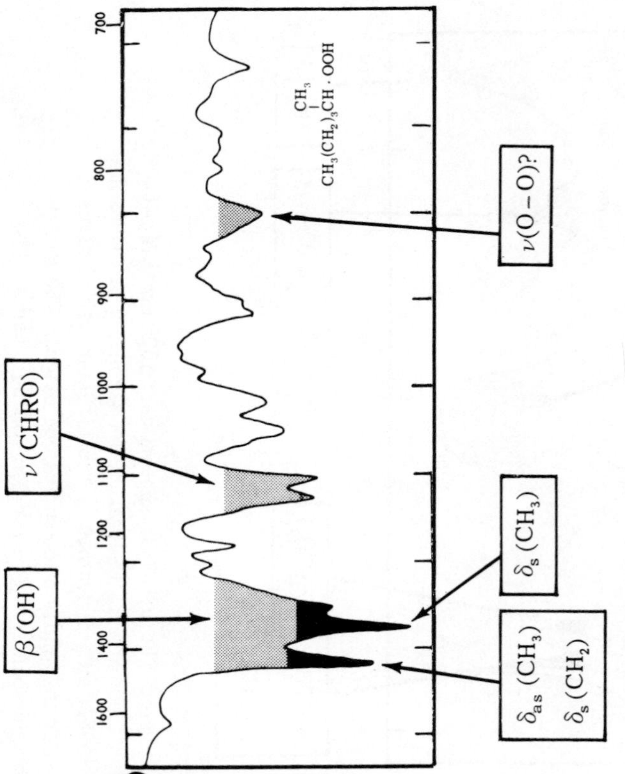

19

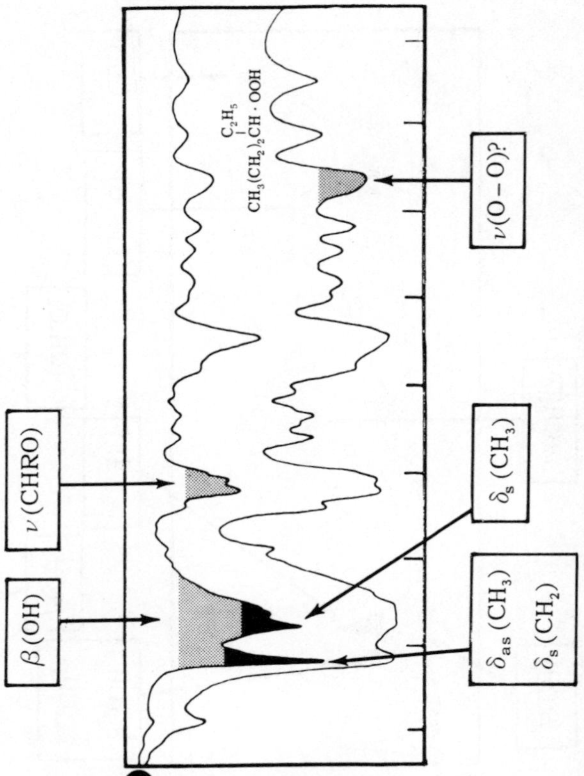

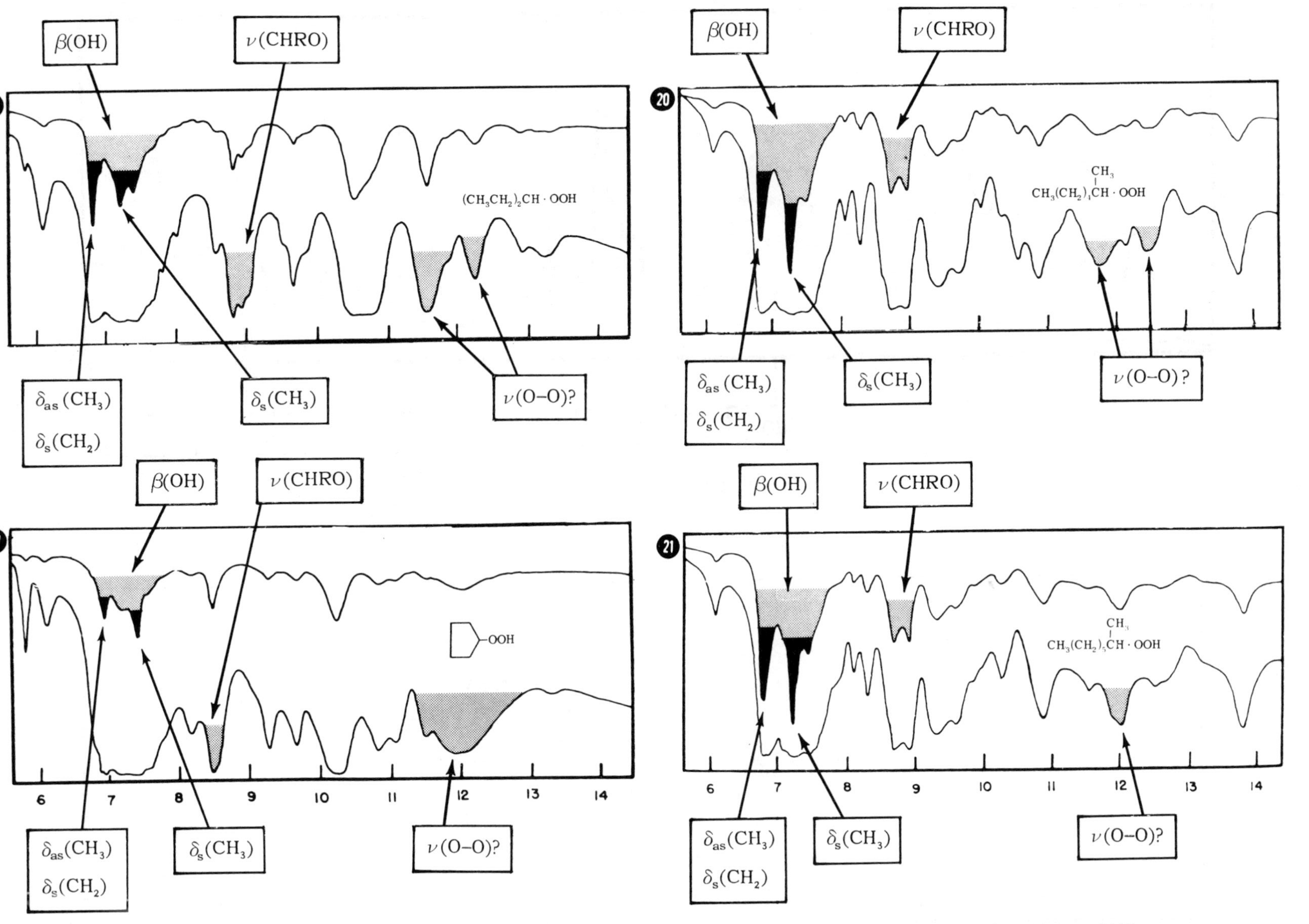

14-21. Here we compare secondary hydroperoxides. Since the group CHRO is present, we expect a ν(C−O) near 1100 cm^{-1}, and a strong band is found here in all examples. There is a strong band near 950 cm^{-1} in many of these examples which is either the ν(O−O) or a vibration due to the branching groups. We shall see in further spectra that the correct assignment is not obvious, but the band does not appear at 950 cm^{-1} except for the secondary hydroperoxides. The author of these spectra suggest that a band near 1330-1335 cm^{-1} is definitive for secondary alkyl peroxides, and bands in the 850-800 cm^{-1} region are due to the OOH group.

Reprinted from Proc. Roy. Soc. London A224 : 176 (1954).

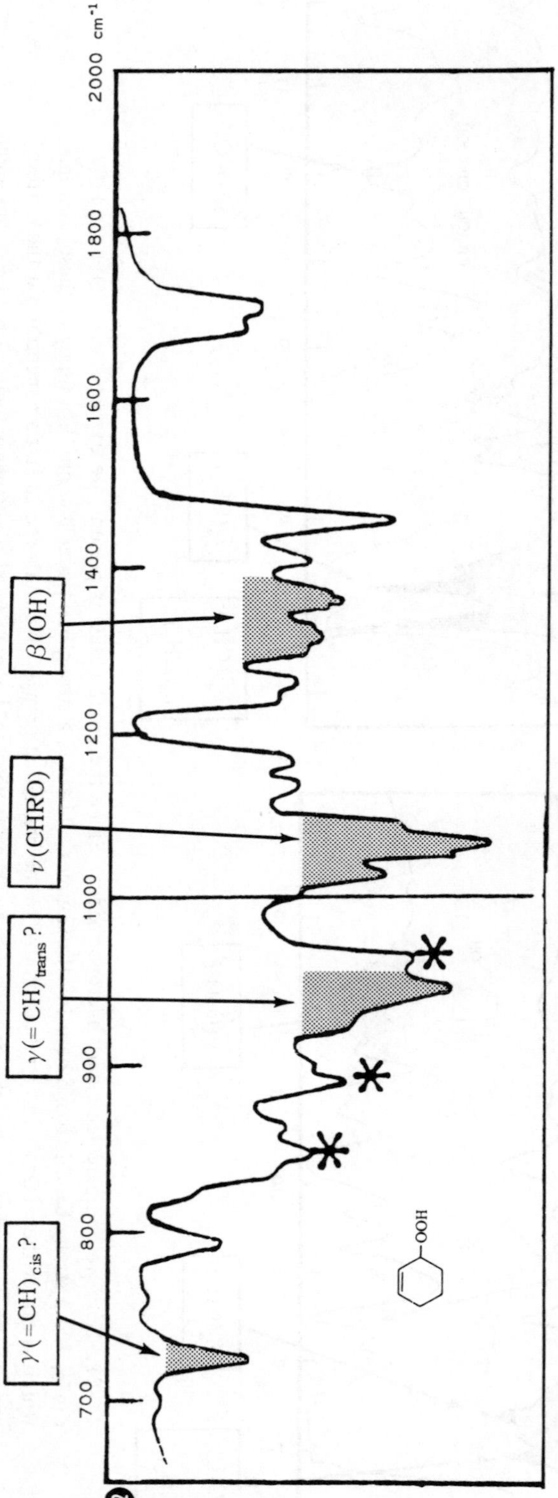

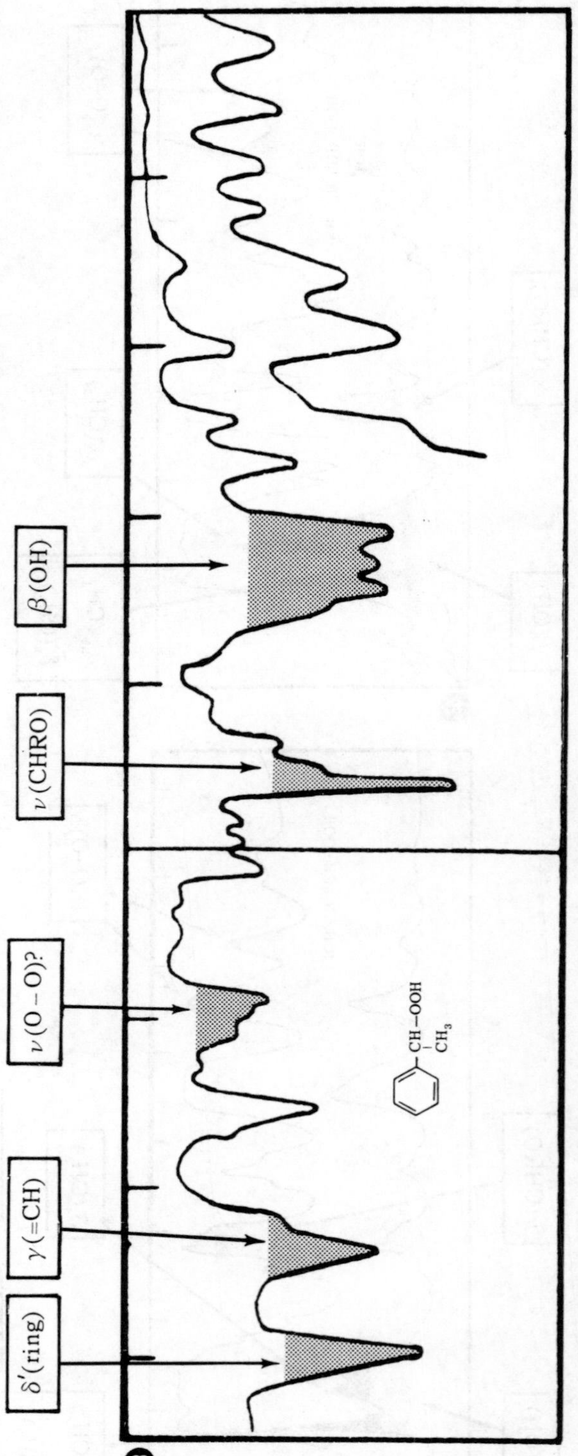

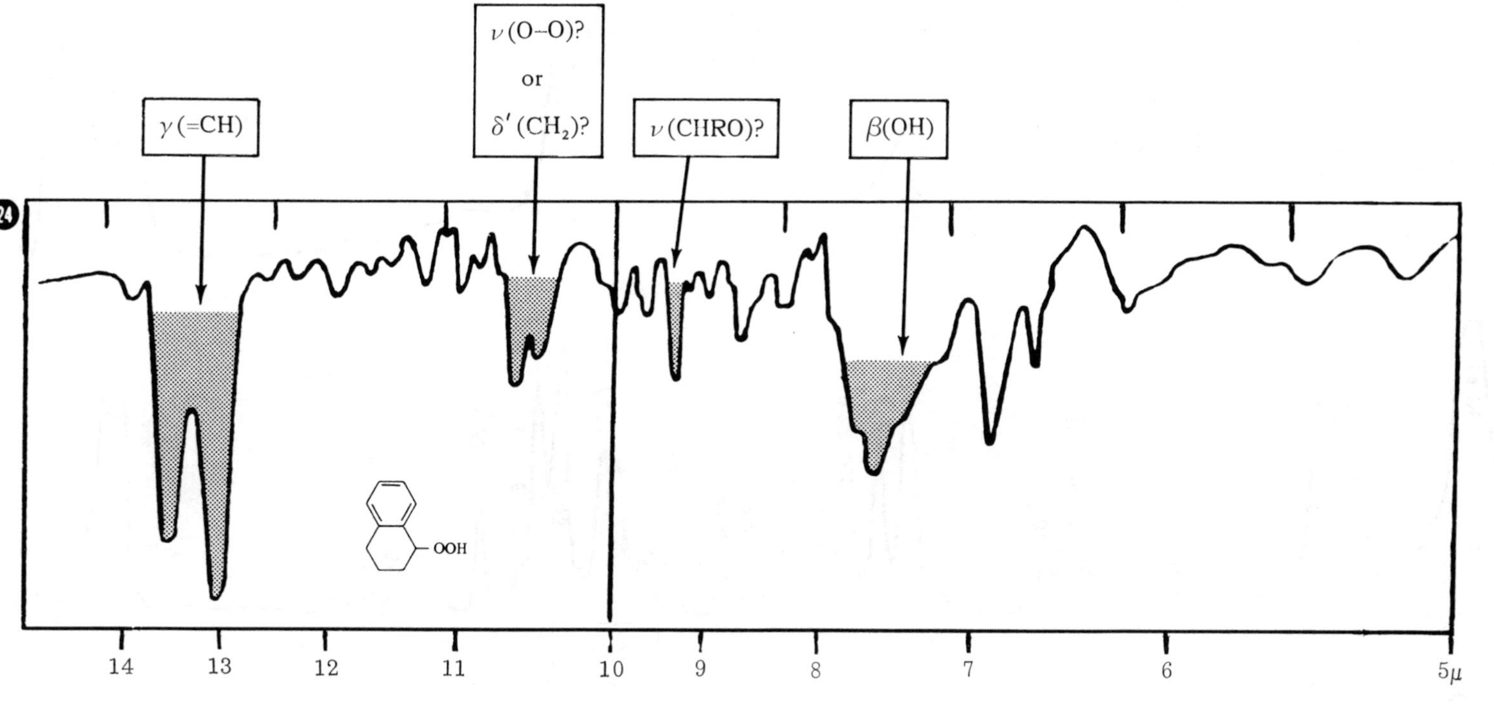

*Asterisked bands denote impurities.

22, 23, 24. The spectra of three secondary hydroperoxides are presented here. These are from the reference reported in the correlation section (p. 211) where the authors suggest that, although a ν(O–O) band appears in the 1000-850 cm^{-1} region, it is usually of medium to weak intensity and obscured by other bands. We feel it is of little value to assign ν(O–O) vibrations, as no consistent band is found. In these spectra, therefore, ν(CHRO) and β(OH) of the hydroperoxide are assigned and a very tentative ν(O–O) is assigned to any strong band near 900 cm^{-1}. The ν(CHRO) assignment is made at 1110 cm^{-1}. Note the absence of the band near 980 cm^{-1} in the aromatic compound, suggesting it is a CH_2 vibration in the bottom spectrum. We call attention to this band since it often occurs as a strong band, and can confuse the ν(C–O) assignment. The β(OH) is probably best assigned as a broad band centered near 1425 cm^{-1}.

Reprinted from Anal. Chem. 23:282 (1951).

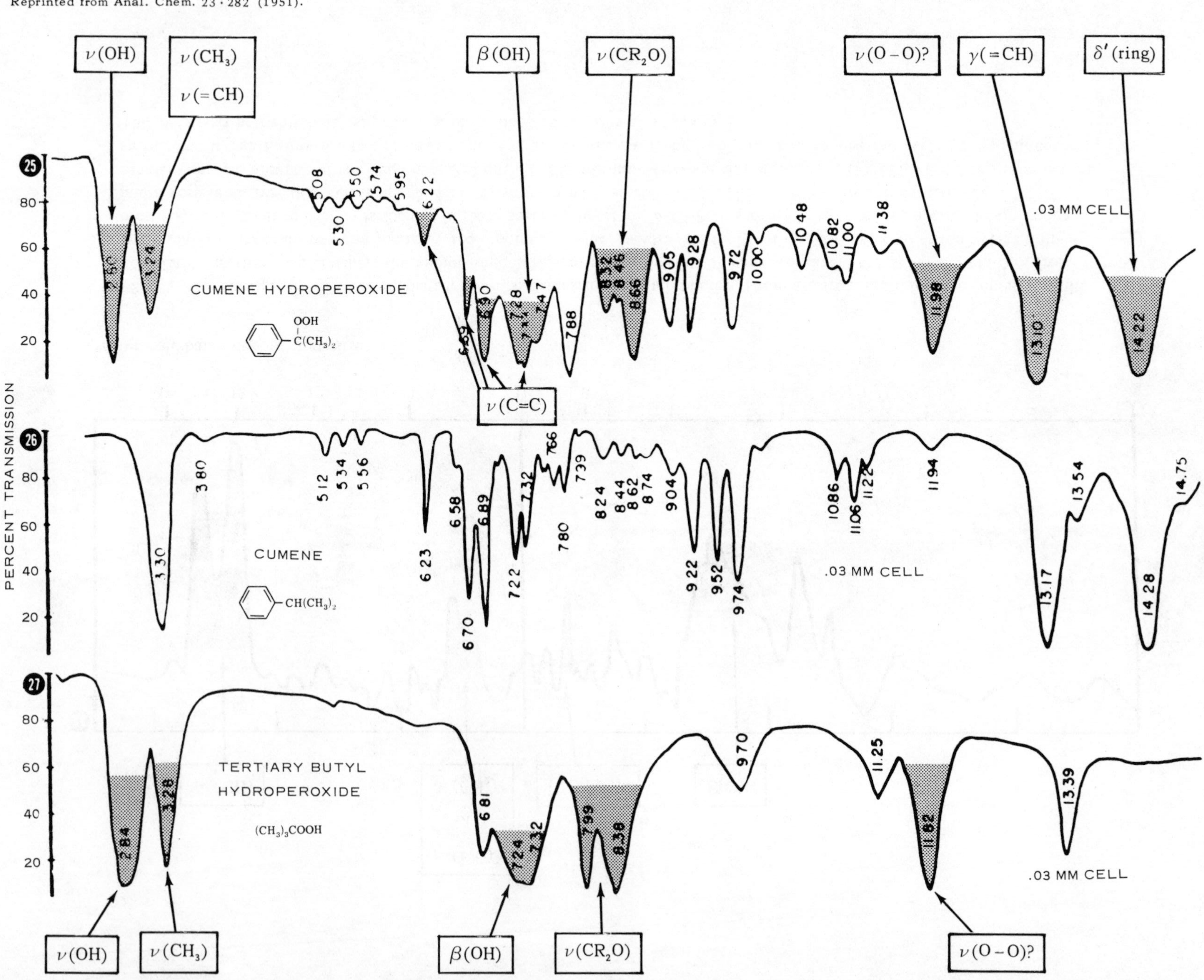

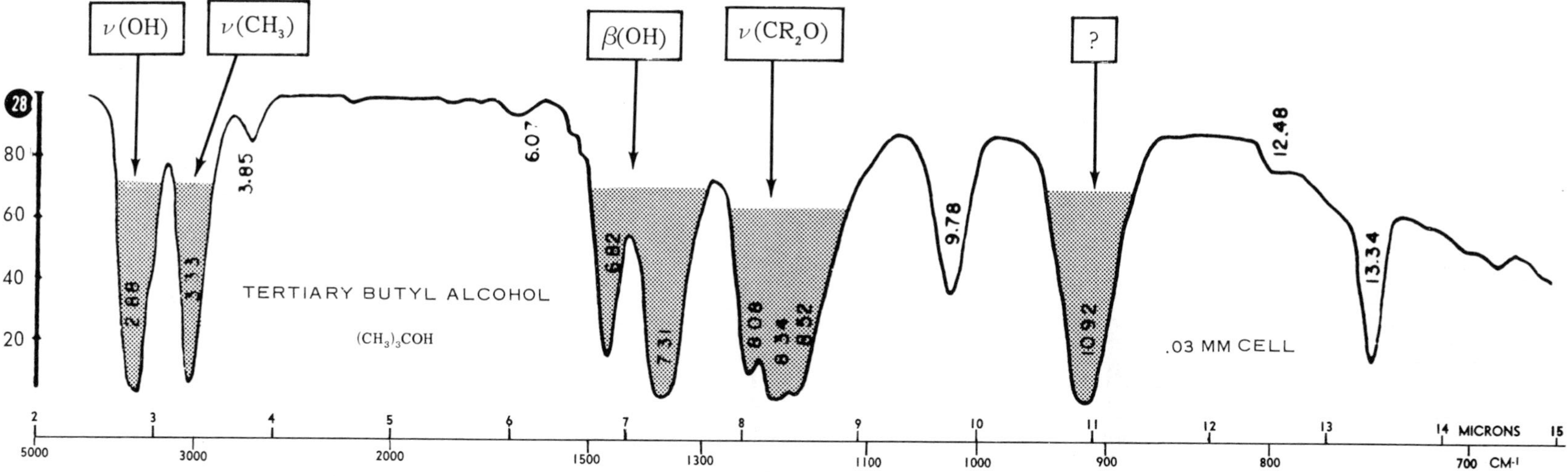

25-28. The comparison is made here between two pairs of related compounds which are also related to a lesser degree to each other. We can compare the lower two spectra first. The bottom one is tertiary butyl alcohol and its spectrum should be compared to tertiary butyl hydroperoxide. We note first a very strong band near 910 cm^{-1}, which apparently shifts to 885 cm^{-1} in the peroxide. This band is not easily assigned and also illustrates how confusing it would be to assign the ν(O−O) vibration of peroxides as a band near 900 cm^{-1}. It is possible the 900 cm^{-1} band is due to the $C(CH_3)_3$ group.

We next can compare the ν(C−O) vibration. In tertiary alcohols it should appear near 1200 cm^{-1} and shift a small degree in the peroxide. If we take the lowest maxima of the alcoholic ν(C−O) as the peak near 1250 cm^{-1}, then the shift of the peroxide is to higher rather than lower frequency. Thus the correlation suggested concerning the lowering of the ν(C−O) of peroxides compared to alcohols fails here.

We can now include the cumene hydroperoxide spectrum in this discussion. For this compound the ν(C−O) is at lower frequency than for the alcohol and tertiary butyl hydroperoxide. This is expected since the ring withdraws electrons and thus lowers the electron density of the C−O group, resulting in a lower frequency (see Volume 2, p. 39, of this series for further discussion of the electron withdrawing effect on the position of the ν(C−O) vibration). Because both hydroperoxides have a band near 850 cm^{-1}, the author of the spectra suggests it may be a ν(O−O) vibration. As we shall see, this is not a good group frequency.

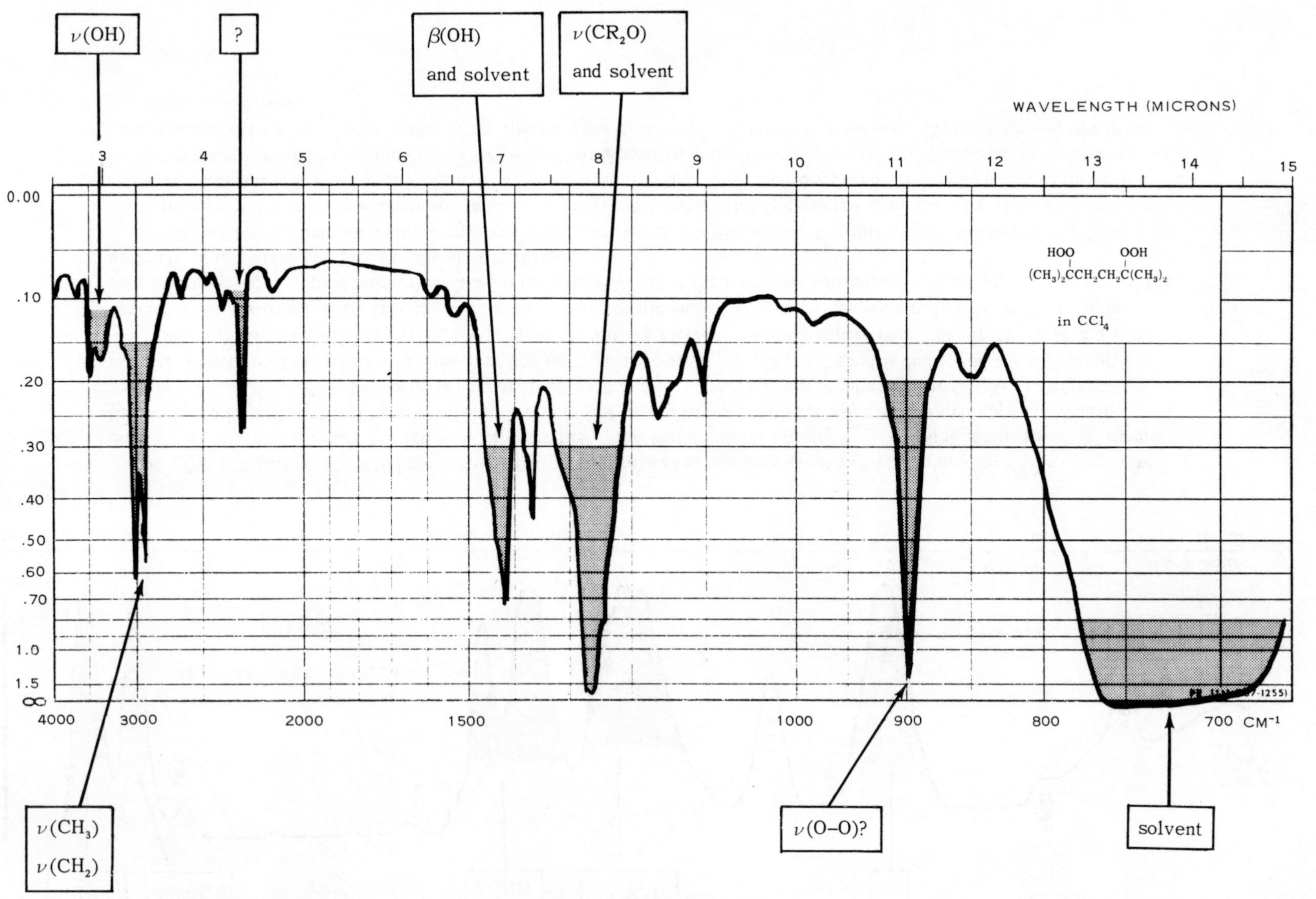

29. The spectrum of 2,5-dimethyl-2,5-dihydroperoxyhexane is presented here. This is tertiary hydroperoxide so the $\nu(CR_2O)$ appears near 1200 cm^{-1}. The $\beta(OH)$ is near 1425 cm^{-1} as in previous spectra. Note the lack of a distinct $\nu(O-O)$ band in the 1000-700 cm^{-1} region. The $\nu(OH)$ band is doubled, but no explanation is obvious. The solvent bands are marked on the spectrum.

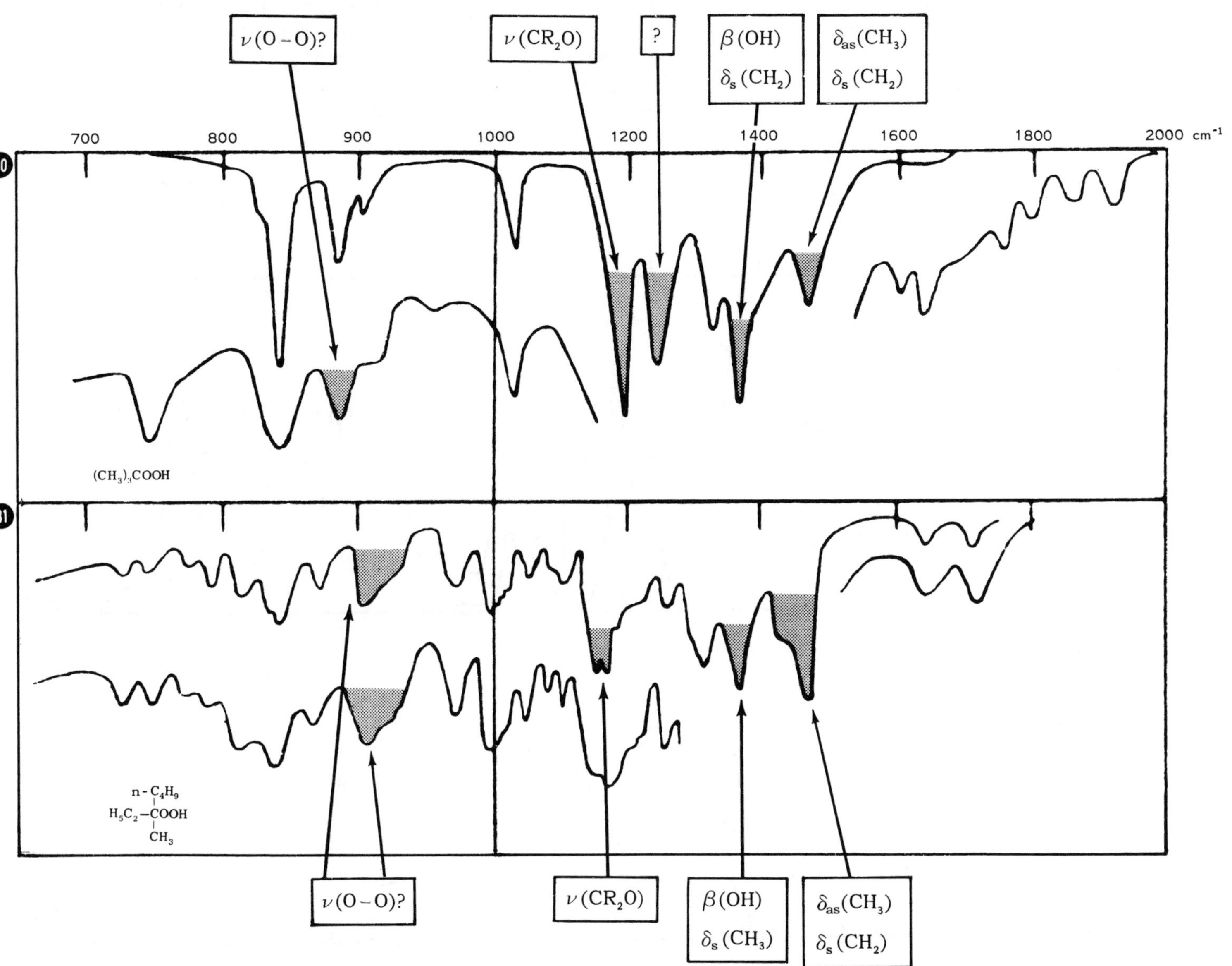

30, 31. These tertiary hydroperoxides have the $\nu(CR_2O)$ and $\beta(OH)$ at the expected positions. There are often strong bands near these group frequencies which are not easily assigned, as they do not persist in all related spectra. Note for example the band near 1250 cm^{-1} in the spectrum of $C(CH_3)_3OOH$. It occurs in a number of CH_3 spectra, and may be a CH_3 vibration. We shall point it out in future spectra.

Reprinted from Proc. Roy. Soc. London A224 : 176 (1954)

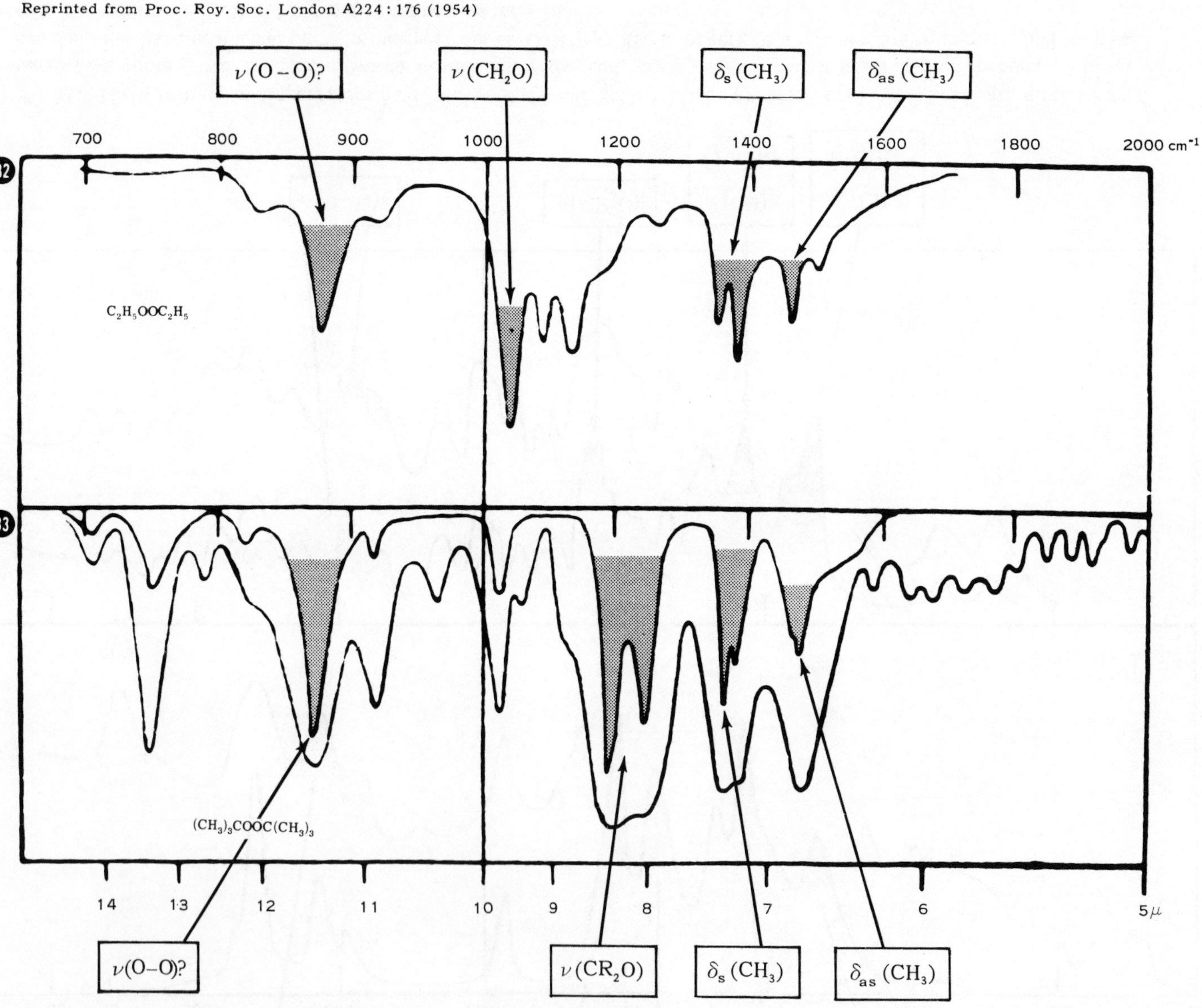

32, 33. These two spectra are the first examples of the peroxides not having OH groups. Their spectra will be similar to the hydroperoxides except the ν(OH) and β(OH) vibrations will not appear, and we can note the regions where these should appear do not have bands. Note the band near 880 cm^{-1} in these spectra. Again the suggestion that this is the ν(O–O) can be made, although, as discussed before, this is not a good group frequency. The strong band near 1200 cm^{-1} in the methyl derivative is the $\nu(\underset{.}{C}R_2\dot{O})$ of a tertiary peroxide, and is in the position found for alcohols, ethers, hydroperoxides, and peroxides having this tertiary group. The primary peroxide has this band near 1025 cm^{-1} as expected.

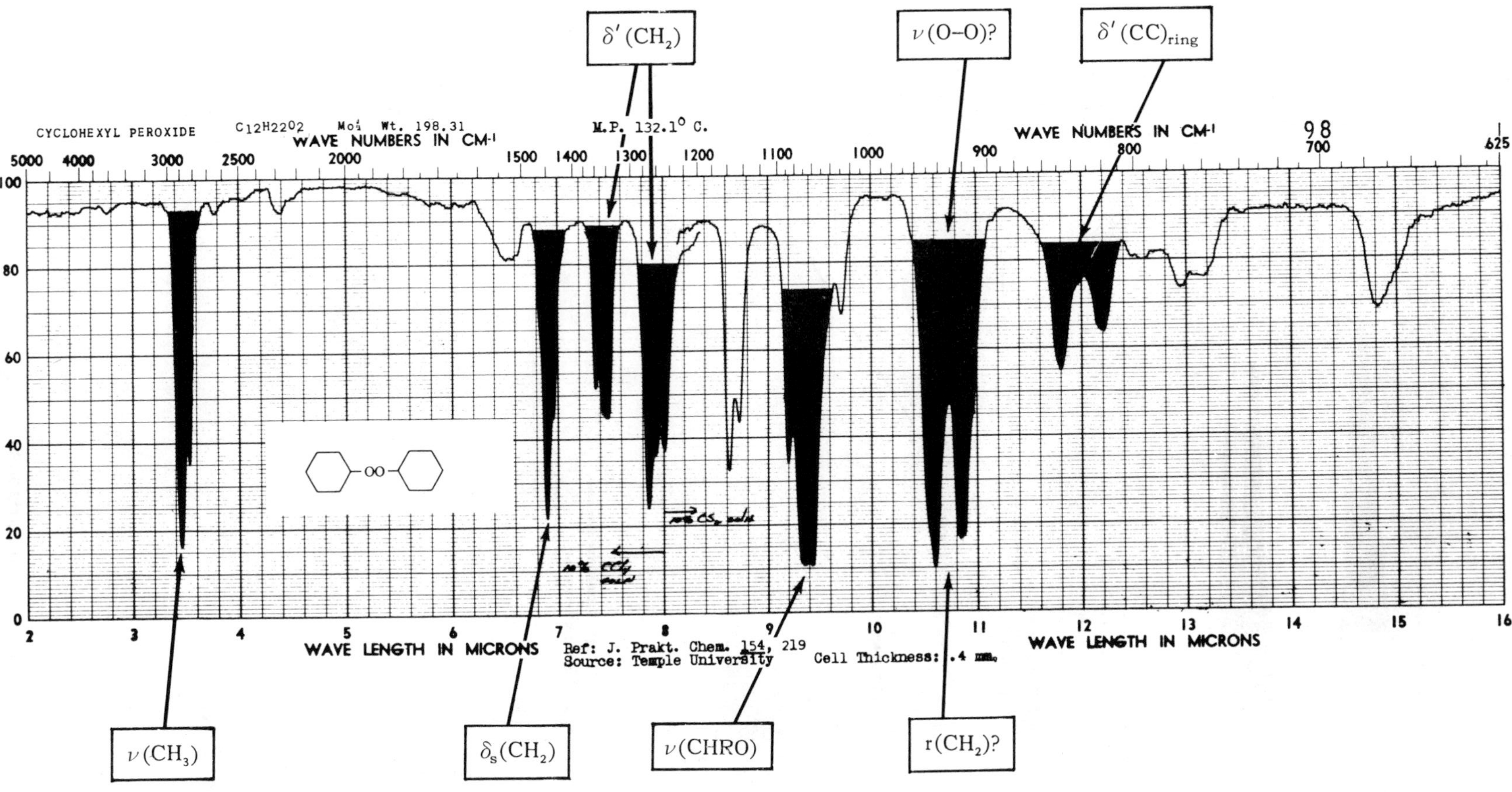

34. The spectrum of cyclohexyl peroxide represents that of a secondary peroxide. The ν(CHRO) should appear near 1110 cm^{-1}. A strong band near 1080 cm^{-1} is assigned to this vibration, but this is lower than expected. We shall see the saturated ring compounds give anomalous results for the position of the ν(C–O). A strong doublet appears near 920 cm^{-1}, but this is where the r(CH_2) of the ring appears. We therefore suggest the doublet is ν(O–O) and/or r(CH_2). In addition, the six-member saturated ring has a δ'(CC) near 830 cm^{-1}, and this band is also observed.

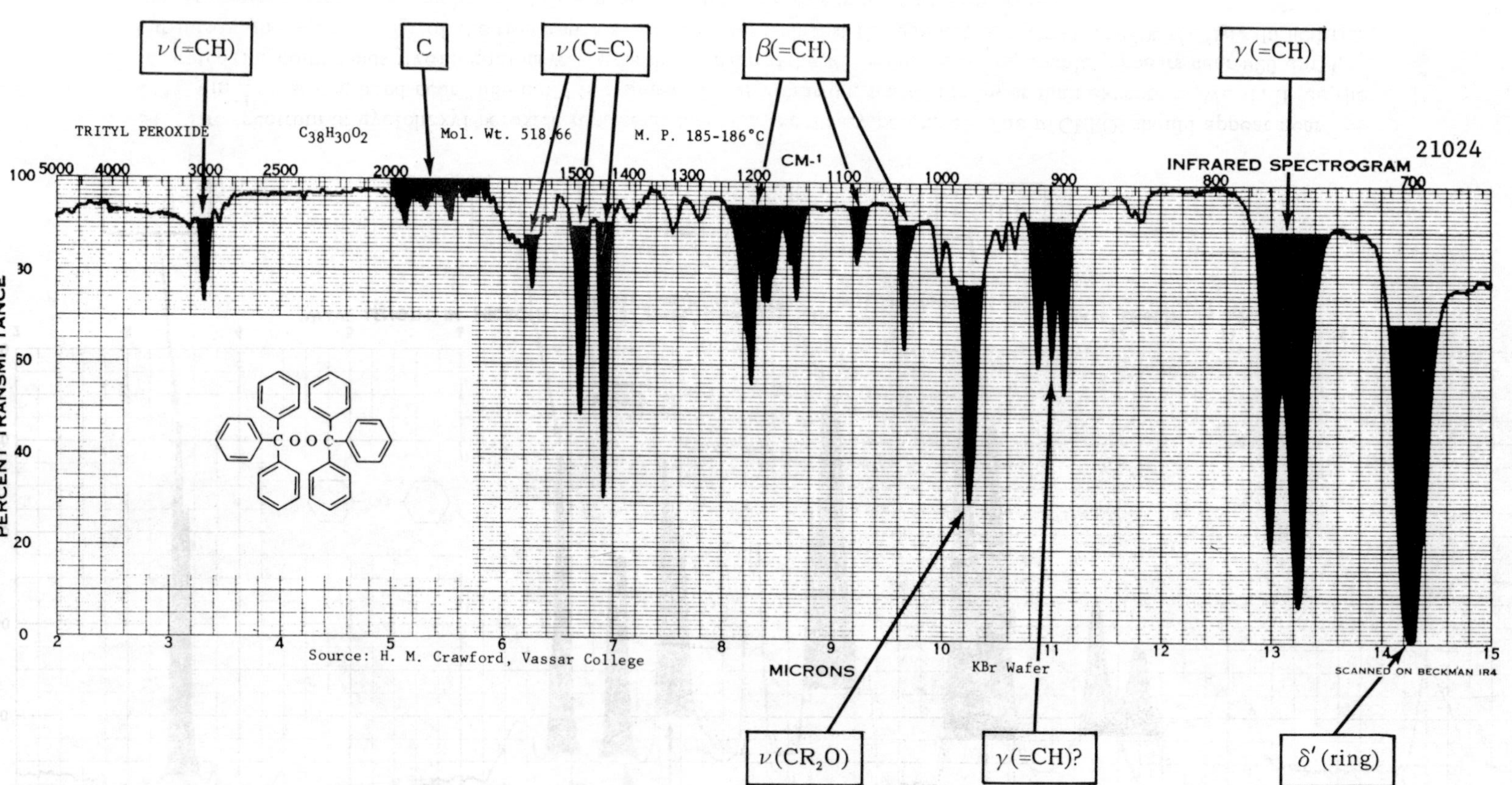

35. This spectrum illustrates a point the author made in Volume 2 of this series. There the low position of the $\nu(CR_2O)$ for the alcohol $(C_6H_5)_3COH$, at 1000 cm^{-1}, was explained as being due to the withdrawing properties of the ring. The position of the $\nu(CR_2O)$ is 975 cm^{-1} for this compound, and this can also be assigned as due to the inductive effect of the six rings.

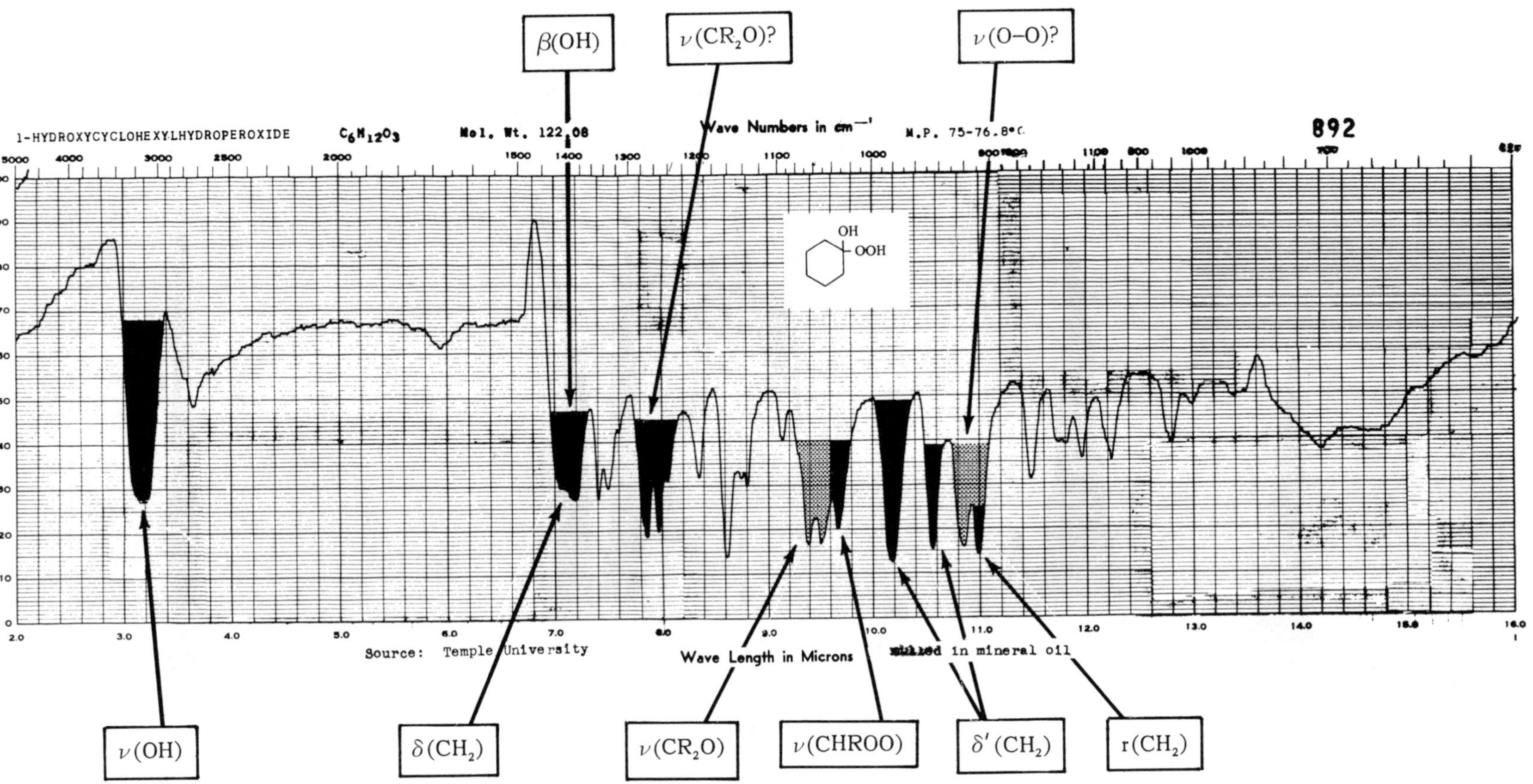

36. We face a dilemma in this spectrum in locating the νC–O), since we expect it near 1200 cm^{-1}, but a strong band occur near 1020 cm^{-1}. This could be a ring vibration, but its great intensity would not be expected. It may represent an impurity band. The very poor baseline suggests large particle size, and its abnormal intensity near 1450 cm^{-1} suggests the Christiansen effect is occurring (see IR–Theory and Practice of Infrared Spectroscopy by this author for explanation of the Christiansen effect). The spectrum in general appears to be a poor one, and no further interpretation of it will be attempted.

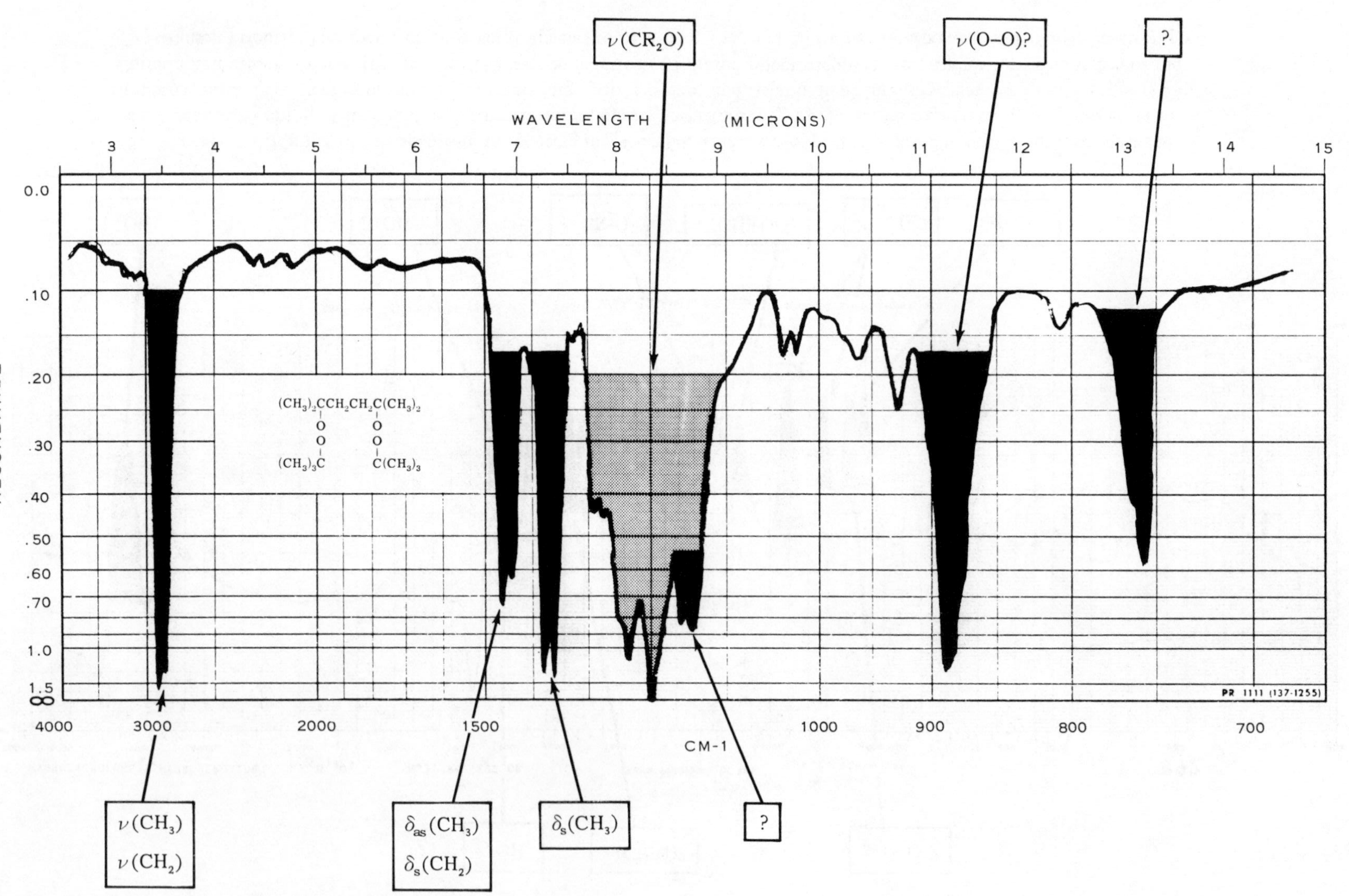

*Discussion below.

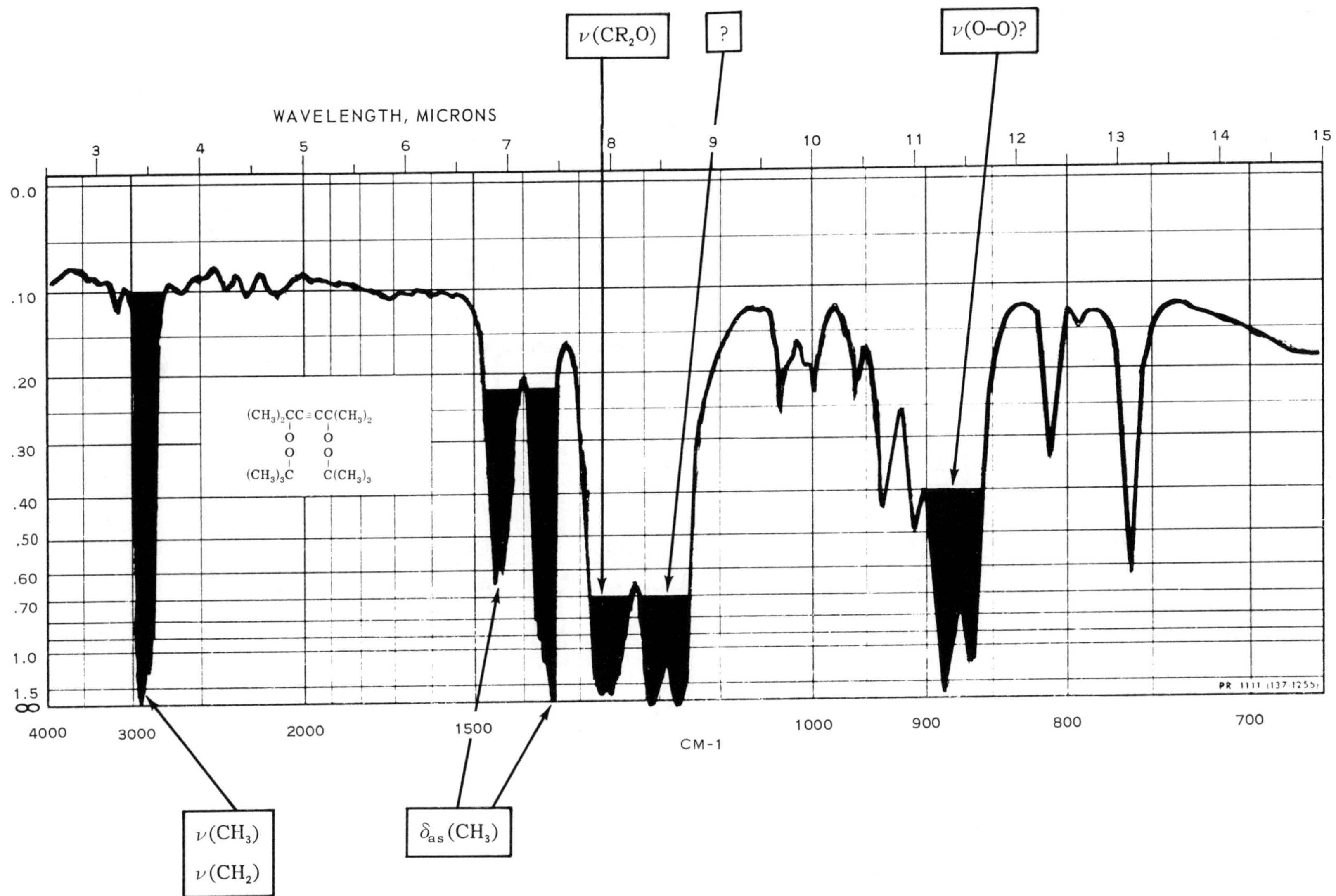

37, 38. These compounds are tertiary peroxides, but since the inductive effect is small, the $\nu(CR_2O)$ band is near 1200 cm^{-1}. The band is doubled here, but if we compare these spectra to that of $C(CH_3)_3OOH$, the bands appear similar, suggesting a CH_3 vibration appears here. Note the absence of the ν ($C{\equiv}C$) for spectrum 37 due to the symmetry of the compound. In Volume 1 the doubling of the 1380 cm^{-1} band was discussed for the grouping $C(CH_3)_2$. The 1380 cm^{-1} band here is a triplet, suggesting this doubling does not occur for complex structures such as this one.

Reprinted from Anal. Chem. 24:638 (1952).

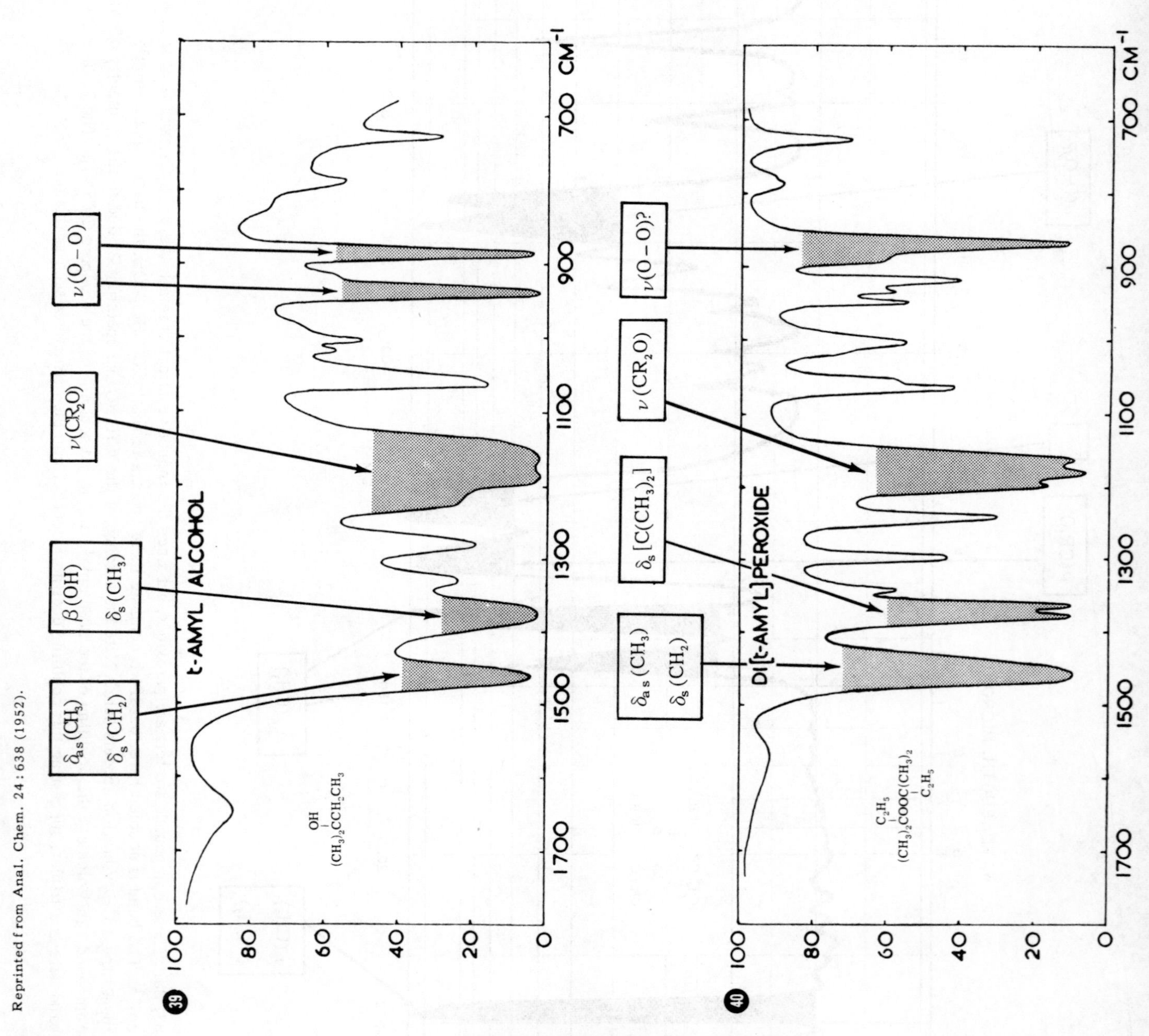

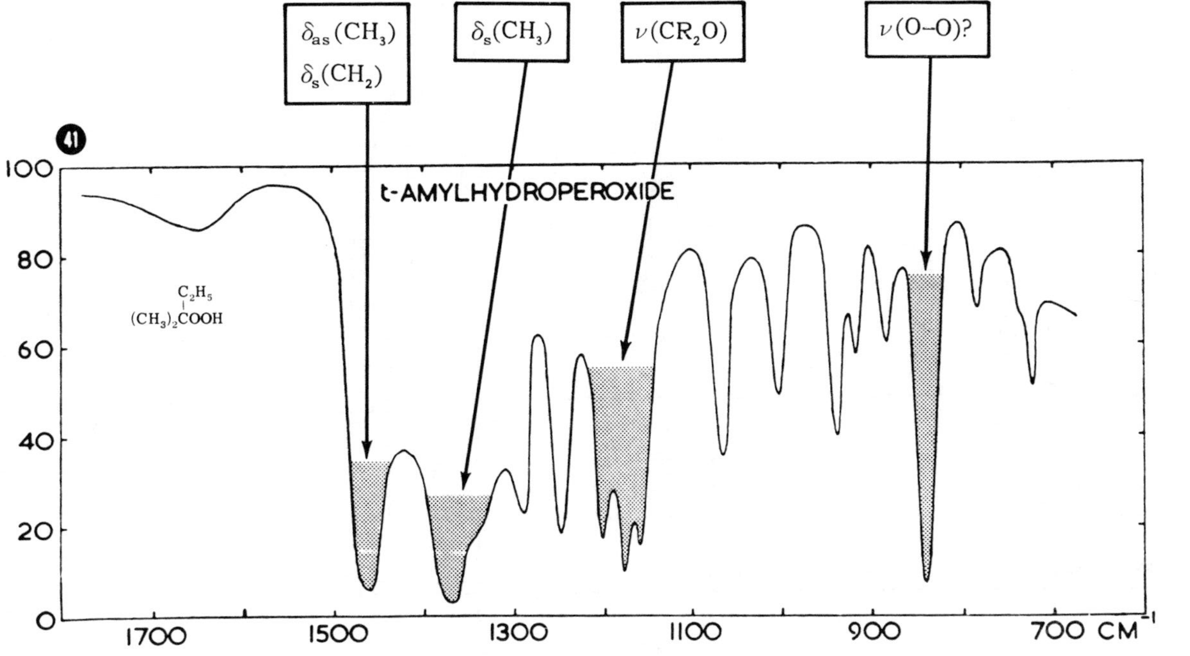

39,40,41. In this series of spectra an alcohol is compared with its related peroxide and hydroperoxide. Having observed the previous examples of peroxides and hydroperoxides, we are ready to consider a series such as this. First we can note the $\nu(CR_2O)$ band appears in the same position for all three compounds, as expected, since we have consistently pointed out how the position of the ν(C–O) depends only on the groups attached to the carbon atom. The position is near 1200 cm^{-1}. The β(OH) vibration for the alcohol and hydroperoxide should appear near 1425 cm^{-1}. It is not as obvious a band in these spectra, except for the broadening of the 1450 and 1380 cm^{-1} bands of the CH_3 and CH_2 groups. We may also examine the 1000-600 cm^{-1} region for coincident bands. Consider the 915 cm^{-1} band for the alcohol, and its shift to 875 cm^{-1} in the peroxide, and 845 cm^{-1} for the hydroperoxide. We shall see this shifting occurring in other tertiary series. Note that this band appears where the ν(O–O) has been assigned, indicating that even in alcohols, strong bands appear which cannot be assigned as ν(O–O). It can be noted that all three compounds have strong bands in the 915-830 cm^{-1} region, thus suggesting the group C_3C–O is responsible for the bands here, and this does not allow one to identify the ν(O–O) band which should also be in this region.

Reprinted from Anal. Chem. 24 : 638 (1952).

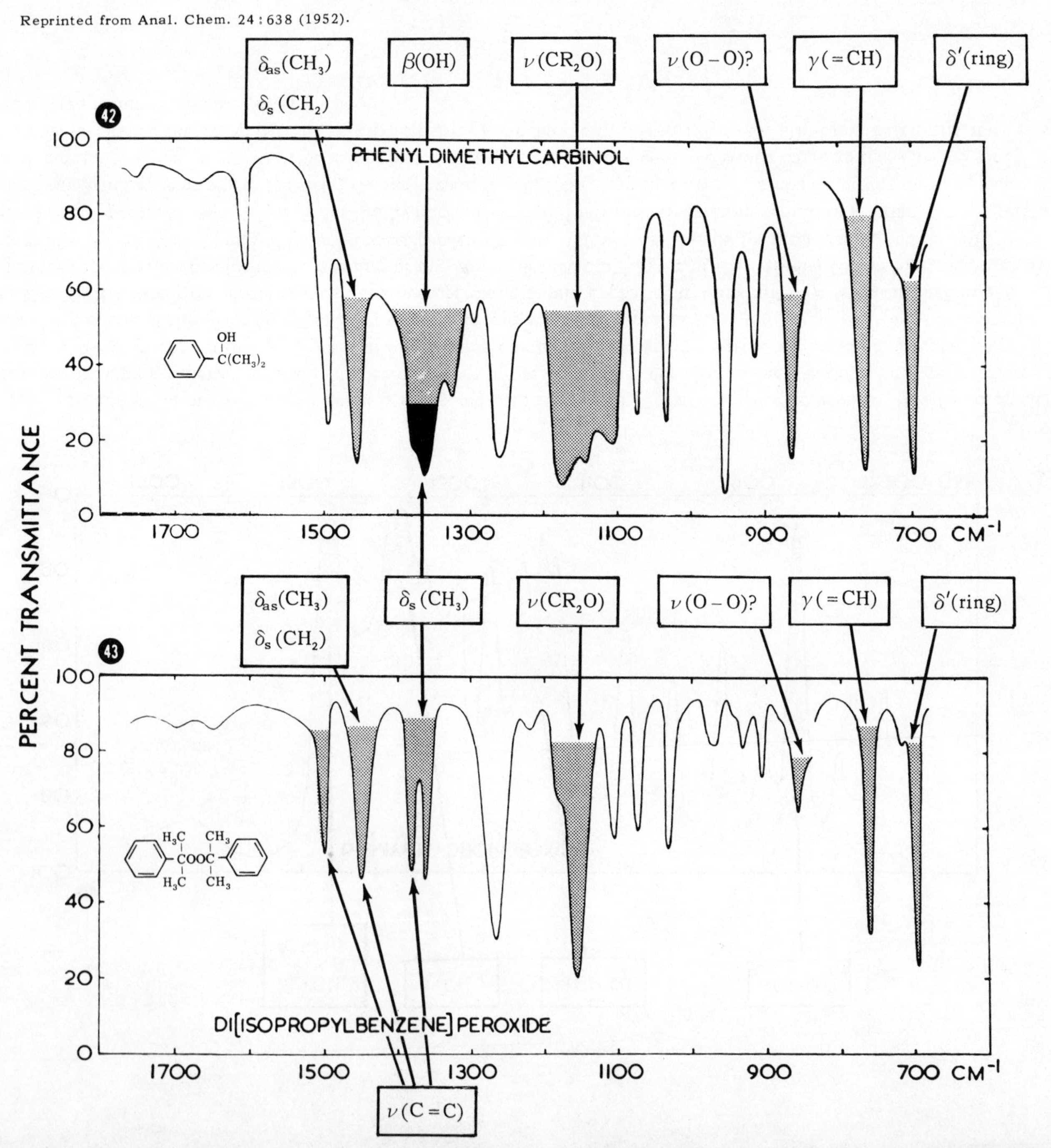

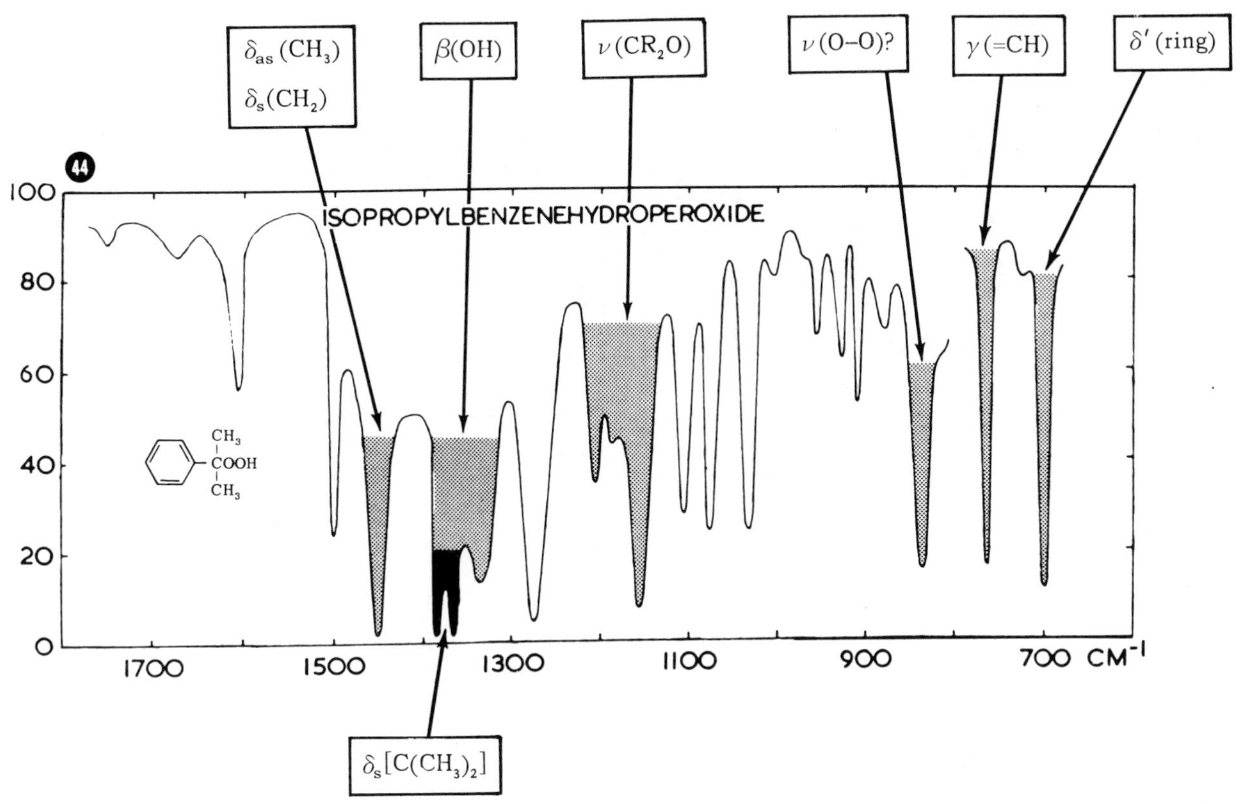

42, 43, 44. We compare here three related compounds. Each has a monosubstituted ring as one substituent on a tertiary carbon atom attached to an oxygen atom. We note first the $\nu(CR_2O)$ for each. In all three spectra it appears near 1180 cm^{-1} as expected; however, for the alcohols it is a broader band. Note it is lower than 1200 cm^{-1} here because of the withdrawing properties of the ring. The β(OH) of the alcohols appears near 1400 cm^{-1} as a broadening of the CH_3 and CH_2 band here. The ν(O–O) band, which should appear in the 950-800 cm^{-1} region, shows no strong or consistent position in this series. Perhaps the band near 850 cm^{-1} comes the closest to retaining a constant position and intensity.

Reprinted from Proc. Roy. Soc. London A224:176 (1954).

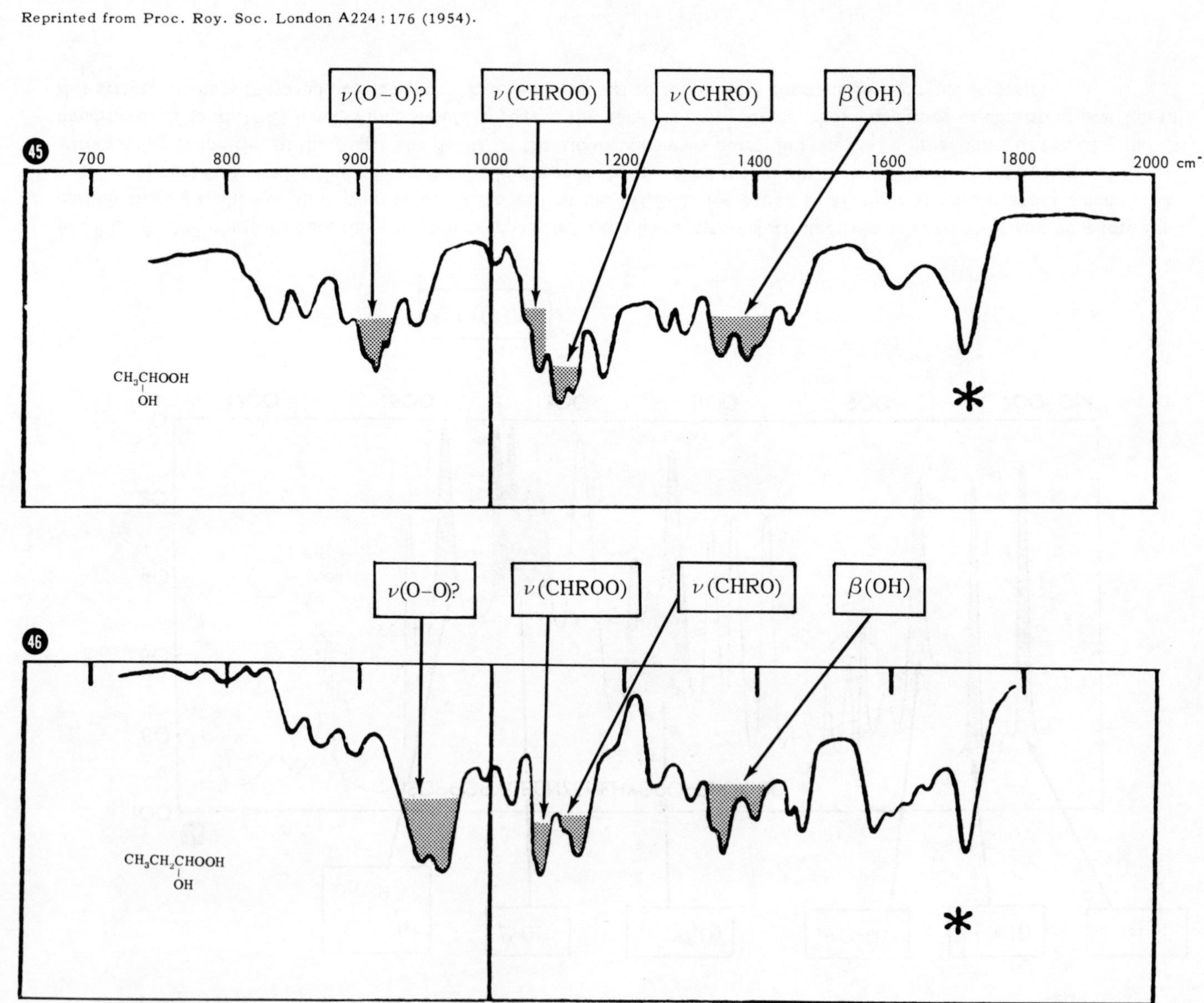

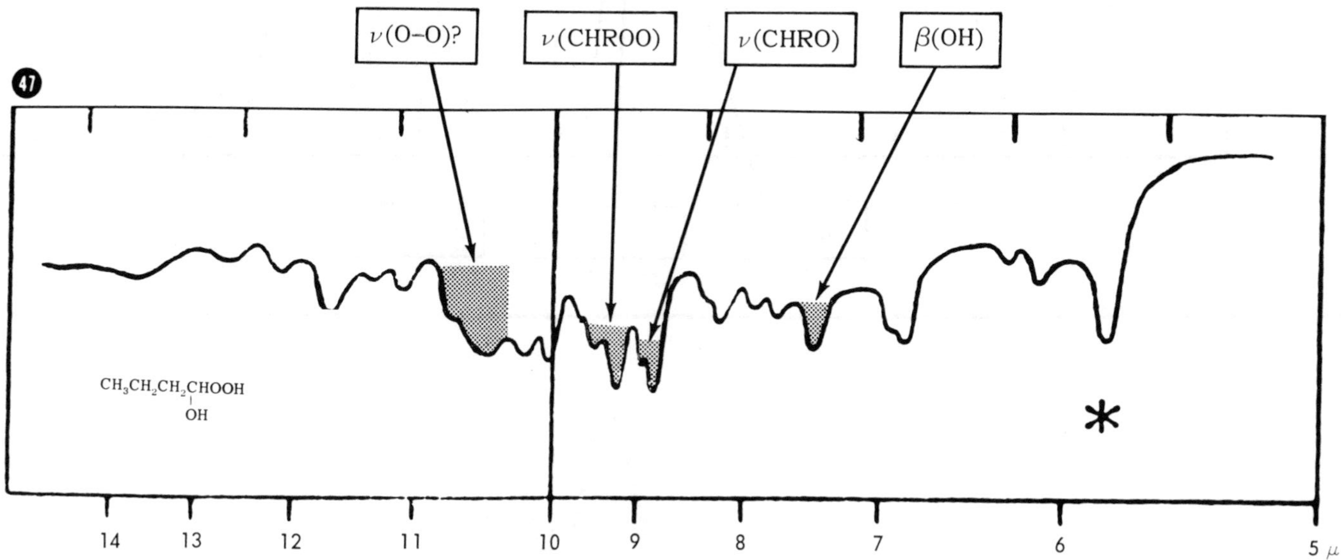

45-47. This series of spectra represent secondary alcohols and hydroperoxides. The $\nu(C-O)$ band for these groups should be near 1100 cm^{-1}, with the hydroperoxide at the low frequency. These assignments are therefore based on this reasoning. Note the band near 900 cm^{-1}. All the secondary hydroperoxides have a strong band here. Possibly this is the $\nu(O-O)$.

Reprinted from Proc. Roy. Soc. London A224:176 (1954).

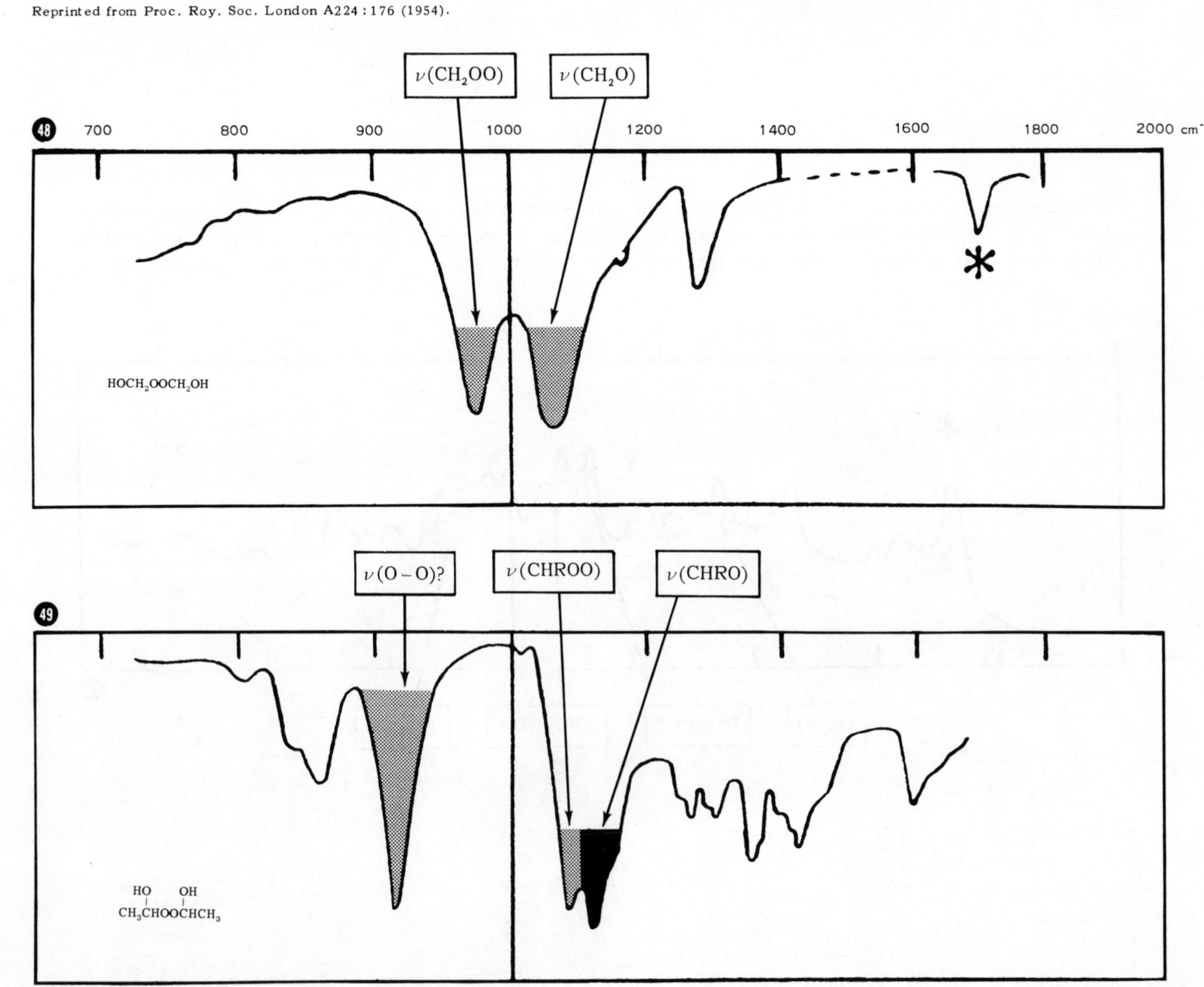

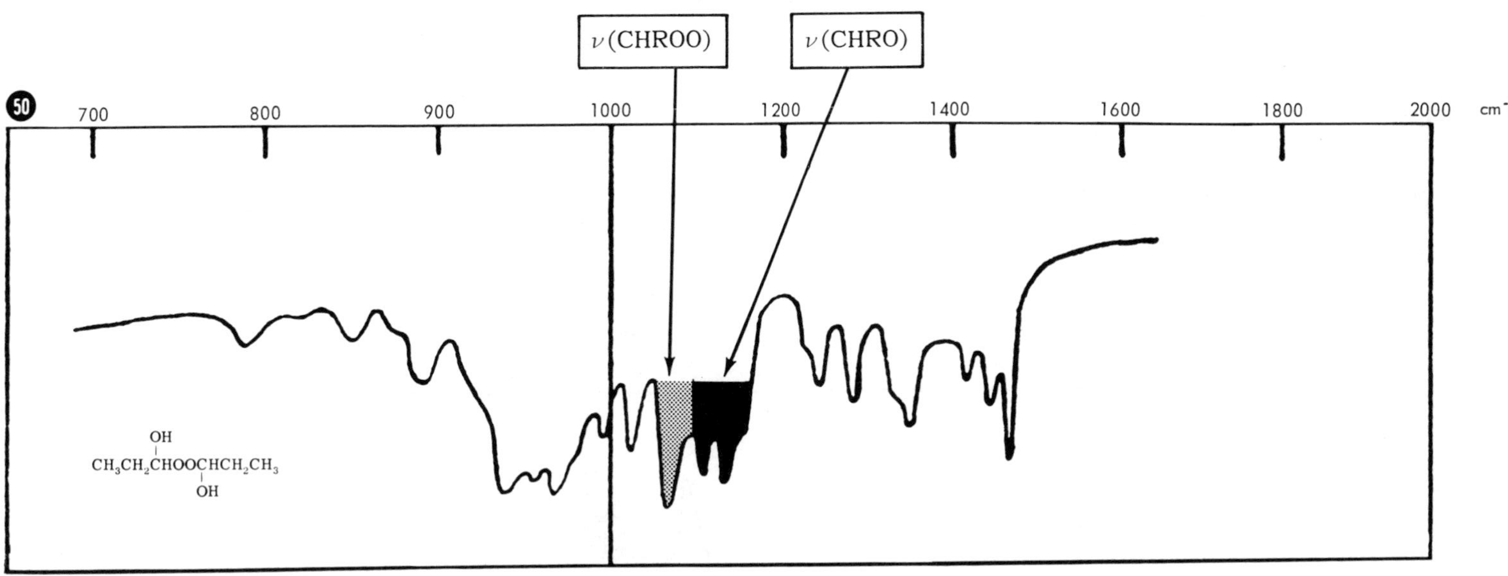

48, 49, 50. There are a number of interesting points which can be made concerning these spectra. First, if the top spectrum is examined, it represents a compound where primary alcohol and peroxide groups are present, and we expect the ν(C−O) to be near 1000 cm^{-1}. Since peroxides absorb lower than alcohols, we assign the band near 980 cm^{-1} as the peroxide C−O stretch. This point is re-emphasized in the second spectrum, where secondary alcohol and peroxide occur. The bands are closer together but are still distinct near 1100 cm^{-1}, the expected position. The ν(O−O) is tentatively assigned as the strong band near 900 cm^{-1}. The bottom spectrum also has two groups, and while the bands are multiple near 1100 cm^{-1} we divide them into a higher alcoholic and lower peroxide band.

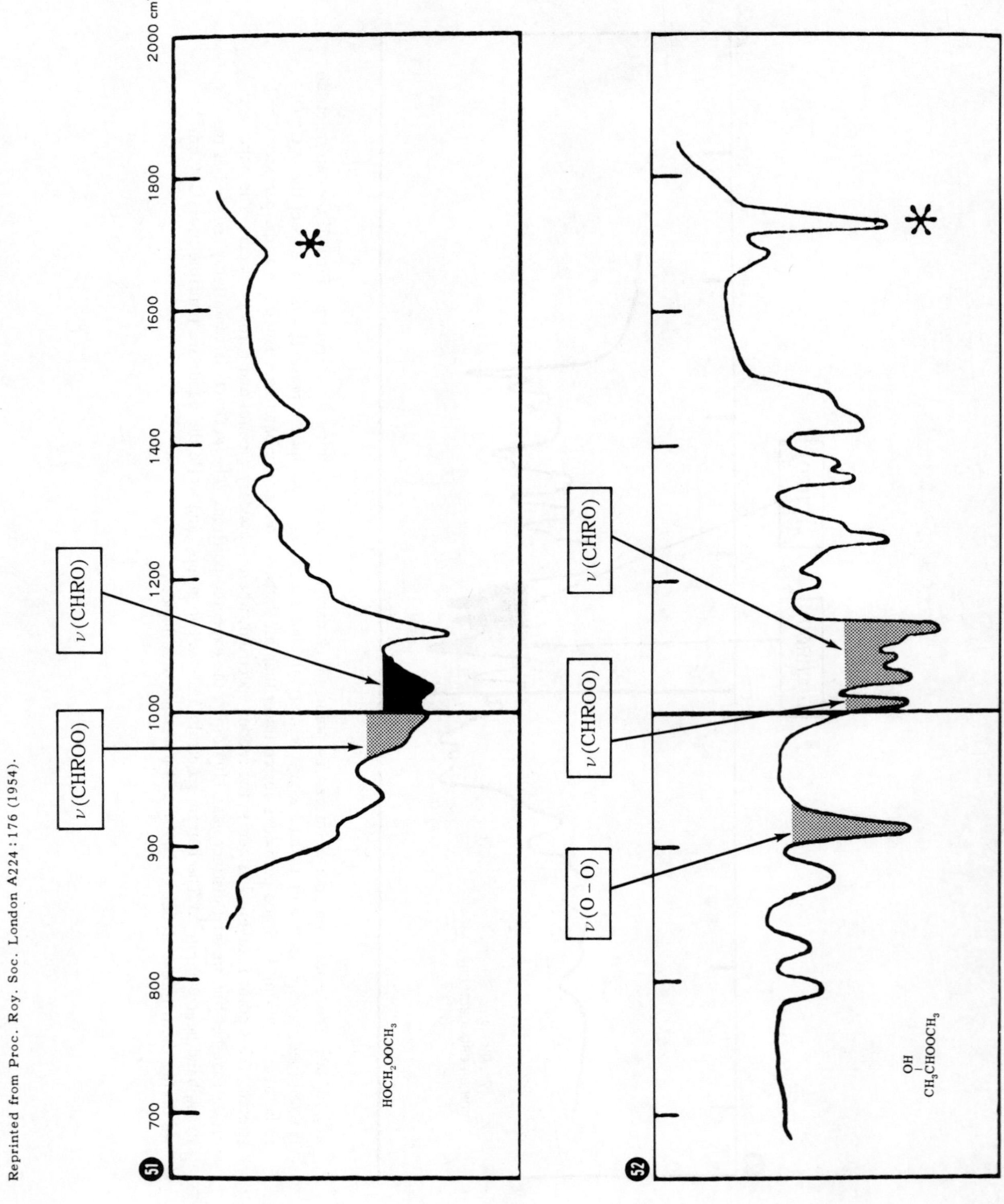

Reprinted from Proc. Roy. Soc. London A224 : 176 (1954).

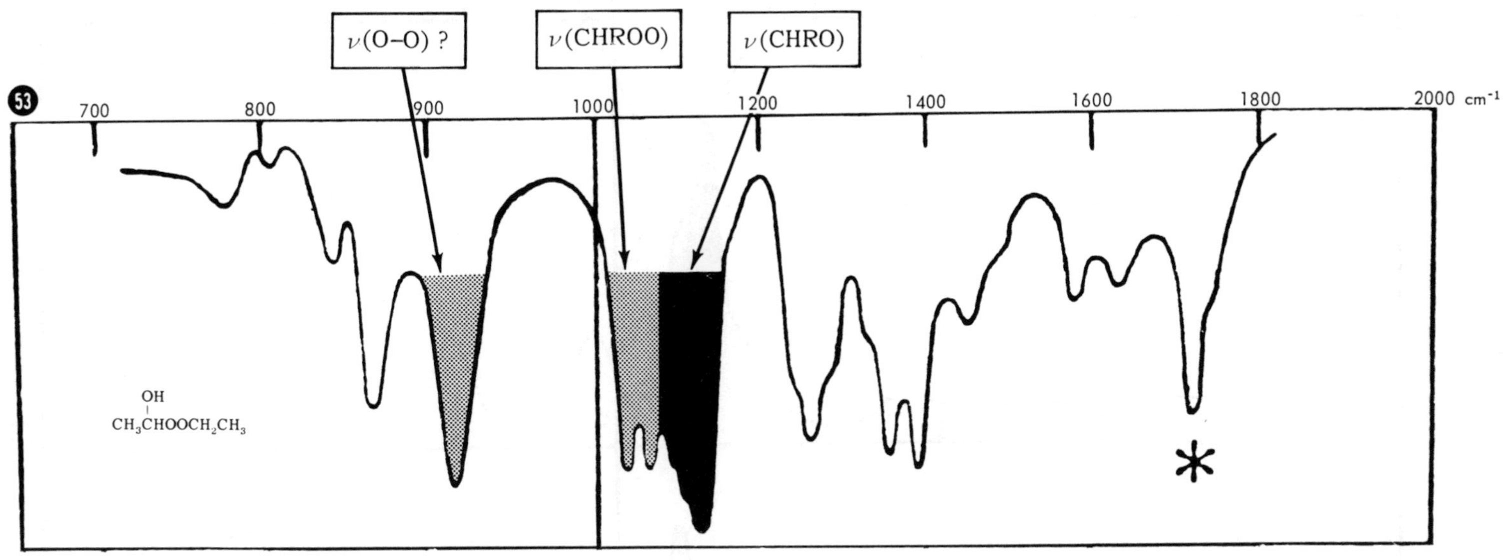

51, 52, 53. While these spectra are not distinct, we can identify the two C−O groups near 1110 cm^{-1}. This is the expected position for the CHRO group, with the peroxide being the lower of the two bands. We can further note that the top spectrum has the ν(CHRO) lower than the other two, but it also has two H atoms on the carbon compounds, and is therefore a primary alcohol (and peroxide). We expect the ν(C−O) near 1000 cm^{-1} for this class of C−O group. A strong band near 900 cm^{-1} is tentatively assigned as ν(O−O).

Reprinted from Proc. Roy. Soc. London A 224 : 176 (1954).

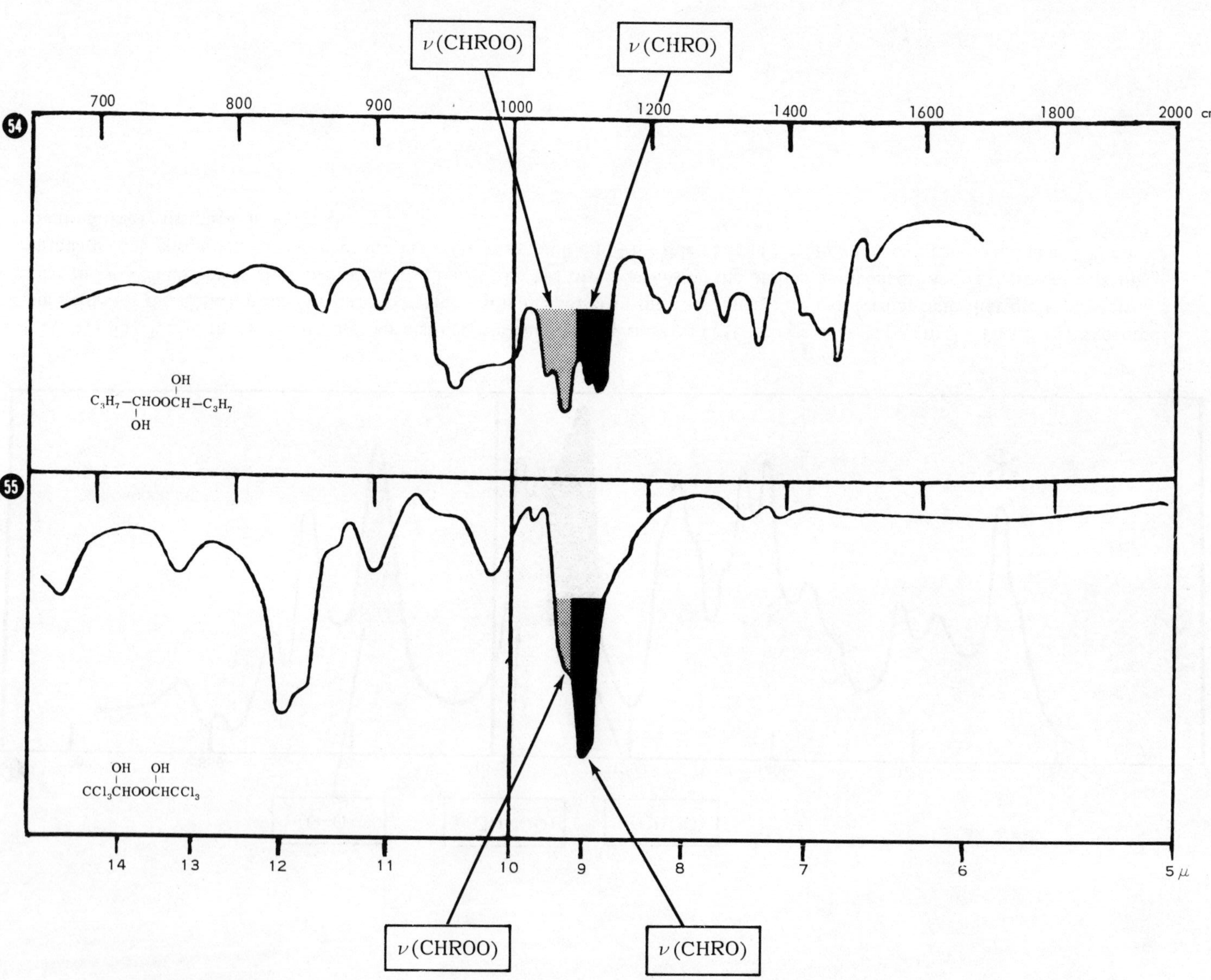

54, 55. The groups are CHRO here, but one is alcoholic and the other peroxide. We expect both vibrations to be near 1100 cm^{-1}, with the peroxide at slightly lower frequency; and the bands are so assigned.

57 PEROXIDES

Reprinted from Proc. Roy. Soc. London A224 : 176 (1954).

56, 57. The combination of a peroxide and alcohol should give two strong bands closely spaced near 1100 cm^{-1}. The lower of the two bands should be the peroxide, as suggested in the correlation section, and is so assigned. The spectrum is not sharp but is illustrative of this type of compound. The strong band near 900 cm^{-1} in the first spectrum is not easily assigned. It may be the elusive ν(O−O).

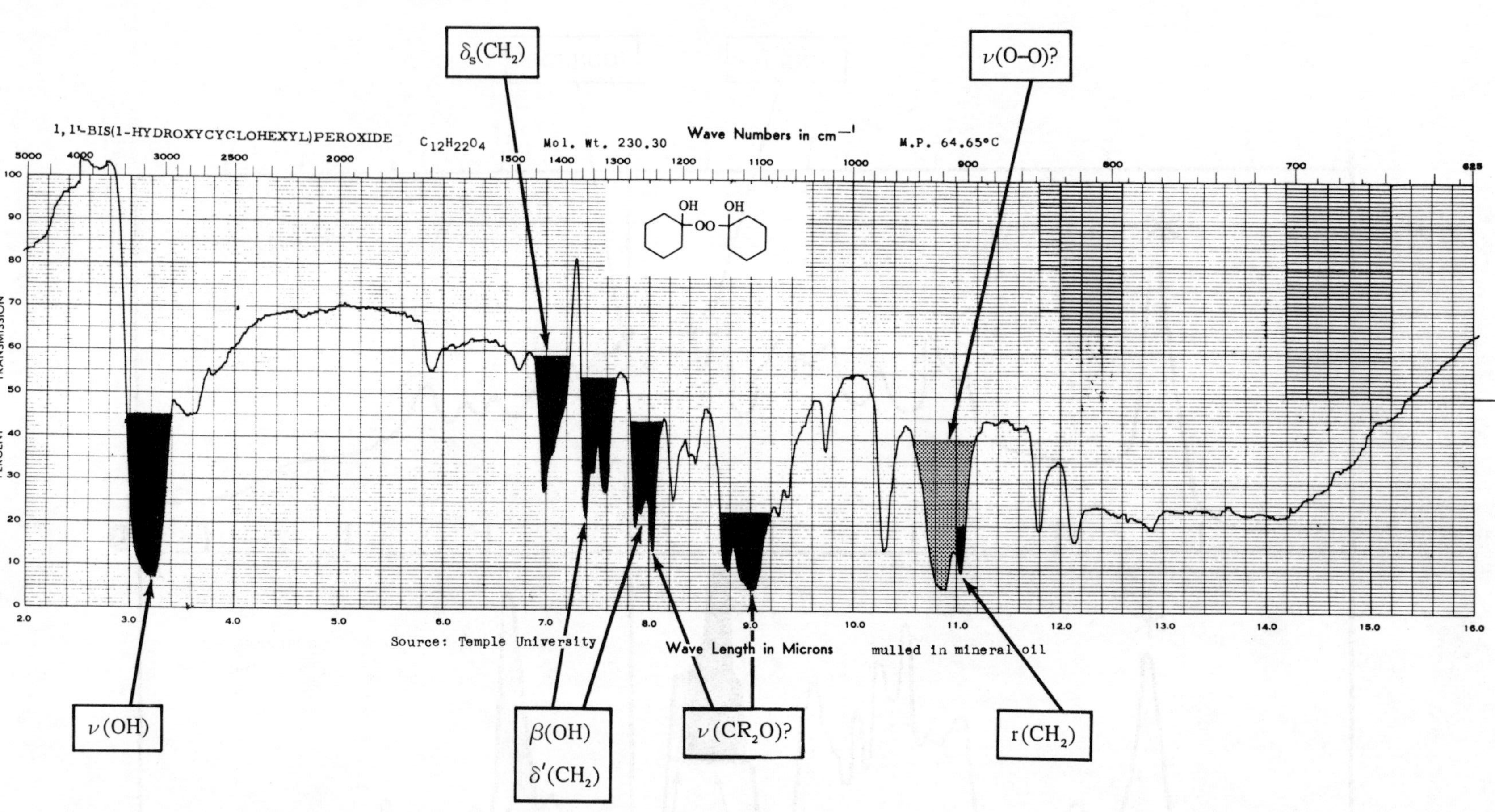

58. The two groups here are CR_2O, one of which is alcoholic and the other ether. We expect the position to be near 1200 cm^{-1}, but a strong band appears near 1100 cm^{-1}. This could be a saturated ring vibration, but this does not appear a satisfactory assignment. Possibly this spectrum does not represent the compound listed for it.

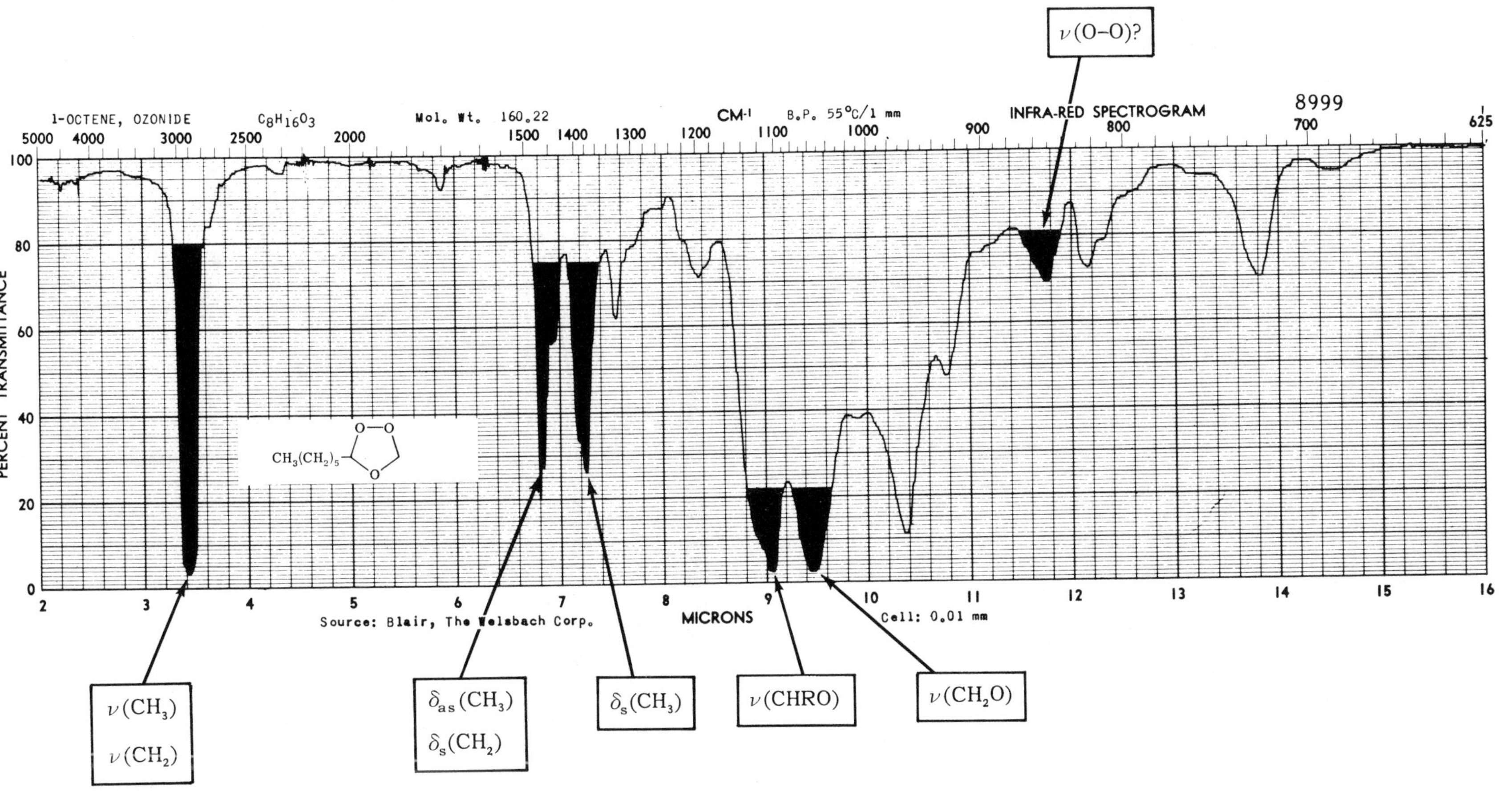

59. This compound has the groups CHRO and CH_2O, and, as expected, bands near 1100 and 1050 cm^{-1} are observed. The ν(O–O) is tentatively assigned as the band near 880 cm^{-1}.

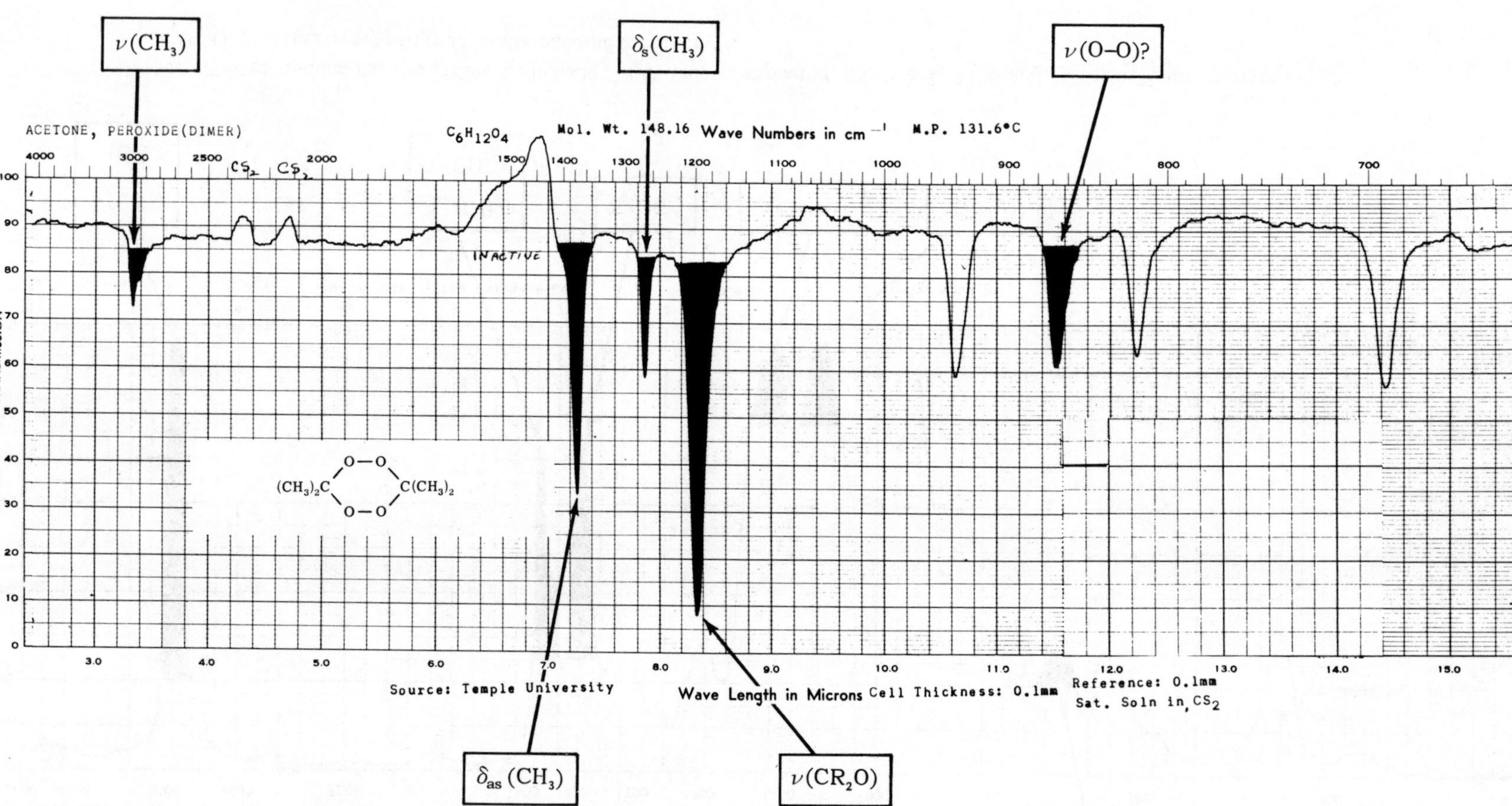

60. Since the group CR_2O is present here, we expect a strong band near 1200 cm^{-1}. This band is observed. There are three strong bands in the 970-870 cm^{-1} region, but it is not obvious which should be assigned as $\nu(O-O)$, since, as we have observed previously, this is not a good froup frequency..

61 PEROXIDES

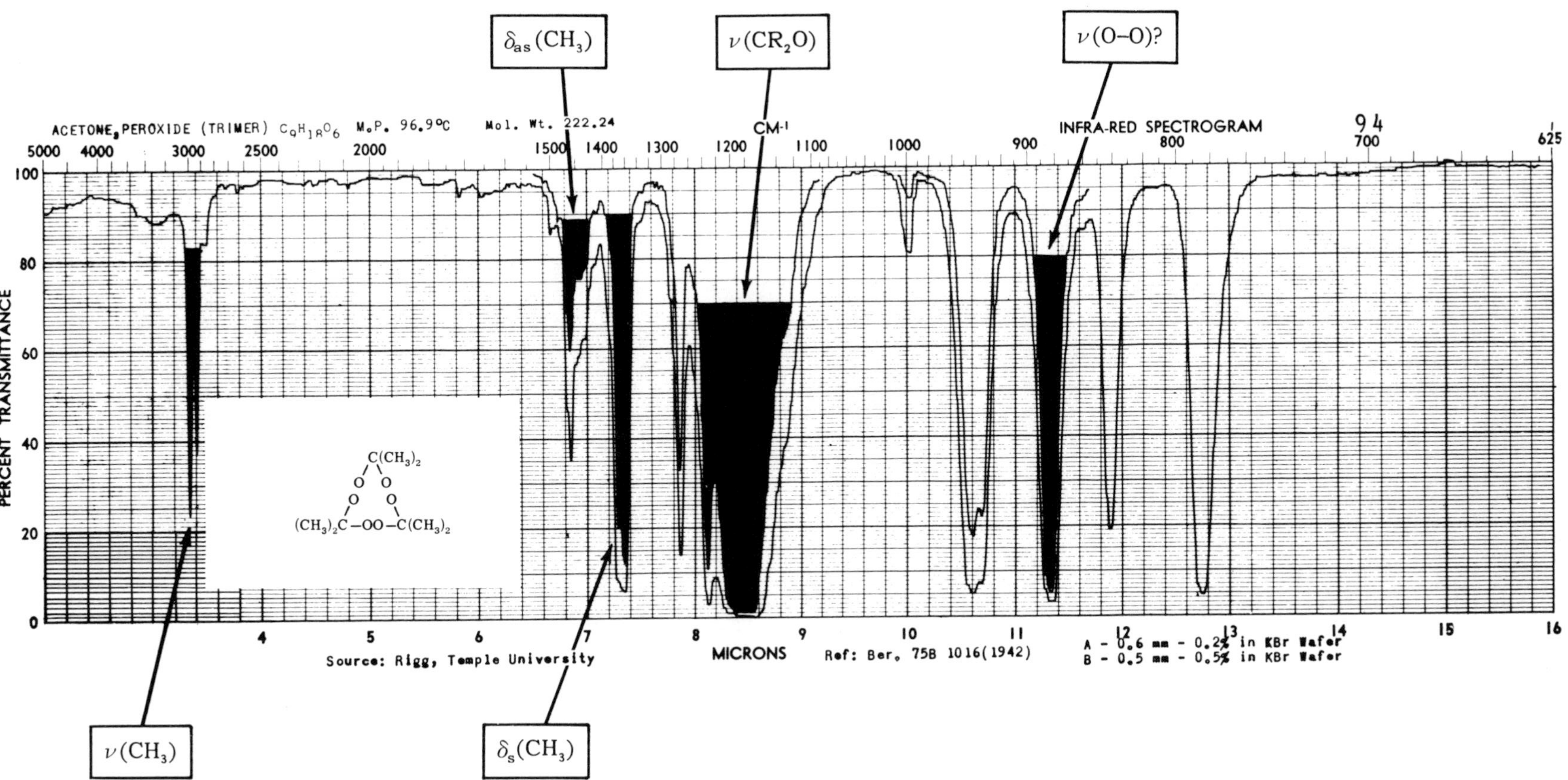

61. Using the general rule that the $\nu(CR_2O)$ band appears near 1200 cm^{-1}, we assign the strong band at this position to this vibration. Apparently the six oxygens here do not result in any shift of this band. The strong bands in the 1000-750 cm^{-1} region are probably due to CH_3 vibrations; however, the $\nu(O-O)$ assignment which has been tentative in all previous spectra is also assigned here.

CUMULATIVE INDEX

Cumulative Index

Compounds whose spectra are interpreted in this series are listed according to empirical formula. The number in parentheses at the bottom of each entry refers to the volume, and the number that follows it to the page on which the spectrum appears.

CUMULATIVE INDEX

$C_3H_8O_2$ $CH_3OCH_2CH_2OH$ (3)93	C_4H_6 $CH_3C\equiv CCH_3$ (2)11	C_4H_8O O (3)196, 201
$C_3H_8O_2$ $(CH_3)_2CH\cdot OOH$ (3)217	C_4H_6O O $-CH{=}CH_2$ (3)179	C_4H_8O $CH_3CH=CHCH_2OH$ (2)88
$C_3H_8O_2$ $HOCH_2CH_2CH_2OH$ (2)44	$C_4H_6O_2$ O O (3)175	C_4H_8O OH $CH_3CHCH=CH_2$ (2)153
$C_3H_8O_2$ OH CH_3CHCH_2OH (2)267	$C_4H_6O_2$ $HOCH_2C\equiv CCH_2OH$ (2)86	C_4H_8O CH_2OH (2)84
$C_3H_8O_3$ OH $CH_3CHOOCH_3$ (3)242	C_4H_8 $CH_3CH=CHCH_3$ cis (1)48	$(C_4H_8O)n$ $\left[\begin{matrix} OC_2H_5 \\ -CH_2CH- \end{matrix}\right]_n$ (3)108
$C_3H_8O_3$ CH_3CH_2CHOOH OH (3)238	C_4H_8 $CH_3CH=CHCH_3$ trans (1)51	$C_4H_8O_2$ O O (3)200
$C_3H_8O_3$ OH $HOCH_2CHCH_2OH$ (2)274	C_4H_8 $(CH_3)_2CH=CH_2$ (1)52	$C_4H_8O_2$ $HOCH_2CH=CHCH_2OH$ (2)89
$C_4H_4Cl_6O_4$ OH OH $CCl_3CHOOCHCCl_3$ (3)244	C_4H_8 (1)170	$C_4H_{10}O$ $CH_3CH_2-O-CH_2CH_3$ (3)89
C_4H_4O O (3)206	C_4H_8O $CH_3CH_2OCH{=}CH_2$ (3)11[illegible]	$C_4H_{10}O$ $(CH_3)_3COH$ (3)225
C_4H_6 $H_2C=CHCH=CH_2$ (1)63	C_4H_8O O CH_2CH_3 (3)177	$C_4H_{10}O$ $CH_3CH_2CH_2CH_2OH$ (2)45

Formula	Structure	Reference
$C_4H_{10}O$	$(CH_3)_2CHCH_2OH$	(2)58
$C_4H_{10}O$	$CH_3CH_2\underset{CH_3}{C}HOH$	(2)112
$C_4H_{10}O$	$(CH_3)_3COH$	(2)222
$C_4H_{10}O_2$	$(CH_3)_3COOH$	(3)224, 227
$C_4H_{10}O_2$	$CH_3CH_2\overset{CH_3}{C}H \cdot OOH$	(3)220
$C_4H_{10}O_2$	$CH_3(CH_2)_3 \cdot OOH$	(3)218
$C_4H_{10}O_2$	$C_2H_5OOC_2H_5$	(3)228
$C_4H_{10}O_2$	$HOCH_2CH_2CH_2CH_2OH$	(2)46
$C_4H_{10}O_2$	$CH_3\overset{OH}{C}H\underset{OH}{C}HCH_3$	(2)113
$C_4H_{10}O_2$	$CH_3CH_2\overset{OH}{C}HCH_2OH$	(2)268
$C_4H_{10}O_2$	$CH_3\overset{OH}{C}HCH_2CH_2OH$	(2)269
$C_4H_{10}O_3$	$HOCH_2CH_2OCH_2CH_2OH$	(3)99
$C_4H_{10}O_3$	$CH_3CH_2CH_2\underset{OH}{C}HOOH$	(3)239
$C_4H_{10}O_3$	$CH_3CH_2\overset{OH}{C}HOOCH_3$	(3)245
$C_4H_{10}O_3$	$CH_3\overset{OH}{C}HOOCH_2CH_3$	(3)243
$C_4H_{10}O_3$	$HOCH_2\overset{OH}{C}H\underset{OH}{C}HCH_3$	(2)275
$C_4H_{10}O_3$	$HOCH_2\overset{OH}{C}HCH_2CH_2OH$	(2)276
$C_4H_{10}O_4$	$CH_3\overset{HO}{C}HOO\overset{OH}{C}HCH_3$	(3)240
C_5H_6		(1)73
C_5H_6	$HC \equiv \overset{CH_3}{C}C = CH_2$	(2)22
$C_5H_6O_2$	CH_2OH	(3)207
C_5H_8		(1)70
C_5H_8	$(CH_3)C = C = CH_2$	(1)77
C_5H_8	$(CH_3)_2CHC \equiv CH$	(2)12
C_5H_8O	$CH_2{=}CHCH_2OCH{=}CH_2$	(3)115
C_5H_8O	$CH_3CH_2\overset{OH}{C}HC \equiv CH$	(2)158
C_5H_8O	$(CH_3)_2\overset{OH}{C}C \equiv CH$	(2)244
C_5H_{10}	$H_2C = CHCH_2CH_2CH_3$	(1)40
C_5H_{10}	C_2H_5	(1)154
C_5H_{10}	CH_3, CH_3	(1)159

CUMULATIVE INDEX

C_5H_{10} (1)191	$C_5H_{10}O_2$ $CH_2{=}CHO(CH_2)_2OCH_3$ (3)120	$C_5H_{12}O_2$ $HOCH_2CH_2{-}OCH_2CH_2CH_3$ (3)97
$C_5H_{10}O$ OH $(CH_3)_2CCH = CH_2$ (2)245	$C_5H_{10}O_2$ OOH (3)221	$C_5H_{12}O_2$ $(CH_3)_2CH(CH_2)_2 \cdot OOH$ (3)219
$C_5H_{10}O$ $CH_2{=}CHOCH(CH_3)_2$ (3)122	$C_5H_{10}O_2$ O CH_2OH (3)198	$C_5H_{12}O_2$ C_2H_5 $(CH_3)_2COOH$ (3)235
$C_5H_{10}O$ HOCHCH$_3$ (2)170	$C_5H_{10}O_5$ OH H HO HO H OH O (3)204	$C_5H_{12}O_2$ $(CH_3CH_2)_2CH \cdot OOH$ (3)221
$C_5H_{10}O$ O H_3C H H CH_2CH_3 (3)186	$C_5H_{12}O$ $CH_3(CH_2)_3CH_2OH$ (2)47	$C_5H_{12}O_2$ CH_3 $CH_3CH_2CH_2CH \cdot OOH$ (3)220
$C_5H_{10}O$ O CH_3 (3)197	$C_5H_{12}O$ $(CH_3)_2CHCH_2CH_2OH$ (2)59	$C_5H_{12}O_2$ $CH_3(CH_2)_4 \cdot OOH$ (3)218
$C_5H_{10}O$ OH (2)200	$C_5H_{12}O$ CH_3 $CH_3CH_2CHCH_2OH$ (2)62	$C_5H_{12}O_2$ OH $CH_3CHCHCH_2CH_3$ OH threo (2)114
$C_5H_{10}O$ O (3)200	$C_5H_{12}O$ OH $CH_3CHCH_2CH_2CH_3$ (2)116	$C_5H_{12}O_2$ OH OH $CH_3CH - CHCH_2CH_3$ erythro (2)115
$C_5H_{10}O$ OH $CH_3CHCH_2CH = CH_2$ (2)154	$C_5H_{12}O$ OH $CH_3CH_2CHCH_2CH_3$ (2)117	$C_5H_{12}O_2$ OH OH $CH_3CHCH_2CHCH_3$ (2)118
$C_5H_{10}O_2$ $HOCH_2CH_2OCH_2CH{=}CH_2$ (3)106	$C_5H_{12}O$ OH $(CH_3)_2CCH_2CH_3$ (2)226, (3)234	$C_5H_{12}O_3$ OH $CH_3CHOOCH(CH_3)_2$ (3)245

CUMULATIVE INDEX

Formula	Structure	Reference
$C_5H_{12}O_3$	OH $HOCH_2CHCH_2CH_2CH_2OH$	(2)277
$C_5H_{12}O_4$	CH_2OH $HOCH_2-C-CH_2OH$ CH_2OH	(2)81
C_6H_6		(1)102
C_6H_6O	OH	(3)22
$C_6H_6O_2$	OH OH	(3)30
$C_6H_6O_2$	OH OH	(3)28
$C_6H_6O_2$	OH OH	(3)23
C_6H_8	$H_2C=CHCH=CHCH=CH_2$	(1)68
C_6H_8		(1)72
C_6H_{10}	CH_3 $H_2C=CCH=CHCH_3$	(1)64
C_6H_{10}	$H_2C=CHCH=C(CH_3)_2$	(1)65
C_6H_{10}	CH_3 $H_2C=CC=CH_2$ CH_3	(1)66
C_6H_{10}	$H_2C=CHCH_2CH_2CH=CH_2$	(1)67
C_6H_{10}	$H_2C=CCH_3$	(1)156
C_6H_{10}		(1)157
C_6H_{10}	$=CHCH_3$	(1)173
C_6H_{10}	$CH_3(CH_2)_3C\equiv CH$	(2)13
C_6H_{10}	$CH_3C\equiv CCH_2CH_2CH_3$	(2)15
C_6H_{10}	$HC\equiv C(CH_2)_3CH_3$	(2)16
$C_6H_{10}O$	$H_2C=CHCH_2OCH_2CH=CH_2$	(3)105
$C_6H_{10}O$	H O H	(3)188
$C_6H_{10}O$	OH $CH_3CH_2CH_2CHC\equiv CH$	(2)159
$C_6H_{10}O$	CH_3 $CH_3CH_2CC\equiv CH$ OH	(2)243
$C_6H_{10}O_2$	OH $CH_2=CHCHCHCH=CH_2$ OH	(2)90
$C_6H_{10}O_2$	OOH	(3)222
$C_6H_{10}O_4$	O HO O CHCH OH	(3)176
C_6H_{12}	CH_3 $H_2C=CCH_2CH_2CH_3$	(1)53
C_6H_{12}	$CH(CH_3)_2$	(1)155
C_6H_{12}	CH_3 H_3C CH_3	(1)160
C_6H_{12}	CH_2CH_3	(1)171

CUMULATIVE INDEX

C_6H_{12} CH_3 (1)196	$C_6H_{12}O_2$ OH OH (2)188	$C_6H_{14}O$ $HOCH_2CH_2CH_2CH(CH_3)_2$ (2)67
C_6H_{12} (1)244	$C_6H_{12}O_2$ OH OH CH_3 (2)207	$C_6H_{14}O$ OH $CH_3CH_2CH_2CHCH_2CH_3$ (2)120
$C_6H_{12}O$ $CH_2{=}CHO(CH_2)_3CH_3$ (3)119	$C_6H_{12}O_3$ OH OOH (3)231	$C_6H_{14}O$ OH $(CH_3)_3CCH_3$ (2)130
$C_6H_{12}O$ OH $CH_2 = CHCH_2CH_2CHCH_3$ (2)155	$C_6H_{12}O_4$ O—O $(CH_3)_2C$ $C(CH_3)_2$ O—O (3)248	$C_6H_{14}O$ OH $CH_3CH_2CHCHCH_3$ CH_3 (2)131
$C_6H_{12}O$ OH (2)174	C_6H_{14} $CH_3(CH_2)_4CH_3$ (1)16	$C_6H_{14}O$ OH $(CH_3)_2CHCH_2CH_3$ (2)133
$C_6H_{12}O$ HO CH_3 (2)239	$C_6H_{14}O$ CH_3 $CH_3CH_2CHCH_2CH_2OH$ (2)60	$C_6H_{14}O$ OH $(CH_3)_2CHC(CH_3)_2$ (2)224
$C_6H_{12}O_2$ CH_3 $HOCH_2CCH_2OH$ $CH = CH_2$ (2)92	$C_6H_{14}O$ CH_2CH_3 $CH_3CH_2CHCH_2OH$ (2)63	$C_6H_{14}O$ OH $(CH_3)_2CCH_2CH_2CH_3$ (2)227
$C_6H_{12}O_2$ OH trans OH (2)179	$C_6H_{14}O$ $(CH_3)_3CCH_2CH_2OH$ (2)64	$C_6H_{14}O$ $CH_3(CH_2)_3OCH_2CH_3$ (3)93
$C_6H_{12}O_2$ OH OH (2)180	$C_6H_{14}O$ CH_3 $(CH_3)_2CHCHCH_2OH$ (2)65	$C_6H_{14}O$ $(CH_3)_2CHOCH(CH_3)_2$ (3)108
$C_6H_{12}O_2$ OH OH cis (2)186	$C_6H_{14}O$ CH_3 $CH_3CH_2CCH_2OH$ CH_3 (2)68	$C_6H_{14}O_2$ $C_4H_9OCH_2CH_2OH$ (3)98

$C_6H_{14}O_2$ CH_3 $CH_3(CH_2)_3CH \cdot OOH$ (3)220	$C_6H_{14}O_2$ OH CH_3 $CH_3CHCH_2CHCH_2OH$ (2)271	C_7H_8O OCH_3 (3)128
$C_6H_{14}O_2$ C_2H_5 $CH_3(CH_2)_2CH \cdot OOH$ (3)220	$C_6H_{14}O_2$ OH OH $(CH_3)_2CCH_2CHCH_3$ (2)284	C_7H_8O OH CH_3 (3)24
$C_6H_{14}O_2$ $CH_3(CH_2)_5 \cdot OOH$ (3)219	$C_6H_{14}O_3$ $CH_3CH_2OCH_2CH_2OCH_2CH_2OH$ (3)100	C_7H_8O CH_2OH (2)95
$C_6H_{14}O_2$ $HOCH_2(CH_2)_4CH_2OH$ (2)48	$C_6H_{14}O_3$ OH $HOCH_2CH(CH_2)_3CH_2OH$ (2)278	$C_7H_8O_2$ OH CH_3 OH (3)45
$C_6H_{14}O_2$ CH_3 $HOCH_2CH_2CHCH_2CH_2OH$ (2)61	$C_6H_{14}O_4$ OH $CH_3CH_2CHOOCHCH_2CH_3$ OH (3)241	$C_7H_8O_2$ OH OCH_3 (3)150
$C_6H_{14}O_2$ CH_3 $HOCH_2CCH_2OH$ CH_2CH_3 (2)74	$C_6H_{14}O_5$ OH OH OH OH $CH_3CH-CH-CH-CHCH_2OH$ Fucitol (2)282	$C_7H_8O_3$ OH CH_3 HO OH (3)67
$C_6H_{14}O_2$ OH OH $CH_3CHCH_2CH_2CHCH_3$ (2)119	$C_6H_{14}O_6$ CH_2OH HOCH HOCH HCOH HCOH CH_2OH Mannitol (2)280	C_7H_{12} CH_2CH_3 (1)71
$C_6H_{14}O_2$ OH OH $CH_3CHCHCHCH_3$ CH_3 (2)132	$C_6H_{14}O_6$ CH_2OH HCOH HOCH HCOH HCOH CH_2OH d-Sorbitol (2)281	$C_7H_{12}O$ CH_3 O H (3)192
$C_6H_{14}O_2$ OH OH $(CH_3)_2CC \equiv CC(CH_3)_2$ (2)253	$C_6H_{15}O$ OH $(CH_3)_2CHCH_2CHCH_3$ (2)134	$C_7H_{12}O$ HO CH (2)171
$C_6H_{14}O_2$ OH CH_3 $CH_3CH-CCH_2OH$ CH_3 (2)270	C_7H_8 CH_3 (1)109	C_7H_{14} $H_2C=CHCHCH_2CH_3$ CH_2CH_3 (1)41

CUMULATIVE INDEX

CUMULATIVE INDEX

CUMULATIVE INDEX

$C_8H_{10}O_2$ OCH_2CH_2OH (3)139	C_8H_{14} $CH_3CH_2CH_2C{\equiv}CCH_2CH_2CH_3$ (2)18	C_8H_{16} CH_3 CH_3 CH_3 cis, cis, cis (1)215
$C_8H_{10}O_2$ $CH{-}OOH$ CH_3 (3)222	$C_8H_{14}O$ $HOCHCH_3$ (2)141	C_8H_{16} CH_3 CH_3 CH_3 cis, trans, cis (1)216
$C_8H_{10}O_2$ $HOCHCH_2OH$ (2)283	$C_8H_{14}O_2$ OH OH $(CH_3)_2CC{\equiv}CC(CH_3)_2$ (2)252	C_8H_{16} H_3C CH_3 CH_3 (1)217
$C_8H_{12}O$ H O H $CH{=}CH_2$ (3)190	$C_8H_{14}O_3$ O OH OH cis, cis (3)205	C_8H_{16} CH_3 CH_2CH_3 (1)222
C_8H_{14} CH_2CH_3 (1)75	C_8H_{16} CH_3 $(CH_3)_3CC = CHCH_3$ (1)58	C_8H_{16} H_3C CH_2CH_3 (1)225
C_8H_{14} CH_3 CH_3 (1)76	C_8H_{16} $(CH_3)_2CHCH_2CH = C(CH_3)_2$ (1)59	C_8H_{16} CH_3 CH_3 H_3C cis, cis, trans (1)226
C_8H_{14} $CH_2CH = CH_2$ (1)210	C_8H_{16} CH_3 $(CH_3)_2CHC = C(CH_3)_2$ (1)62	C_8H_{16} CH_3 CH_3 H_3C cis, trans, cis (1)227
C_8H_{14} $HC = CH_2$ (1)265	C_8H_{16} $CH_2CH_2CH_3$ (1)198	C_8H_{16} CH_2CH_3 (1)253
C_8H_{14} CH_2CH_3 (1)284	C_8H_{16} $CH(CH_3)_2$ (1)204	C_8H_{16} CH_3 CH_3 cis (1)272
C_8H_{14} $CH_3CH_2C{\equiv}C(CH_2)_3CH_3$ (2)17	C_8H_{16} H_3C CH_3 CH_3 (1)214	C_8H_{16} CH_3 CH_3 trans (1)273

CUMULATIVE INDEX

$C_9H_{12}O_3$ CH_2OH, OCH_3, OCH_3 (3)144	C_9H_{18} H_3C, CH_3, CH_3 (1)278	$C_9H_{18}O$ CH_3, OH, CCH_2CH_3, CH_3 (2)240
$C_9H_{16}O$ CH_2OH (2)94	C_9H_{18} H_3C, CH_3, CH_3 (1)279	$C_9H_{18}O$ OH CH_3 CH_3 $(CH_3)_2C-C-C=CH_2$ CH_3 (2)247
$C_9H_{16}O$ OH, CH_2 (2)204	C_9H_{18} CH_3, H_3C, CH_3 1-cis-3-trans-5-Trimethylcyclohexane (1)280	$C_9H_{18}O_6$ $C(CH_3)_2$ O O O O $(CH_3)_2C-OO-C(CH_3)_2$ (3)249
C_9H_{18} H_3C $(CH_3)_3CCH_2$ (1)158	C_9H_{18} CH_3, H_3C, CH_3 1-cis-3-cis-5-Trimethylcyclohexane (1)281	C_9H_{20} CH_3 $(CH_3)_3CCHCH_2CH_2CH_3$ (1)22
C_9H_{18} $CH_2(CH_2)_3CH_3$ (1)172	C_9H_{18} H_3C, CH_2CH_3 (1)287	C_9H_{20} CH_2CH_3 $(CH_3)_2CHCHCH(CH_3)_2$ (1)23
C_9H_{18} $CH_2(CH_2)_2CH_3$ (1)199	C_9H_{18} CH_3, CH_2CH_3 cis (1)291	$C_9H_{20}O$ $CH_3(CH_2)_7CH_2OH$ (2)53
C_9H_{18} $H_3CCHCH_2CH_3$ (1)205	C_9H_{18} CH_3, CH_2CH_3 trans (1)292	$C_9H_{20}O$ CH_3 $(CH_3)_3CCH_2CHCH_2CH_2OH$ (2)68
C_9H_{18} $C(CH_3)_3$ (1)206	$C_9H_{18}O$ OH, CH_3, H_3C, CH_3 (2)194	$C_9H_{20}O$ OH $CH_3(CH_2)_3CH(CH_2)_3CH_3$ (2)127
C_9H_{18} $CH_2CH(CH_3)_2$ (1)207	$C_9H_{18}O$ OH, CH_3, H_3C, CH_3 (2)196	$C_9H_{20}O$ OH $(CH_3)_2CHCH_2CHCH_2CH(CH_3)_2$ (2)145
C_9H_{18} $CH_2CH_2CH_3$ (1)254	$C_9H_{18}O$ OH, H_3C, H_3C, CH_3 trans (2)199	$C_9H_{20}O$ CH_3 $(CH_3)_2CHCH-CCH_2CH_3$ OH CH_3 (2)148

CUMULATIVE INDEX

$C_9H_{20}O$ OH CH$_2$CH$_3$ $CH_3CHCH_2CH_2CHCH_2CH_3$ (2)149	$C_9H_{20}O_2$ $CH_2CH_2CH_2CH_3$ $HOCH_2CCH_2OH$ CH_2CH_3 (2)75	$C_{10}H_{12}O_2$ H_3C O H_3C–C O (3)187
$C_9H_{20}O$ OH $(CH_3)_2C(CH_2)_5CH_3$ (2)228	$C_9H_{20}O_3$ CH_3 CH_3 $HOCH_2CCH_2CHCH_2OH$ CH_2OCH_3 (3)102	$C_{10}H_{12}O_2$ H O H H CH_2 O H (3)189
$C_9H_{20}O$ OH $CH_3CH_2C(CH_2)_7CH_3$ CH_3 (2)231	$C_9H_{20}O_3$ CH_2OH $CH_3(CH_2)_3CH_2CCH_2OH$ CH_2OH (2)76	$C_{10}H_{12}O_2$ OOH (3)223
$C_9H_{20}O$ CH_3 CH_3 $CH_3CH_2C - CCH_2CH_3$ HO CH_3 (2)132	$C_{10}H_8O$ OH (3)43	$C_{10}H_{12}O_3$ HO– –CH=CHCH$_2$OH OCH_3 (3)71
$C_9H_{20}O$ CH_3 OH $(CH_3)_3CCH-C(CH_3)_2$ (2)134	$C_{10}H_8O_2$ HO OH (3)42	$C_{10}H_{14}$ CH_2CH_3 CH_2CH_3 (1)118
$C_9H_{20}O$ CH_3 $(CH_3)_3CCCH_2CH_2CH_3$ OH (2)135	$C_{10}H_8O_2$ OH HO (3)41	$C_{10}H_{14}O$ $O(CH_2)_3CH_3$ (3)133
$C_9H_{20}O$ H_3C CH_3 $(CH_3)_2CHC-CHCH_2CH_3$ HO (2)136	$C_{10}H_{10}O$ OH $H_3CCC\equiv CH$ (2)262	$C_{10}H_{14}O$ OH C_4H_9 (3)25
$C_9H_{20}O$ CH_3 $(CH_3)_3CCCH(CH_3)_2$ CH_3 (2)137	$C_{10}H_{12}$ CH_3 (1)162	$C_{10}H_{14}O$ OH C_4H_9 (3)31
$C_9H_{20}O_2$ C_2H_5 $CH_3(CH_2)_3CHOCH_2CH_2OH$ (3)112	$C_{10}H_{12}O$ OH (3)39	$C_{10}H_{14}O$ OH H_3C CH_3 H_3C CH_3 (3)66
$C_9H_{20}O_2$ $CH_3(CH_2)_8 \cdot OOH$ (3)219	$C_{10}H_{12}O$ CH_3 $C=CHCH_2OH$ (2)109	$C_{10}H_{14}O$ OH CH_3 $CH(CH_3)_2$ (3)40

CUMULATIVE INDEX

$C_{11}H_{16}O$ OH $C(CH_3)_3$ H_3C (3)47	$C_{11}H_{24}O$ OH $CH_3CH(CH_2)_8CH_3$ (2)129	$C_{12}H_{16}O$ OH trans (2)212
$C_{11}H_{16}O$ OH H_3C CH_3 H_3C CH_3 CH_3 (3)69	$C_{11}H_{24}O$ OH $(CH_3)_2C(CH_2)_7CH_3$ (2)130	$C_{12}H_{16}O$ HO cis (2)213
$C_{11}H_{16}O$ OH $CH_2CH_2CH(CH_3)_2$ (3)32	$C_{11}H_{24}O_2$ OCH_2CH_2OH $(CH_3)_2CHCH_2CHCH_2CH(CH_3)_2$ (3)126	$C_{12}H_{16}O$ HO (2)214
$C_{11}H_{16}O$ OH C_5H_{11} (3)29	$C_{11}H_{24}O_3$ CH_3 $(CH_3)CCH_2CCH_2OH$ $O(CH_2)_3OH$ (2)123	$C_{12}H_{16}O_3$ O O $CH_2OC_4H_9$ (3)195
$C_{11}H_{16}O_4$ OCH_2CH_3 OCH_2CHCH_2OH OH (3)148	$C_{12}H_{10}$ (1)103	$C_{12}H_{18}$ $CH(CH_3)_2$ $CH(CH_3)_2$ (1)119
$C_{11}H_{16}O_5$ OH H_3CO H_3CO OCH_2CHCH_2OH (3)147	$C_{12}H_{10}O$ O (3)127	$C_{12}H_{18}$ CH_2CH_3 H_3CH_2C CH_2CH_3 (1)129
$C_{11}H_{16}O_5$ $OCH_2CHOHCH_2OH$ OCH_3 OCH_3 (3)145	$C_{12}H_{10}O_4$ HO OH HO OH (3)44	$C_{12}H_{18}O$ OH $(CH_3)_3C$ CH_3 CH_3 (3)55
$C_{11}H_{20}$ (1)246	$C_{12}H_{16}$ (1)266	$C_{12}H_{18}O$ OH H_7C_3 C_3H_7 (3)54
$C_{11}H_{22}$ $(CH_3)_2CCH_2CH_3$ (1)261	$C_{12}H_{16}O$ OH trans (2)210	$C_{12}H_{18}O$ $(CH_3)_3CCHCH_2OH$ (2)99
$C_{11}H_{22}O$ $CH_2=CH(CH_2)_8CH_2OH$ (2)91	$C_{12}H_{16}O$ OH cis (2)211	$C_{12}H_{18}O$ OH $CH_2CH_2CCH_2CH_3$ CH_3 (2)259

CUMULATIVE INDEX

$C_{14}H_{12}$ CH = CH cis (1)112	$C_{14}H_{14}O$ CH_2OCH_2 (3)107	$C_{14}H_{22}O_2$ OH $C(CH_3)_3$ $(CH_3)_3C$ OH (3)64
$C_{14}H_{12}$ CH = CH trans (1)113	$C_{14}H_{14}O_2$ CH_2OH CH_2OH (2)96	$C_{14}H_{26}$ CH_3 CH (1)255
$C_{14}H_{22}$ CH_2 C (1)114	$C_{14}H_{18}$ $HC \equiv C(CH_2)_4C \equiv C(CH_2)_4C \equiv CH$ (2)21	$C_{14}H_{26}$ $CH_2CH_2CH_2$ (1)282
$C_{14}H_{14}$ (1)105	$C_{14}H_{20}$ $CH_2CH_2CH_2$ (1)212	$C_{14}H_{26}O_2$ CH_3 CH_3 $(CH_3)_2CHCH_2CC \equiv CCCH_2CH(CH_3)_2$ OH OH (2)255
$C_{14}H_{14}$ CH_3 CH_3 (1)122	$C_{14}H_{20}$ CH_2CH_2 (1)267	$C_{14}H_{28}O$ O $(CH_2)_{11}CH_3$ (3)180
$C_{14}H_{14}$ H_3C CH_3 (1)125	$C_{14}H_{20}$ CH_3 CH (1)268	$C_{14}H_{30}O_3$ CH_2OH $CH_3(CH_2)_3CH_2CCH_2OH$ CH_2OH (2)79
$C_{14}H_{14}$ CH_3 CH_3 (1)137	$C_{14}H_{20}O$ trans-3,3-Dimethyl-5-phenylcyclohexanol H_3C CH_3 H H OH (2)216	$C_{15}H_{12}O$ $C \equiv CH$ C OH (2)261
$C_{14}H_{14}$ CH_3 CH_3 (1)138	$C_{14}H_{20}O$ H OH CH_3 H CH_3 (2)221	$C_{15}H_{16}$ CH_3 C CH_3 (1)108
$C_{14}H_{14}$ CH_3 CH_3 (1)139	$C_{14}H_{22}$ $CH_2(CH_2)_6CH_3$ (1)110	$C_{15}H_{16}O$ CH_2OH C CH_3 (2)101
$C_{14}H_{14}$ CH_3 CH_3 (1)141	$C_{14}H_{22}O$ H_3C OH $CH_3CH_2C-CCH_2CH_3$ CH_3 (2)260	$C_{15}H_{16}O$ CH_2CH_2OH CH (2)107

CUMULATIVE INDEX

CUMULATIVE INDEX

CONVERSION TABLE

FOR USE IN CHANGING FROM WAVELENGTH IN MICRONS TO WAVENUMBER AND VICE VERSA

n	$1000/n$	n	$1000/n$
0	∞	50	20.00000
1	1000.0000	51	19.60784
2	500.0000	52	19.23077
3	333.3333	53	18.86792
4	250.0000	54	18.51852
5	200.0000	55	18.18182
6	166.6667	56	17.85714
7	142.8571	57	17.54386
8	125.0000	58	17.24138
9	111.1111	59	16.94915
10	100.0000	60	16.66667
11	90.90909	61	16.39344
12	83.33333	62	16.12903
13	76.92308	63	15.87302
14	71.42857	64	15.62500
15	66.66667	65	15.38462
16	62.50000	66	15.15152
17	58.82353	67	14.92537
18	55.55556	68	14.70588
19	52.63158	69	14.49275
20	50.00000	70	14.28571
21	47.61905	71	14.08451
22	45.45455	72	13.88889
23	43.47826	73	13.69863
24	41.66667	74	13.51351
25	40.00000	75	13.33333
26	38.46154	76	13.15789
27	37.03704	77	12.98701
28	35.71429	78	12.82051
29	34.48276	79	12.65823
30	33.33333	80	12.50000
31	32.25806	81	12.34568
32	31.25000	82	12.19512
33	30.30303	83	12.04819
34	29.41176	84	11.90476
35	28.57143	85	11.76471
36	27.77778	86	11.62791
37	27.02703	87	11.49425
38	26.31579	88	11.36364
39	25.64103	89	11.23596
40	25.00000	90	11.11111
41	24.39024	91	10.98901
42	23.80952	92	10.86957
43	23.25581	93	10.75269
44	22.72727	94	10.63830
45	22.22222	95	10.52632
46	21.73913	96	10.41667
47	21.27660	97	10.30928
48	20.83333	98	10.20408
49	20.40816	99	10.10101

n	$1000/n$	n	$1000/n$	n	$1000/n$	n	$1000/n$	n	$1000/n$
100	10.000 000	175	5.714 286	250	4.000 000	325	3.076 923	400	2.500 000
101	9.900 990	176	5.681 818	251	3.984 064	326	3.067 485	401	2.493 766
102	9.803 922	177	5.649 718	252	3.968 254	327	3.058 104	402	2.487 562
103	9.708 738	178	5.617 978	253	3.952 569	328	3.048 780	403	2.481 390
104	9.615 385	179	5.586 592	254	3.937 008	329	3.039 514	404	2.475 248
105	9.523 810	180	5.555 556	255	3.921 569	330	3.030 303	405	2.469 136
106	9.433 962	181	5.524 862	256	3.906 250	331	3.021 148	406	2.463 054
107	9.345 794	182	5.494 505	257	3.891 051	332	3.012 048	407	2.457 002
108	9.259 259	183	5.464 481	258	3.875 969	333	3.003 003	408	2.450 980
109	9.174 312	184	5.434 783	259	3.861 004	334	2.994 012	409	2.444 988
110	9.090 909	185	5.405 405	260	3.846 154	335	2.985 075	410	2.439 024
111	9.009 009	186	5.376 344	261	3.831 418	336	2.976 190	411	2.433 090
112	8.928 571	187	5.347 594	262	3.816 794	337	2.967 359	412	2.427 184
113	8.849 558	188	5.319 149	263	3.802 281	338	2.958 580	413	2.421 308
114	8.771 930	189	5.291 005	264	3.787 879	339	2.949 853	414	2.415 459
115	8.695 652	190	5.263 158	265	3.773 585	340	2.941 176	415	2.409 639
116	8.620 690	191	5.235 602	266	3.759 398	341	2.932 551	416	2.403 846
117	8.547 009	192	5.208 333	267	3.745 318	342	2.923 977	417	2.398 082
118	8.474 576	193	5.181 347	268	3.731 343	343	2.915 452	418	2.392 344
119	8.403 361	194	5.154 639	269	3.717 472	344	2.906 977	419	2.386 635
120	8.333 333	195	5.128 205	270	3.703 704	345	2.898 551	420	2.380 952
121	8.264 463	196	5.102 041	271	3.690 037	346	2.890 173	421	2.375 297
122	8.196 721	197	5.076 142	272	3.676 471	347	2.881 844	422	2.369 668
123	8.130 081	198	5.050 505	273	3.663 004	348	2.873 563	423	2.364 066
124	8.064 516	199	5.025 126	274	3.649 635	349	2.865 330	424	2.358 491
125	8.000 000	200	5.000 000	275	3.636 364	350	2.857 143	425	2.352 941
126	7.936 508	201	4.975 124	276	3.623 188	351	2.849 003	426	2.347 418
127	7.874 016	202	4.950 495	277	3.610 108	352	2.840 909	427	2.341 920
128	7.812 500	203	4.926 108	278	3.597 122	353	2.832 861	428	2.336 449
129	7.751 938	204	4.901 961	279	3.584 229	354	2.824 859	429	2.331 002
130	7.692 308	205	4.878 049	280	3.571 429	355	2.816 901	430	2.325 581
131	7.633 588	206	4.854 369	281	3.558 719	356	2.808 989	431	2.320 186
132	7.575 758	207	4.830 918	282	3.546 099	357	2.801 120	432	2.314 815
133	7.518 797	208	4.807 692	283	3.533 569	358	2.793 296	433	2.309 469
134	7.462 687	209	4.784 689	284	3.521 127	359	2.785 515	434	2.304 147
135	7.407 407	210	4.761 905	285	3.508 772	360	2.777 778	435	2.298 851
136	7.352 941	211	4.739 336	286	3.496 503	361	2.770 083	436	2.293 578
137	7.299 270	212	4.716 981	287	3.484 321	362	2.762 431	437	2.288 330
138	7.246 377	213	4.694 836	288	3.472 222	363	2.754 821	438	2.283 105
139	7.194 245	214	4.672 897	289	3.460 208	364	2.747 253	439	2.277 904
140	7.142 857	215	4.651 163	290	3.448 276	365	2.739 726	440	2.272 727
141	7.092 199	216	4.629 630	291	3.436 426	366	2.732 240	441	2.267 574
142	7.042 254	217	4.608 295	292	3.424 658	367	2.724 796	442	2.262 443
143	6.993 007	218	4.587 156	293	3.412 969	368	2.717 391	443	2.257 336
144	6.944 444	219	4.566 210	294	3.401 361	369	2.710 027	444	2.252 252
145	6.896 552	220	4.545 455	295	3.389 831	370	2.702 703	445	2.247 191
146	6.849 315	221	4.524 887	296	3.378 378	371	2.695 418	446	2.242 152
147	6.802 721	222	4.504 505	297	3.367 003	372	2.688 172	447	2.237 136
148	6.756 757	223	4.484 305	298	3.355 705	373	2.680 965	448	2.232 143
149	6.711 409	224	4.464 286	299	3.344 482	374	2.673 797	449	2.227 171
150	6.666 667	225	4.444 444	300	3.333 333	375	2.666 667	450	2.222 222
151	6.622 517	226	4.424 779	301	3.322 259	376	2.659 574	451	2.217 295
152	6.578 947	227	4.405 286	302	3.311 258	377	2.652 520	452	2.212 389
153	6.535 948	228	4.385 965	303	3.300 330	378	2.645 503	453	2.207 506
154	6.493 506	229	4.366 812	304	3.289 474	379	2.638 522	454	2.202 643
155	6.451 613	230	4.347 826	305	3.278 689	380	2.631 579	455	2.197 802
156	6.410 256	231	4.329 004	306	3.267 974	381	2.624 672	456	2.192 982
157	6.369 427	232	4.310 345	307	3.257 329	382	2.617 801	457	2.188 184
158	6.329 114	233	4.291 845	308	3.246 753	383	2.610 966	458	2.183 406
159	6.289 308	234	4.273 504	309	3.236 246	384	2.604 167	459	2.178 649
160	6.250 000	235	4.255 319	310	3.225 806	385	2.597 403	460	2.173 913
161	6.211 180	236	4.237 288	311	3.215 434	386	2.590 674	461	2.169 197
162	6.172 840	237	4.219 409	312	3.205 128	387	2.583 979	462	2.164 502
163	6.134 969	238	4.201 681	313	3.194 888	388	2.577 320	463	2.159 827
164	6.097 561	239	4.184 100	314	3.184 713	389	2.570 694	464	2.155 172
165	6.060 606	240	4.166 667	315	3.174 603	390	2.564 103	465	2.150 538
166	6.024 096	241	4.149 378	316	3.164 557	391	2.557 545	466	2.145 923
167	5.988 024	242	4.132 231	317	3.154 574	392	2.551 020	467	2.141 328
168	5.952 381	243	4.115 226	318	3.144 654	393	2.544 529	468	2.136 752
169	5.917 160	244	4.098 361	319	3.134 796	394	2.538 071	469	2.132 196
170	5.882 353	245	4.081 633	320	3.125 000	395	2.531 646	470	2.127 660
171	5.847 953	246	4.065 041	321	3.115 265	396	2.525 253	471	2.123 142
172	5.813 953	247	4.048 583	322	3.105 590	397	2.518 892	472	2.118 644
173	5.780 347	248	4.032 258	323	3.095 975	398	2.512 563	473	2.114 165
174	5.747 126	249	4.016 064	324	3.086 420	399	2.506 266	474	2.109 705